Overcoming Darkness Journey

Deliverance & Discipleship Training Program

WORKBOOK

Paula Cross

paula@overcomingdarknessjourney.com

www.overcomingdarknessjourney.com

Cover Design by Paula Cross
Interior Module Headers Designed by Kjpargeter / Freepik

Ordering Information:
Quantity sales. Special discounts are available on quantity purchases by corporations, associations, and others. For details, contact Paula Cross at the address above.
Published Siebert Publishing LLC

First Printing in the United States of America : August 2020

ISBN   978-0-9991646-3-1

Table Of Contents

Table of Contents Continued

Section Two:

Table of Contents Continued

Meditate on God's Love

You will find random heart drawings throughout this book indicative of God's Love. We know coloring is said to be therapeutic. I've included these peaceful renditions of love for you to color while simultaneously meditating deeply upon the truths of God's love. Most of us don't relate or feel God's love and presence because darkness blocks it just as storm clouds block out the sun. We must remember that just as the sun hasn't gone anywhere, neither has God & neither has His love for us. He is here with us - loving us. Meditate declaring with every stroke of color the wonder of God's love, your gratitude for it, and for all things right & true. **Forbid yourself from thinking on ANYTHING else**. Permit **ONLY** thoughts pertaining to God's love & goodness. Even and ESPECIALLY if you don't feel it. Your soul will transform & Faith will increase, eventually ripping the dark clouds wide open so that you can see the SON & feel His warm love!

Introduction

This program is not just for the oppressed, but for those the Lord has been speaking to about alignment and coming into the fullness of His Kingdom -and the full stature of Christ.

Have you been going in the same circles for years or even decades? Are you on a financial, physical, spiritual, or an emotional roller coaster? Are you stuck in a mediocre Christian walk doing all the right things but going nowhere? Are you frustrated that you know the Word but struggle to fully apply it, obey, and LIVE it? Are you weary, knowing there's more but you're stifled? Worse yet, despite following Christ, is your life plagued with oppression, peculiar injustice, violations, defeat at every turn, or even demonic manifestations?

30 Years of Deliverance in this Program!

The founder and developer of the ODJ Program, Paula Cross, spent 30 years coming out of the dominion of darkness. Though born again in May of 1988 and rescued from the dominion of darkness and transferred into the Kingdom of God's dear Son at that time according to Colossians 1:13, the enemy maintained legal holds and authority over Paula's life. She would cry out through the years, *"God, you are above all the power of the devil and I'm your daughter! I follow you, pray, serve and worship you. I do my best to obey and repent when I fail. Why does the darkness prevail against me?"*

Unbeknownst to Paula, God had begun working to unravel this mystery to her in 1989, long before she ever sought understanding. It was through dreams, visions, and other encounters whereby God addressed her faulty belief system and ignorance, and unveiled the truths of His Word which, as she came into alignment with them, escorted her into manifest freedom, authority and well-being. She was once dominated, severely oppressed and saw her circumstances continually manipulated by darkness without relent - despite being a child of the Most High God. But now she's completely DELIVERED!

True deliverance by the power of God is real and permanent! But it must be laid hold of. And the Overcoming Darkness Journey Program, developed by the inspiration of the Holy Spirit, is here to provide clear and solid teaching, prayer and guidance for those who are ready to live in the manifest reality of the kingdom of God.

When we were born again, we were supposed to begin our journey down the narrow path. This journey includes a new identity, a transformation process, authority in Christ, and direct access to the throne room in Heaven via the Holy Spirit who now lives in us.

Unfortunately, most of us have yet to lay hold of who we are. Many struggle with coming into the fullness of Christ, and into all His benefits. Though the answers that guide us to victory are all in the Bible, the majority of us are only getting so far.

Paula Cross began her journey in 1988 and despite genuinely giving her all, she lived defeated for her first 20+ years as a believer. But because of her desperate pursuit for answers as to how this was so, as well as her longing to experience what she knew the Bible said, Holy Spirit worked with her on her level, giving her dreams, visions, and encounters whereby truths of the Bible came to life for her.

Consequently, Paula's journey was a very slow, but steady, climb. And now the countless truths the Holy Spirit taught her have Paula increasingly and effectively living in the manifest reality of her identity in Christ Jesus, and over the power of the devil. The walls that once barricaded her have been torn down! She has been prospering in every possible way! Paula Cross has been completely delivered and now works diligently to bring the same to the body of Christ.

This ODJ Program workbook is a compilation of many of the scriptural lessons and revelations that the Holy Spirit taught her over the course of 30 years. Though it all reflects teachings we're well versed in, the WHOLE picture of God's message is presented in a fresh way with keen insight and intricate tweaking from the many ways we've been off kilter. Every scriptural truth is taught by someone with first-hand, experiential revelation. And everything is laid out in such a way that, if studied from beginning to end, will bring deeper understanding of the scriptures to truth seekers like never before. And for those who apply what's taught here, they will experience complete deliverance over every power of the enemy! And they'll come into the literal power of God!

Jesus spoke in parables when He was here for a reason. But the hour of clear understanding through the Holy Spirit, through His teachers and genuine, Holy Spirit-breathed programs like this one, is upon us.

Those who take this program can expect to be refined in their belief system and, thereby, greater alignment with the kingdom of God. They should anticipate the puzzle pieces coming together. They should also expect plenty of light bulbs to go off. They should anticipate powerful encounters with the Holy Spirit. And they should anticipate that where there has been confusion and debilitating strongholds, there will now be clarity and ever-increasing stability. Those who take this program should gear up to finally grasp the whole point of the Gospel like never before.

This deliverance and discipleship workbook actually began as an online weekly email training program which is overcomingdarknessjourney.com.

But various members expressed the challenge of extensive online reading which required the production of this workbook.

Please understand the intent of the weekly email program was to provide teaching bit by bit in conjunction with prayers because, as Paula learned over 30 years of coming out from the rule of darkness, our journey is a step-by-step process. Just as we cannot pick up the Bible, read it in one sitting, and master all it conveys. There are endless points of refinement, rhema, enlightenment, and more to be experienced over the course of our lives. Likewise, the contents of this workbook cannot be digested in a single sitting, let alone a rushed one. There are many truths conveyed in this workbook that require time to digest, process, ponder, and work out with God via our personal situations and application.

That being said, as you read the modules, and if you should discern the Spirit of God in these teachings and see their parallel to the written Word of God, please remember they were intended to be digested or contemplated slowly. Do please take your time with the modules. Please work with God concerning everything that He illuminates. Do not be hasty to complete the book and throw it aside.

Take notes! Of course, you don't need to be told to do this but it is necessary to emphasize the importance of it. ***Also, please be sure to write your name in the spaces provided in the prayers throughout this book to personalize them.

You are strongly advised to record all that God illuminates in the note taking sections provided in this book. Record all that you need to work on, all that you see changing, all applicable scriptures you need to consume, and even your prayers in given moments. You will revisit these modules and need to see your growth.

A Note From the Author

I want to address something I come across regularly concerning people who worry or wonder if they are truly saved, so they aren't sure the program will work for them. If you resonate with this, I want to encourage you that the fact is you are here because **your spirit desires God and truth**. Your spirit could NOT do that if you didn't belong to Jesus. If you aren't yet born again, you will be by the time you finish the program for sure. So, I speak to all worry, anxiety and fear to stand down right now. Take these captive and get them off the table. You're here. That's what matters. Focus on what matters. Again I say... Focus on what matters. Do not focus on your concerns.

Another thing I hear a great deal from those who reach out in desperation is *"I've been through deliverance! Nothing works! Things only get worse!"* If you've been through deliverance and it hasn't made a difference, get this off the table, too. Lay this concern down. What's done is done. This is a new day; this is your turning point. This program is REAL deliverance. So again, all worries, anxiety and fear, stand down right now. Take these captive. Put them out. We are going to the feet of Jesus to pray to the Father. Do not bring worry, anxiety, or fear with you. They are banned from the altar. Now let's pray:

> *Dear Heavenly Father,*
>
> *I lift _____ up to You, Lord. Father, we know that because we were born into a world ruled by darkness that you sent Jesus to deliver us from all the power of the enemy. **But Father, we need your help to lay hold of this.** You say in your Word all we have to do is believe. Yet, though we do believe that Christ Jesus is God in the flesh and that He is the only way back to you, the enemy has done very*

well to finagle with our belief systems, interfering with our connection to you and all your truths and goodness! So, Father, I pray for _____ to finally be set free from the dictates of darkness!

*Father, **let this day be marked in their history as the day the dark systems and control in their lives began to be <u>rapidly dismantled</u>!** Father, your will be done in every aspect of their lives. Please break them free from every false system, deception, addiction, every form of unbelief, every idol, and especially of every false perspective of you!*

By the authority of Jesus Christ, I speak to every dark system that's been in place in the lives of every ODJ member since their birth: the Lord rebuke you foul workers of iniquity who trespass on that which belongs to Jesus. I call you to be dismantled right now. Your deceptive reign over these ODJ members ends right now!

Father, pull these members close to you right now, taking your stand against the evil empire that's been wreaking havoc in their lives! Speak assurance to their spirits that you've got them and are not letting them go!

*Please forgive and have mercy on them. Lord, you know they chose this program because **they choose you** despite where they are in their walk with you. Regardless how deeply entangled with sin they may be. Even if they're not born again yet, Father, please forgive their every sin. Wash them clean right now, right this moment. Let the seed of Life and Truth of the kingdom of Christ take root in them right now! Make them whole, Father, by the blood of Jesus Christ. You are such a wonderful God. We do not deserve such grace. But it's your* *way and your PASSION, to recreate anyone that believes and asks for such cleansing. Praise you, Father!*

Now please help this ODJ member to be still and rest in the truth of your compassion, love, and great mercy. I ask for added protection, wisdom and guidance over every ODJ member, future and past. Lord, meet them right where they are. Please open the eyes of their spirit to see and understand your truths like NEVER before! And please... begin to expose whatever agreements they may have with darkness deep within. Being sure to guide them out of it and into your truth.

I speak TRUTH, WHOLENESS, and PROSPERITY over and into the souls of every ODJ member right now!

In Jesus' Name, Amen!

Before you get started, record any concerns and/or confusion you have. Then give them to God and take your focus off of them. God is with you. Also, record any scripturally based questions you long for God to answer. If they aren't answered or resolved *after* you finish this workbook, please email me at info@paulacross.com and let me know. I may not have the answer but maybe we can seek clarity or direction from God together. **But thoroughly completing this book first is required.**

_____

_____

_____

_____

_____

_____

_____

_____

_____

_____

_____

_____

_____

_____

_____

_____

_____

_____

_____

Pre-Program Intro

As per the online training, there is a section members go through before beginning the main program. The reason this section is set apart is because it speaks to the most common and severe aspects of oppression in the Church. Mind you, the entire program was developed to bring Christians into permanent deliverance from darkness. But this PRE section is a serious, very pointed jump-start concerning the severity of dark reign over believers as well as its obscurity in being realized.

Now if you are here more for the discipleship training to bring you into the full stature of Christ and think the discussions on "oppression" in the PRE-PROGRAM won't pertain to you, that's not the case. Even if your life is going fine, you need to review these discussions. It is absolutely necessary for ALL members to complete this preliminary section. In it, you'll acquire a well-rounded perspective that will definitely help you whether you're struggling in this life or not. It's important to have a grip on the full scope of things, regardless of what's specifically going on in your every day-to-day.

Now let's pray...

> *Heavenly Father, Thank You that You are training us up in the truth like never before! Thank You that You are opening the eyes of our understanding like never before. Now Lord, I ask You to please give _____ a clear mind to receive and understand everything that's important in these teachings! You are the Almighty God. I ask in all Your mercy for you to grant supreme wisdom and extra protection, putting a shield about their mind, heart and soul right now.*

Father, You are the Author of life and Master over every member that completes these teachings. So please have Your way in them. I take authority over all foul spirits, instructing all workers of darkness to stand down, to cease and desist in any attempt to thwart Your plans for _____ right now! Guard them and let them encounter Your presence more completely than they have in a long time! Praise God. Thank You for being so good to Your children, Lord. Have Your way, Father. Have Your way.

In Jesus' Name, Amen.

Most Are Oppressed And Just Don't Know It!
Pre-Program 1

It's likely you purchased the ODJ Program discipleship and deliverance workbook because you know there's more to walking with Christ than the majority of Christians live or experience. But did you know this "lack" in the body is oppression? Everyone knows oppression can be a severe thing, but we fail to recognize that subtle oppression is equally terrible; especially in the body of Christ.

It's obvious that when someone is oppressed, this is a very problematic situation. The very definition of oppression is "prolonged cruel or unjust treatment or control, the state of being subject to unjust treatment or control, and mental pressure or distress".

But, note how it says "the state of being subject to...control." This is the *not-so obvious* form of oppression we'll be discussing here. Because, though the majority of Christians are oppressed, only a fraction experience the cruel, unjust type. **The rest have no idea they're oppressed because they do not experience prolonged, cruel or unjust treatment. They do not live in mental distress ongoing.** In fact, many people who assert that Jesus is the Son of God and Savior of the world, live wonderful, productive lives - having no clue that they're oppressed by darkness.

If you look up the definition of oppression, you'll find that a few of its synonyms are: repression, suppression, subjugation and even enslavement.

These terms are all affiliated with *being under dominion*. "Repression" more specifically has to do with restraint, prevention, or inhibition. While "suppression" has to do with subduing, defeat, and prevention. Note that these don't necessarily have to involve cruelty or ongoing distress. You can be enslaved without being mistreated by your master, for example. You can be restrained, inhibited or prevented from doing something, without cruelty or blatant distress as well.

As I came into freedom from dark kingdom dominion, I began to recognize that part of the oppression I was in included powerlessness over the devil. Indeed that goes without saying, but what hit me was that pretty much everyone else I knew as Christians were just as powerless over the devil as I had been! Yet, they weren't "distressfully" oppressed like me. The most wonderful church I belonged to in my baby years was full of very lovely men and women of God that didn't have dark clouds hanging over their heads, for the most part. They were relatively established, excelling in their lives with their families, careers, and all else. Yet, I don't recall ever seeing the authority of Christ exercised over the power of the devil by any of them. And I don't recall seeing healing miracles. Even in "crusades". I've never witnessed anything like what we see in the Bible. Testimonies were always very general. Sickness and disease remained all around.

Jesus said we would do even greater miracles than Him, yet, though I have personally cast out and took authority over demons as well as a few other "small" but very real miracles in recent years, I've done NOTHING comparable to Jesus let alone 'greater'. Not anywhere close! My faith is still being tweaked in this department. Because at the end of the day, it's all about faith.

But the point is the power that the few of us do have (even to overcome sin or strongholds) is minimal compared to what it's supposed to be. Most of us never walk in victory over the flesh or sin, and every power of the devil. *And this is a level of oppression.* This is a form of restraint, inhibition and prevention that's on the children of God. Indeed, there are some big name evangelists or healing ministers called into the five-fold ministry that do (or did) exercise power over the devil. In fact, there are many miracles reported on the internet daily. But this is not the experience of the corporate body as a unified whole. Most of us never see, practice or experience authority over darkness like this. Despite the fact that Jesus said, "And these signs shall follow them that believe; In my name shall they cast out devils; they shall speak with new tongues. They shall take up serpents; and if they drink any deadly thing, it shall not hurt them; they shall lay hands on the sick, and they shall recover". Mark 16:17-18. Yet, demons are permitted to sit in the pews (or chairs) right along with the congregation in every church I've ever been in.

Well, if we all *believe*, then what's the problem?

The problem is the enemy has infiltrated and tinkered with our belief system. And why blame the devil? Because he HAS to keep the power of God at bay. Satan is powerless against God's power. But if he can legally prevent or inhibit a person from exercising that power, don't you think he'll be sure to work tirelessly to do so? Satan has a lot to lose if just one believer rises up in who they are in Christ. Just one Christian that walks in God's power can "put a thousand to flight", Deuteronomy 32:30. Now that's scary for the devil!

You know what's amazing is Christians are so busy being afraid of the devil -instead of being afraid of God *for* being afraid of the devil! Meanwhile, it's the devil that's really afraid. Because he cannot afford to allow those who receive the Word of God, who are born again, to come into their inheritance and power. So, **since God's people are still accessible to the devil on earth, he's quite busy working to restrain them.** True, believers will be held accountable for apathy and not persisting in the fight to victory, if they fail to. But the devil is right there doing everything he legally can to subdue believers so they won't excel in the power that will defeat him in their lives and the world around them!

Just because a Christian's life looks clean and pretty doesn't necessarily mean it is. But even if it is clean, as in no hidden sin or secret darkness, and they are excelling in the things of this life, that still doesn't mean they are excelling in Christ. If Jesus said that those who believe will cast out demons and heal the sick, and they aren't, then the devil has them right where he wants them. Powerless.

Don't confuse the gifts of the Spirit with what Jesus said in Mark 16:17-18. This doesn't mean we're all going to be walking around healing and prophesying to the same degree as one called into the apostolic field. What it does mean is that Christians who truly believe will be able to take care of any devils in their own lives and even in the lives of those in their surroundings, in whatever way is required at the time. True, sometimes prayer and fasting is required to establish one's faith enough to contend with particular demonic high powers according to Matthew 17:20-21. The primary point of that passage being that it was due to the disciples' "unbelief" which prevented them from successfully exercising authority. That's on us, yes, but the dark kingdom works diligently luring us away by the lusts of our flesh and the deceptions of our heart, to prevent us from consecrating ourselves by going into deep prayer and fasting when and where necessary.

And what about the fruit of the Spirit? The Bible tells us that we should bear much fruit of the Spirit of God (Galatians 5). Though there's some, the majority of those who claim to be Christian have very little. The Church looks like the world. She deals with life with the same anxiety, selfishness, pride, resentment, and lack of self-control as the world does, to one degree or another. Especially behind closed doors.

And then what about the full stature of Christ discussed in Ephesians 4? We won't even go there, for now. Just to say, here is another demonstration that the corporate body of Christ is being held back. Regardless how pretty she might look, regardless of her works and services, how much of the above does the Church truly exhibit?

Again, the devil is not exclusively at fault. But, the point, however, is that the corporate body at large is not walking in victory over sin or in the power and authority of Christ, doing what God said we could do, if we believe, because we're allowing the enemy to reign in our lives even unwittingly. And, though we must take full responsibility for this individually, please understand that the Church at large is most definitely under the oppression of the dark kingdom.

But not for long. God is bringing forth the WHOLE truth of the gospel of His kingdom that will finally set believers on course. This program is one of those sources. And I pray the revelational teachings here will help equip the body of Christ and bring her out of the restraints and inhibitions of the kingdom of darkness. And for the Christians who also experience relentless cruel and unjust treatment at the hands of dark kingdom dominion, I pray you'll latch on to every point of truth here, and rise up into victory, manifest freedom, and the authority of Christ once and for all! Amen.

Notes/Prayers

Cycles

Pre-Program 2

Is your life a cycle of ups and downs? Do you want to move forward through Christ, but find yourself going in circles with the same old things?

Many people, despite belonging to Jesus, spend decades inching along in the Christian walk, never really getting where they know they're supposed to be. This is because, though under the blood of Jesus, they're still vulnerable to the kingdom of darkness. And in many cases, the dark kingdom maintains dominion over their lives to some measure. When this is the case, the believer will have the following symptoms ongoing, or off and on through the decades:

- lethargy
- cycles of defeat
- hopelessness
- poverty or
- financial setbacks
- never getting ahead
- opportunities that always hit dead ends
- a sense of powerlessness
- a sense of suffocation
- a sense of limitation
- feeling constricted
- feeling trapped
- feeling paralyzed
- lack of motivation / ambition
- procrastination

- lack of focus
- easily distracted
- foggy mind
- aimless/loss of vision/direction
- indifference
- apathy
- consistent weariness
- suicidal thoughts
- isolation
- depression
- inability to pray
- inability to worship
- inability to study the Word of God
- feeling inferior to peers
- feeling inadequate
- feeling you're a disappointment
- feeling people think poorly of you
- being qualified but overlooked
- doing great things but getting nowhere

When these symptoms are cyclic or, worse, constant, to whatever degree if even subtle, you can be sure that these believers are likewise prone to or have a history of any number of the following behavioral tendencies:

- bitterness
- resentment
- anger
- worry
- anxiety
- fear
- self-pity
- pessimism
- selfishness

- insecurity
- inferiority
- self-hatred
- not understanding or comprehending God's love
- doubting anyone can love them
- pride
- promiscuity
- fornication
- lust
- addictive tendencies
- suspicious
- divisive
- being defensive
- self-preservation
- needing to be heard
- needing to be understood
- needing to be recognized
- needing the approval of man
- fearing disapproval of man
- being needy period
- self-indulgence
- self-destruction
- over-indulgence
- impulsive
- obsessive
- confusion
- being manipulative
- self-medicating
- idolatry
- etc.

Now many of these behavioral tendencies could possibly be the result of a medical condition such as an imbalance in brain chemistry or a methylation or hormonal issue in which case I believe even these are a result of very strategic works of darkness. Regardless, these behavioral tendencies are often coping mechanisms people take on due to their history of bad experiences and their seduction into alignment with darkness. For example, a child that experiences repeated rejection will take on fear of rejection, insecurity, need for recognition, pride, self-preservation, self-defense, etc. A child that isn't loved will take on any number of behaviors such as anger, self-medicating, idolatry, and more. A child that is ridiculed will align with spirits of self-loathing, self-harm, resentment, hatred and bitterness, etc. That's not to say a child born into a stable home life where Satan doesn't have legal authority can't or won't also take on these dark behaviors. There are other reasons people have these issues. But I'm addressing those who've taken on these cycles because of their history under the indoctrination and programming of evil spirits that had legal authority over them.

The following is a list of strategies of various tactics implemented early on against heirs of salvation that the enemy knows will grow up to become a threat. Especially in homes that have not given dominion to Jesus, where the dark kingdom has legal access to these children. Their guardian angels are with them protecting and ministering tirelessly to combat the legal assaults of darkness. But sadly, the enemy successfully works through parents, siblings, other family, guardians, teachers, playmates, and even strangers in the following ways to train the child to only comprehend, relate to, and anticipate evil:

- abandonment
- negligence
- bullying
- terrorizing
- antagonizing
- tormenting
- repetitive disappointment
- defeat

- injustice
- heart break
- scorn
- repetitive rejection
- belittling spirits
- controlling spirits
- rigid, cold, insensitive spirits
- intimidating spirits
- manipulative spirits
- condescending spirits
- critical spirits
- not being loved
- lack of affirmation
- not being believed in
- being despised
- being disappointed in
- not being valued
- abuse (verbal, sexual, emotional, mental, etc)
- repetitive loss
- repetitive violations
- repetitive injustice
- repetitive trauma

When a child or even an adult undergoes such continual, strategic assault(s) as listed above, they are programmed in the soul to operate out of fear and many other non kingdom of God conditions for survival's sake. Even after they get to know Jesus, their souls are very indoctrinated and programmed to operate independently from the truths of God, in doubt of Him and confident in the let-downs, in an effort to protect or validate themselves because "nobody else will". Regardless, operating in these ways if even to a minor degree is <u>an agreement with and submission to the dark kingdom</u> and gives the enemy legal ability to adversely influence or dominate their lives, which is why they can't overcome the above symptoms no matter how hard they try. What the believer needs to do is come out of submission to this wrong programming in their soul and into security in Christ in order to be delivered from the dominion of darkness, and for the power of the enemy to be broken off their lives.

If you recognize what's discussed here as your personal experience, be it to a small or large degree, please realize that God's already been working to bring your soul out of the false programming it has been operating in. If you feel overwhelmed or hopeless, please remember that the power is in your faith, not in your will and certainly not dependent upon what you've experienced. To date, most everything you've experienced was likely a big show put on by darkness to convince you how afraid of them you should supposedly be - and to convince you how much God doesn't care about you or how incapable He is to bother stepping in to help.

You know faith comes by hearing the truth of the Word of God. And you may know many aspects of God's truths. But what I've found is when our souls are indoctrinated via a lifetime of dark kingdom rule, we struggle to connect the dots of truth in order to grasp it so that it will make the change in us. I have found in my personal life that it was not until I connected the dots of truth that my freedom became manifest. And that's what this program is here to accomplish. This page alone has revealed truth to you which should have begun connecting some dots, which will serve to set your freedom into motion. **Realize, the truth really does set us free**. The only reason the enemy has ever gotten away with anything in anyone's life is because he lured them AWAY from God's infallible truth and into agreement or fear or alignment with wrong ideals and lies. Therefore, coming out of alignment with these false perspectives, beliefs, and practices **literally nullifies the power of the devil *on the spot***. Which is why the enemy works so very hard to keep you discombobulated, overwhelmed, confused, preoccupied, sidetracked, flustered, upset, feeling guilty or ashamed, beating yourself up, disappointed, hopeless and/or weary. **So that you don't connect to the truth and power to overcome.**

So do not be discouraged. Please spend some time right now just thanking God. Put all the bad down and meditate on that which is GOOD. (Use one of the coloring pages if it helps.) If you are not feeling it, that's okay. Do it anyway. It's called a sacrifice of praise which means you're doing it because God deserves it even if you are upset and don't care that He does. Just do it. You'll be activating God's power, putting God's reality into motion - regardless of what you feel. Gradually you'll FEEL God, not the darkness. Because that which you focus on is what increases. Don't think, "Well, I'll be lying if I praise God right now because I'm feeling negative/angry/hurt". Not true. You are not lying. God is still worthy even if you aren't feeling how worthy He is.

You may also feel like you'll never overcome your personal issues and false programming. But that is NOT TRUE. I don't care how you feel right now. If your feelings are anything other than assurance, then they need kicked to the curb. The truth is what's relevant and needs expounded upon so that IT is what grows and manifests. Please believe me. I lived in a very defeated place for decades! I know what it is to feel like it's hopeless and that nothing will ever change - including me! But as I shifted my focus and confidence onto God despite whatever song and dance the devil was doing, things began to change! KNOWING the truth. And not just knowing it in my head - but **knowing it in my innermost being, deep down in my soul! When my soul got it, things changed! So, take that position on purpose, defying your feelings, if that's all you can do right now.** God has brought you to this program to shed light on the truths you need that will do the work in you. You cannot overcome false programming and false behavioral tendencies EXCEPT that you honor and unite with the power of God that is in you. And the only way to unite with it is to take your eyes off the lies, discover the contrary, and believe it. Which is what you are doing right now. Amen.

Notes/Prayers

Dark Systems

Pre-Program 3

We know that God is sovereign. There is none like Him. And He is above all things - including every power of the enemy. But it appears the enemy has the upper hand in the world and EVEN in the lives of God's people! Countless believers don't experience victory over the devil but, instead, routinely suffer great assaults. I'm not talking about trials that God permits for the sake of refinement. I'm talking about believers who have unexplainable dark clouds following hard after them. And this is baffling. It leads many into confusion or despair wondering why God won't deliver them.

Though this will sound cliché, it's true nonetheless: **God HAS delivered everyone that believes on Him!** But see, that's the point... His deliverance is manifest for those that believe! Now I know you are obviously a devout follower of Christ who certainly believes in Him, or you wouldn't be here! But hear me out.

Several years ago, while consecrating myself to the Lord, He said, "Paula, you believe *but you don't believe.*" The thing is that though I adamantly believed Jesus was the Son of God, God in the flesh, the Great I Am, that His ways were right and true, and that His death redeemed me of my sins, **there were so many aspects of His kingdom that I was not walking in alignment with**. And the fact is, alignment with truth is one and the same as believing. On one hand, yes, I totally believed. On the other hand, I didn't.

God showed me that the hidden areas of my unbelief were to my downfall. Because where I didn't believe God, I unwittingly placed confidence in the ideals of the dark kingdom. Unbeknownst to me, I was bowing to the devil which gave him legal access to me. Consequently, he had a measure of freedom to interfere with my circumstances!

There were many dark systems in place in my life whereby just about everything I put my hand to was derailed or sabotaged! Walls continually barricaded me, and injustice may as well have been my middle name. Because there was dark interference with everything I did. Again, it wasn't about the types of trials everyone deals with once in a while . This was about being followed by dark clouds. And despite pressing forward against the resistance for decades, I never got anywhere. Because the dark systems methodically made sure of it. All I ever managed to do was just get by.

Briefly, just as God assigns His angels as ministering spirits to help and serve His children, the devil has his own angels assigned to God's children as well. Of course, their mission is broad. First, they strive to keep the person from submitting to God and receiving Christ as long as possible. Second, they strive to inundate the person with as many false ideals, idols, and perspectives as possible so that when they do come to Jesus, they'll be confused deep down and will lack clarity of heart and conviction. Third, once the person does submit to Jesus, the dark strategists strive to keep the person bowing and yielding to old ways and old belief systems so that they won't excel in Christ, and especially in His power and authority; and so they have legal rights in their lives. And finally, in so much as the dark powers maintain legal rights, they strategically set up dark systems with various dark angels each having their own organized assignment to keep the person where they want them. For example, one minion might be assigned to setting the person up for sin or failure. Another's job is to keep reminding the person of certain things that trigger downward spirals. Another might be responsible for making sure friends, family and colleagues poke and jab them in the particular ways that will incite certain negative responses. Still another might be assigned to not allowing the person to accomplish whatever endeavor they are attempting, such as getting the promotion that they truly deserve, or even finding a job that pays properly. And yet another might be assigned to their dreams, to taunt them or stir up painful memories or wounds to keep them bound and aimless. While another might be assigned to keep them from connecting with the relationships God has for them; or keep them from receiving the blessings, provisions, gifts, or even wisdom that God sends to them. And on and on it goes. It's very well orchestrated and very real. Of course, these dark systems are only possible and effective where there is legal access - and when a believer doesn't know how to exercise the authority of Christ.

These were the types of dark systems that dominated my life for decades. I'm sure there are many more. Regardless, they are no longer effective in my life. I believe they've been dismantled or merely become devoid of power. Either way, these mighty forces are no longer mighty against me! And let me say, after beating your head against the wall for years over being at the mercy of such darkness, you can't imagine the joy of finally seeing it all dismantled - all because you finally came into alignment with truth! I am living proof that God delivers. But I'm also proof that deliverance directly correlates with one's belief system! **I WATCHED my life CHANGE as my belief system did!**

Oh, the enemy is still around. I still discern the dark kingdom and recognize the strategies they still attempt. That's par for the course so long as we're still on earth. Trials are still a part of life, also, just as Jesus said there would be. But, what's different when your belief system comes into alignment with the real, complete truth of the Word of God, is the enemy loses legal access! The devil suddenly has difficulty getting anything over on you to hold you back. True, he may score here and there, but he knows the control and liberty he once had over your life via the profound dark systems he had in place which successfully confounded you... are behind you! Once you come into this place, there's no going back. You cannot unlearn what you know. So, the devil is defeated.

Satan KNOWS this. He knows that if your belief system is brought into alignment with the truth and you grow up in Christ's authority that not only is the power he's had over your life going to be lost to him forever, but that you'll become a PROBLEM for his kingdom. So he is working VERY hard right now to thwart you from this. Understand that the devil doesn't want you to begin and COMPLETE this program. Because he'll lose his reign over your soul. So, please... Be sure to complete this program if it's all you do. And watch as the dark systems are disabled.

Now I'd like to ask you to consider taking some time to write out an assessment of your belief system. **Ask God to open your eyes to seeing where you are strong in your faith vs where you are weak.**

For example, are you secure in God's love for you? If you don't "feel" loved, then you aren't secure in His love for you. Do you "know" He is on your side in your innermost being? Do you "know" He shows up to help EVERY time you need Him - despite what the enemy has accomplished against you? If you said no to any of the above, this is a form of unbelief. Not comprehending God's love is not your fault. But it's still a form of not believing Him. This is one major way your belief system could be off. Write this down and talk to God about it. Take notes on anything He tells you. And ask Him to illuminate where you do have doubts or fail to believe or trust Him. *Even ask Him where you have more confidence in the dark systems that have been reigning in your life.*

As God shows you these things, repent and be cleansed of these false beliefs. Not because it's your fault, but, though unintentionally, because you yielded and submitted to the lies, system and policies of darkness. Repenting establishes your renouncement.

Next, ask Father God to give you scriptures to meditate on that will drive the applicable truth into your soul whereby it will take root and change you. **Note that He will add to this list ongoing throughout your journey.** You will likely not hear answers immediately but they will appear when least expected. When you receive any insight as to your belief system status, record it here and discuss it with Father.

Scriptures that speak Truth against the dark systems in my life:

_____

_____

_____

_____

_____

_____

_____

_____

_____

_____

_____

_____

_____

_____

_____

_____

_____

MY BELIEF SYSTEM ASSESSMENT

_____

_____

_____

_____

_____

_____

_____

_____

_____

_____

_____

_____

_____

_____

_____

_____

_____

_____

_____

_____

_____

_____

_____

_____

_____

_____

_____

_____

_____

_____

_____

_____

_____

_____

_____

_____

_____

_____

_____

_____

_____

_____

_____

_____

Now I know that:

_____

_____

_____

_____

_____

_____

_____

_____

_____

Notes/Prayers

You may find this strange, but hear me out. As I'm sure you already realize, there is an assault against the physical and mental well-being of mankind in this last hour. That's overstating the obvious but things have been set up in our world (depleted over-processed foods, chemicals and heavy metals in the air, water and foods, big pharma, EMF radiation, etc) which inundate, disturb and break down the physiological, chemical and biological processes of our bodies. We've known all that, but have we realized, **the enemy can manipulate and oppress humans through these vast physiological vulnerabilities**?

One of the tools set into place to pummel the well-being of mankind is the inundation of electrical field toxicity, simultaneous to our separation from the earth's electrons. So, you can imagine that if a believer has particularly weak genes unawares, it's the perfect opportunity for the dark kingdom to take advantage of this and do all it can to assault these vulnerabilities by luring such believers into tremendous exposure to these invisible toxins?

It is a scientific fact that the earth is loaded with electrons that, when connected to any living thing including plants, animals and humans, they transfer life into them, and perform many amazing processes in these living things to keep them well and thriving. One of the processes is the electrons are antioxidants which collect toxins to remove them from the body via the body's elimination systems. I have personally researched this and experimented with the validity of the power of earth's electrons to improve the well-being of living things. The first test I did was on a plant I had in my house. Two weeks after purchasing my poinsettia, it began to wither, petals began turning black to fall off. I remembered about the earth's electrons and connected the poinsettia to the earth (research 'earthing' to find out how). Within a week it looked brand new, full of vitality and brilliance. And it lasted for three more months! By St. Patrick's Day, it was time to say good-bye. I saw with my own eyes, the power of the electrons of the earth!

But since the 60s and 70's when leather (conductive) soles on shoes were replaced with rubber or plastic, mankind has become more and more separated from the earth and its electrons. Rubber, plastic and things like dead wood and asphalt separate the feet from the earth's vitality. Consequently, we became less connected to one of the most powerful life bearing sources available to mankind. It's amazing how we'll spend billions of dollars a year on health products to get well while most are clueless to the best health resource available in the ground they no longer walk on. I've come to understand that the earth's electrons are as important to our well-being as sunshine, water and fresh air. In fact, seeing how there are millions of nerve endings in our feet which transport these electrons all throughout the body instantly upon contact, there's no question - God put electrons in the earth to help us be well. Yet, not only do we overly protect our feet with shoes that forbid the electrons from reaching us, but we live in buildings that are not grounded themselves. Even in high rises that are all the more separated from the electrons the higher you go.

Simultaneous to the separation from earth's electrons, the world is polluted with insanely high levels of electrosmog. Long before cell towers and wifi, even. Ever since electricity was introduced, where it's not grounded and shielded as well as it could be, it causes both electrical fields and magnetic fields to fill its surroundings. Especially in enclosed areas. I know this for a fact because I have various meters and have measured it all. I can tell you that in my own home which was built in the 50s, where the upstairs wiring was not grounded as opposed to the downstairs wiring which was, the readings on my laptop or cell phone chargers are insanely high upstairs while they are only slightly high downstairs. So these fields have been plaguing us for many decades already.

Then along came antennas for radio and later television. More fields. More frequencies. And finally, along came the inundation of the high frequencies put off by cell phones, towers and any wifi device. Not only are these devices EXTREMELY high in magnetic fields AND electrical fields, **especially while charging**, they're also super high in radio frequency fields while communicating with the towers.

It's all too much to lay out here. Please research it more deeply. For now, I am just giving you an idea of the facts behind what I'm about to tell you to do. The bottom line is if you live in a home or work in a building:

- built before 1980
- even worse, that is high off the ground
- even worse, with power lines attached to your bedroom wall or where you spend a great deal of time
- even worse, that's near major, high tension power lines and / or antennas or cell phone towers
- in a dense city as opposed to lesser populated areas
- and you use electronic devices a lot (be it a computer, tablet, video games, cell phones)
- even worse, in enclosed rooms
- and you never really have contact with the earth

Then you need to go touch the earth right now - if even for two minutes! Go touch the bare earth or even a tree, with your hands or feet, if possible. If it's cold outside, even **just one minute will drastically help.** Another thing that helps you discharge is if your plumbing is all metal, your bath or shower may be grounded which means showering will help as well because the water should be carrying the electrons from the earth through the grounded pipes. However, if it is not easy to make any contact with the electrons in the earth even for just a few minutes a day, there are earthing products on the market you can use in your home (although I made my own). See earthing.com. They sell bands or mats you use to connect to the ground outside so that the electrons can travel through them to your body when you wear the band or touch the mat. (Just be sure to connect the products directly to the earth outside using one of their 40' cords and rods. Do not trust plugging the band or mat into your outlets even if the tester says they're grounded. I've seen where even grounded outlets are unreliable!)

Please understand, **the enemy knows you need electrons and counts on your not getting them**. And he knows the influx of electrosmog is very toxic to the body - especially the more disconnected from the electrons you are! Worst of all, the enemy knows the chemical, physical, biological, neurological imbalances that all this causes and HE USES IT TO HIS ADVANTAGE! **An imbalanced mind and body is very vulnerable**.

We know the Bible tells us the spirit is willing but the flesh is weak. Well, when the flesh is infiltrated with mass electrical, toxic chaos (on top of all other chemical and environmental toxins), it struggles all the more to live by the spirit!

So, do whatever you can to touch the earth even with your hand if it's too cold to go outside barefoot!

Next, STOP touching your keypad on your laptop while it is plugged in and never put it on your lap! Get a wired keyboard if possible to reduce electro toxic influx. Also, **DO NOT HOLD YOUR PHONE, TABLET or IPAD while it is CHARGING**. I have measured these fields and they are astronomical while they are charging, and this goes straight into the body - which I also measured!

Next, keep your devices 4 feet away from your body while sleeping, keep your wired alarm clock far away from your bed (they're extremely high in fields!) and do not sleep or hang out in spots where power lines are attached to the outside walls, where your wifi router is located, and where electrical panels are. Try to put a MINIMUM of ten feet between yourself and these high EMF field locations. And do not hang out in an enclosed room where your router is. Crack the window from time to time to allow the fields from the router to escape. Ideally, it would be best if you could get ethernet cords and turn off the airborne wifi signal from the router to your devices. That's what we do and it makes a huge difference.

Of course, this won't remove all of the inundation that you may be working or living in, but those are the most excessive, ridiculously high offenders. Making these adjustments and touching the earth at least a couple minutes each day to discharge and grab some life bearing electrons will help you to stabilize and not be so vulnerable to the assaults of darkness.

But just what does electro-toxicity have to do with demonic assaults?

I know for a fact the enemy uses the electrical toxicity in the body to taunt people because someone I know who has been oppressed by darkness for decades stayed in our home once - and the bed he slept in was directly where the power lines are attached to the house. I did not know any of this back then to know what was going on, but he was convinced my house was haunted because of the things that happened while in that spot, and how badly he was tormented in his sleep. He refused to ever sleep here again. (Btw, I know our home was not haunted because one time I saw a perimeter around the home whereby a particular demon assigned to me was forbidden from crossing to enter the home. However, the demons assigned to the man that had been successfully ruling him for decades had a field day (no pun intended) when he entered the very high electric, magnetic fields in that spot. His personal demons were able to torment him far more intensely than usual.)

And I know a Christian woman that was oppressed by darkness as well, who frequently experienced peculiar demonic things I won't go into. She was often distressed with their blatant taunting. I came to discover she lives in an older home with power lines attached to her house right where her head was while sleeping, along with her alarm clock right there AND their wifi router beneath her night stand table, AND with a bunch of cords under her bed! Her toxicity made her so vulnerable to the demons which continually harassed her. I don't know how or why the spirit world has better access to people through their electrical imbalances and instability, but they do. God revealed and confirmed this clearly.

The final reason I know the enemy somehow utilizes electrical toxicity is years ago I personally would have night terrors of demonic assault, sometimes even waking to a demon straddling me and trying to choke me to death. Of course, the Name of Jesus was sufficient to its defeat. But the night terrors were relentless. Only to find out later, this was when I slept in the other highest electric field smog in my home! So, I'm telling you... the enemy DOES use electro toxicity against children of God. Even if you are not experiencing such blatant manifestations, if you aren't feeling well, have inflammation, lethargy, pain in your body, mental fog, and many other things including disease, you are likely suffering EMF toxicity. And it helps the enemy's cause against you. So, seriously...

GO TOUCH THE EARTH AND REDUCE YOUR ELECTRICAL TOXICITY STARTING RIGHT NOW! Before even attempting to start the program! And then do your best to slowly become electrically balanced. This will bring physical, psychological and emotional healing to your body, in addition to delivering you out from being electrically vulnerable to demonic attack. In fact, if you ever feel the heavy pressing of darkness on your being, go touch the earth immediately and praise the Lord. You'll see darkness flee on the spot.

If this reading right now finds you in the middle of distress, worry, frustration, or something along those lines, I pray you will *stop in your tracks and gaze upon Jesus for a few minutes right now*. We know He is our light and joy. True, it is so difficult to care about that when we're in the middle of trying situations that have us conscious of everything BUT the wonder of our Jesus. Yet, I have found that learning to get caught up in Jesus, and the Father, DESPITE IT ALL, and staying there, totally dismantles the effect the circumstances of life can have on us. **And the longer we stay there, the more the circumstances in our lives begin to reflect and manifest God's kingdom reality, not the devil's.** Living a destitute life becomes overridden with living our destined life. Bottom line - looking up, choosing peace, choosing joy, choosing love, choosing forgiveness, choosing humility, choosing confidence in God's love, choosing assurance that He is there, choosing kindness, choosing self-control (etc.) causes the injustice and unruly dark forces surrounding us to lose more and more ground. Eventually our surroundings look more and more like GOD'S KINGDOM INSTEAD even IF the demonic forces still rule the people around us.

Dear Heavenly Father,

You brought your kingdom to us and we know that Jesus has overcome this world, but we're still learning how to walk in YOUR REALITY as opposed to the only reality we have ever known. Father, forgive us for buying into the presentations of the devil - and not fully believing your reality that's absolutely here with us. Please help us to do so. Help us not be naive, believing the charades of darkness. Help us to not be disturbed by the situations in our lives. Father, help us to see the real reality, that you are who you are, and that you are on your throne IN US, always and forever, and that all the evil in the world will never change that. And that if that's your reality, then that's OUR reality.

Father, please help us connect with the reality that because you are always on your throne, and because you are forever for us, nothing else matters. Everything that transpires in opposition to your love and favor for us is dead noise. But we struggle to see it like this. These things impact our lives in terrible ways, making life difficult so this is what we focus on. And it's wrong. Father, help _____ go to a deeper level in responding to what's REAL according to your design and not the devil's infiltration. We know you allow trials for different reasons. And we know you cause all things to work together for the good for those who love you and are called according to your purpose. So help us to be secure in this, secure in your goodness that despite the issues of this life, you have us - ___**and this is what's good.**___

Father, I ask you to release a deeper level of understanding of your love so that we place less and less dependence upon the things of this life in order to feel good about it. I declare the truth... that this day is good despite whatever is going on, because YOU ARE. You made this day. Oh Father, how majestic you are, having done what no man can do. How you have carried us through this life even when we felt abandoned and alone. How you have been so close to us despite our having no awareness of it! Father, let _____ be fully aware of this reality from now on. Change our perspectives from that of being clueless of your passion and your profound involvement in every detail of our lives, to that of having full consciousness of it. Let us see, God! Let us see you. And let us bask in what YOU are doing... not what the enemy has been doing. Help us to know in our innermost being that all that matters is... You.

Father, I call _____ out of the old and into the new. _____, don't let your past experiences continue to color your perspective of God. Don't let what you've known continue to suggest that it was truth, because it wasn't. Though things truly transpired, they weren't "of" truth, so you can choose to discount them, deeming them irrelevant to your existence except for what God would use it for.

Heavenly Father, I ask again that you bring this understanding into _____'s soul, and replace the false programming where all the rigmarole of darkness has held relevance. Father, help _____ to be resolved about the truth that so long as you are on your throne, life is good.

Amen.

--------------Feeling Guilty? Defeated? Like a Failure?--------------
Here's My Prayer For You

If you feel guilty for not being on top of this program thus far, the devil is trying to use it to remind you what he's been drilling into you for years - that *"you are a failure"* or something to that effect. If that's the case, STOP.

Listen, we're all works in progress and spiritual fatigue or lethargy is a sickness. But let me tell you that the first line of defense against this particular sickness is Vitamin C--- which is Confidence!

Be CONFIDENT that the Father has called you out of spiritual defeat! Do not judge yourself for not yet overcoming the lethargy that comes with it! Stop feeling guilty for not measuring up to your ideal you yet. You know healing is oftentimes a process. I know you may have been in this condition for years or decades but being down on yourself for not moving faster is NOT HELPING. It's, instead, bowing to the devil's suggestion to beat yourself down. Please realize that every time you are discouraged or disappointed in yourself, feeling guilty, etc., where you lose heart, you are agreeing with the enemy and giving him approval. You are likewise NOT resting in grace. You're dissatisfied that Jesus had to cover your failure. You must resist all this from now on. When God convicts you, you won't feel beat down. You'll feel remorse but liberated for having been forgiven. You'll feel inspired to move forward and do better, not sit there in shame and disgust with yourself. That's the devil!

Meanwhile, be CONFIDENT that God's got you and is helping you move forward. If all you can do now is take baby steps, AWESOME. **It's anti-christian to be down on yourself for being where you are** - and allowing yourself to dread it will help KEEP you there!

Heavenly Father, Thank You for the ability to learn and grow in your truth. Lord, I lift up the ODJ members into your hands right now, asking you to please place a hedge of protection about their bodies, minds, spirits and souls as they endeavor to dig into your reality all the more. Father, your truth is all powerful and I ask for it to break through and into every soul today, to do a mighty work like only your truth can. I speak to all barriers and shells, blockades and deceptions to fall off of _____ and all other members' eyes right now as they persist in studying your truth. Open the eyes of their spirits and enlighten them like never before. I speak life into their souls now. And I speak that the deceptions and lies that have attached themselves to your children will disintegrate as we speak, Lord.

Father, you know they are yours but, for those who are wondering if it's too late, or if they really aren't yours, I command that lie to come off of them right now in the Name of Jesus! If there's sin, Lord, help them to lay it all at your feet right now, no matter how big or small, and trust that You are capable of cleansing them from it!

Father, if they haven't been able to trust you because of all the work of darkness that's worked against them all their lives, please forgive them. And please expose the liar and give _____ and the rest of the ODJ members clear understanding of the TRUTH that's been hidden from them! I speak TRUTH into their souls right now. Hallelujah!

Now please stay close to them as they move forward, Father. And I speak to every adversary to STAND DOWN now in Jesus' mighty Name! You may not interfere with the work the Lord is doing in _____ right now.

Have Your way, Father. Have Your way. In Jesus' Name, Amen.

Meditate while coloring: "God loves me! His help is here! He cares about this situation! God is with me no matter how thick the darkness. You are beautiful, Jesus. Thank You for being ever perfect and sovereign. I rejoice in You, my King! You are ALL that matters!", and so on.

Because you are taking the ODJ Program which demonstrates a desire to come into the full stature of Christ, I'm going to assume you're a genuine disciple of Christ which presents two strong possibilities as to why you are likely oppressed by darkness, be it severely or not.

The first (obvious) reason is that the world (including "Christians" who aren't disciples) doesn't like disciples. True disciples are truth bearers and truth lovers. They are the salt of the earth. Salt is known to be used to purify and keep things from rotting. Being salt to the earth, then, is having a life that, in all its purity, either cleanses or stings the world around it - or both! Believers that are truly salt to the earth tend to hold people accountable to righteousness. They tend to speak up about the truth when necessary. And let's face it - almost nobody wants to hear the truth anymore! So, being salt to the earth means you aren't going to be very liked.

Not to mention, disciples are also the light of the world according to Matthew 5:14. And we know that, "Light has come into the world, but people loved darkness instead of light because their deeds were evil. Everyone who does evil **hates the light**, and will not come into the light for fear that their deeds will be exposed", John 3:19-21. If disciples are the light and the world hates the light, then the world hates disciples. Though this is obvious, many disciples struggle to accept this reality. Otherwise they would not be so stunned or even debilitated by it. And the bigger issue is, though we know the Bible tells us this, we don't recognize that the various types of adversity that go on in our personal lives is because of this very reason. Many disciples are repelled by the world - even in the workforce - because of the light in them. Even if these light bearers aren't preaching, witnessing, testifying or saying a single word, they're still emitting light. And the darkness dislikes it.

But there's far more. Another reason true disciples are oppressed by darkness to one degree or another is if they were born into households that were dominated by darkness - as in, the family didn't follow Christ.

When children are born, the devil knows which among them will not only become born again believers someday, but will be the salt of the earth. Hebrews 1:14 says, "Are they not all ministering spirits, sent forth to minister for them who shall be heirs of salvation?" Well, just as there are different people with various purposes and gifts, there are different types of angels, each with specific ways to minister to the heirs they're appointed to. The devil plainly sees what types of angels are assigned to a newborn and can deduce what type of threat to the dark kingdom that child will become. Babies that are marked as the "salt of the earth" are some of the worst threats the enemy faces. So, these little grains of salt are targeted early on by the dark kingdom to be pummeled by darkness.

Now if the child is born into a household dominated by the kingdom of darkness, where Satan has great influence, their task to indoctrinate the child with lies and flood the child with distress throughout their youth is quite easy. Not because the child's angels are too weak to protect him, but because of legalities. If the parents do not give the household to Christ and truly submit to, trust and rely upon His headship, the dark kingdom has legal rights and direct access to the child. And how do we know this? Because the Bible says Satan is the prince of the air, Ephesians 2:2. It also says that believers have been rescued from the dominion of darkness and transferred into the kingdom of God's dear Son in Colossians 1:13. Therefore, if a family doesn't truly believe in and follow Jesus, their children are subject to the rule and inundation of darkness. And the babies born into a household dominated by darkness that have anointings and the call of God on their lives become mega targets by the powers assigned to that household. Those children end up going through hell growing up - in order to hinder their capacity to believe the Lord with all their soul, one day.

Let me reiterate. The children born as grains of salt who will one day find Jesus are severely targeted by the dark minions assigned to the family. As these babies grow up, they are strategically stripped of their value and any sense of dignity through any assortment of assaults be it rejection, bullying, neglect, trauma, mental, physical or sexual abuse, or anything that will serve to program fear and defeat into them, and crush their spirits. It's a very methodical system at work in these young lives which trains their souls to be insecure and doubt God. But they have no clue this is happening to them. All they know is they routinely endure being reminded, perhaps, how inferior, useless or alone they are. Whatever works best, the minions will orchestrate circumstance after circumstance to control the child through dysfunction. Then when the day comes that they do find Jesus, their souls remain profoundly vulnerable to the control of darkness through their subconscious minds and belief system. Where, at the surface they are believing and following God, but subconsciously they're still in fear of the next failure, violation, or let down.

This may not be your situation, but I venture to say that if you are severely oppressed and have been going through the same cycles for decades despite following Jesus for years, you most likely were born into a family where the enemy had charge and had legal access to your life growing up. And if that is the case, then realize that the reason all the terrible things that happened to you in your childhood and beyond is because the devil knew you were a true disciple of Christ, even before you did. And he had to fashion your belief system to make it faulty and unstable, whereby you'd be more confident in him than the One you call Your King.

Realize that if this is your situation, even if not severely, all you need is to be delivered from the devil's deep-rooted programming and be brought into full alignment with truth. That's what you're here for, after all. But get excited because the blockage, barriers, lethargy, defeat and all else as you've known it will be dismantled. If you commit to thoroughly going through this program, I assure you, oppression will become a permanent thing of the past!

Now the reason Satan must put these forces against the grains of salt that are born in the earth is because he learned over the ages that if he can get a stronghold on these grains early on in their lives, if he can get them rooted deeply in lies of defeat and hopelessness, **it will be difficult for them to come into the POWER and AUTHORITY OF CHRIST once they give Jesus their lives. They'll be double-minded, believing God at the surface but doubting Him in their subconscious, thus creating a disconnect between them and the power of the truth.** So their ability to be salt, though still there, will be hindered because of their instability. The devil mangles the souls of these children so well in hopes that, when they're grown and following Jesus, they'll spend more time in despair over his relentless works against them than being the victorious salt to the earth that they really are.

As for why Satan can continue to get away with influencing and incessantly disrupting the lives and destinies of true disciples, it's because these disciples unwittingly still agree with or bow to the deep-rooted strongholds he instilled in them throughout their lives. Disciples that continue to operate in fear, insecurity, inferiority, hopelessness, anger, bitterness, jealousy, pride, and so on, "believe" in the enemy and this gives him a measure of access and authority. But this program will help you sort through your faulty belief system which will bring you out of alignment with darkness - which will deem the enemy POWERLESS over your life once and for all.

Meanwhile, if you were a victim of rejection or some other form of hateful acts against you in your life, remember that Jesus told His disciples, "This is my command: Love each other. (But) if the world (even your family) hates you, keep in mind that it hated me first. If you belonged to the world, it would love you as its own. As it is, you do not belong to the world, but I have chosen you out of the world. That is why the world hates you. Remember what I told you: 'A servant is not greater than his master.' If they persecuted me, they will persecute you also", John 15:17-20.

And, in Matthew 5:11, Jesus says, "Blessed are you when people insult (revile/abuse) you, persecute you and falsely say all kinds of evil against you because of Me. Rejoice and be glad, because great is your reward in heaven, for in the same way they persecuted the prophets who were before you. You are the salt of the earth. But if the salt loses its saltiness, how can it be made salty again? It is no longer good for anything, except to be thrown out and trampled underfoot". In other words - DON'T QUIT BEING SALT no matter how painful it is to continue.

Finally, I'd like to ask you to please ponder for a moment what the life of a prophet in the Old Testament must have been like. Take Jeremiah. God continually told him to tell the Israelites that they were disobedient and that God was going to crush them. Does such a person have many friends, if any at all? Especially when all he does is preach and nothing happens. It took over 20 years for Jeremiah's "doomsday" prophecy to occur. Imagine the nuisance Israel must have perceived him to be. He saw things as they really were and constantly declared it. Unfortunately, just as it is today, nobody wanted to hear the truth. And note that Jeremiah wasn't speaking to the world, but to his own people; to the people of God. And they didn't like him. Well, chances are high that you are somewhat like Jeremiah, if even on a much smaller scale. If you're reviled (abused and mistreated, always putting up with flack one way or another), then Jesus equates you with the prophets of old and says you will be greatly rewarded!

There's no question that believers who hunger for righteousness and strive in a deeper way after truth end up having more than their share of pain and problems in this life, because the people of the world and even in the Church tend to dislike them. Consequently, the most sincere of all believers who aren't secure in Christ yet take this personally, feeling defective or inadequate for being different.

It's been my experience and also what I observed with others, that it's hard to connect with people in a real way when they are okay with the ways of this world. Truth lovers tend to only want to connect in a "truth way". So, it's not possible to be real and connect with people that are not "in" the "truth way". And since there's so few who are "in" the "truth way", this makes life on earth kind of lonely for those who are.

Plus, if you are compelled for truth and righteousness, then this life presents challenges at every turn because you're at odds with just about everything that goes on! And this can make you look or feel like the bad guy. Since most of the world, including the Church, is not interested in the whole truth and real righteousness, this tends to cause righteousness-seekers to be outcasts and isolated in heart. From there, they can be tempted to take on false self-perspectives and feel like something is wrong with them. Perhaps even hating being so different. Being set apart can feel like a "dark" place despite the fact that it's actually a place of profound light.

But, you know... This tendency is only likely if we're still earth-minded (as opposed to eternal-minded), if we're not secure in God's love, and if we're not yet rooted, grounded, and established in God's Word.

It's true that the kingdom of darkness has dominion over the earth. But, as I've said, children of God "have been rescued from the dominion of darkness and transferred into the kingdom of God's dear Son", Colossians 1:13. So, **we no longer have to be subject** to dark policies, veils, walls, clouds, or any other form of evil rule and oppression. If we are still dominated, stifled, confounded or perplexed to any degree by darkness, it's because of at least one (or more) of the following:

- we do not yet know how to contend with trespassers
- we are blind to an aspect of God's truth which makes us vulnerable
- or we're likely in agreement with or yielded somehow, somewhere, someway, to policies of darkness.

There may be several things you have to learn before you will no longer be vulnerable to the dark kingdom. That's what this program is all about. By the time you finish it, you will be well rooted and established, firm in the truth, and untouchable.

But what about right now?

Though you may not be established yet, *there is still a way to be completely untouchable right now*, and it's by hiding under the Almighty's wing. And the way to get there is, first, by believing that Jesus is the way to the Father. So, answer this: *Did Jesus make the way for you to connect with the Father?* If yes, you can continue on. If you have any hesitancy in saying yes, you need to search God and discover this reality. **You need to truly believe this.** Otherwise, the rest of the program from here on out is irrelevant to you.

Now, if you KNOW Jesus made the way for you to get to the Father, you must now do the following:

- Get alone with God, somewhere private so that there's no distractions.
- Humble yourself. Remind God that you know that you were bought with a price and that He is the author of your life; that this life is not your own. If you've been chasing your desires and seeking your life, even well-being and healing, OVER seeking God first, repent.
- Repent for all other sins, including all unbelief and doubt. Ask God to create in you a clean heart and to renew an established spirit within you.
- Now, take your eyes off what the devil is doing. Take your eyes off the assault(s) even. I know it's hard. Especially if you've just taken a serious blow. It hurts. **But look away from it right now**. In fact, lay the situation, the offenders, the knife that was used, the pain, the consequences, all of it, at the feet of Jesus; and leave it there. Realize that the more you look at the garbage, the bigger it becomes and the worse it smells. **Take your eyes off the garbage, regardless of how violated you were, and lay it all at the feet of Jesus.**
- Now look at what matters. And what does matter? **The only thing that matters is that God is what's good, holy, eternal, constant, unending, perfect, wonderful and just.** That even while there is nothing reliable in this life, Jesus is. That even though you are pummeled, this Ancient One remains upon His throne, never shaken; never hindered, never defeated. That even though you suffer now in a broken world, the Majestic One has made a way for you to be one with Him in eternal bliss some day and offers you supernatural

peace in the storms of this life - if you'll lay hold of it. The only thing that matters is HE IS WORTHY despite the injustice and wickedness on earth. I repeat: The only thing that matters, the only thing of significance, the only thing of relevance, the only thing worthy of our attention, is that **God is worthy despite everything**. God is absolute. God is beyond wonder. God is above all the raging darkness in the earth. God is the only thing that matters. So go to that place. Come into that reality. Step over into the conscious resolve for the only thing that matters. Reject all else. No matter how disturbing it all is. I'm telling you, none of it actually matters. Seriously. Don't bow to the disturbing aspects of this fallen, broken world! It's momentary, having no eternal effect. It does not matter. It is not relevant to who you are or your destiny. Mind the reality that matters. Humble yourself to this truth. **Jesus really is the only thing that matters.** Am I telling you anything I've never done? No! In my darkest moments, I chose to focus on the fact that GOD IS STILL ON HIS THRONE, and wonderfully so. It is comforting to bask in that which is certain, beautiful, perfect and infinite when everything around you is falling apart. I learned to look past it all to that which is absolute and constant; and my joy was full despite the pain. I learned the truth as to how God literally is my refuge and strength in times of trouble, Psalm 46:1. Because HE IS. He simply and forever... IS. This is what kept and still keeps me. Discovering and laying hold of this helped change my life. In my darkest hours, I now know to just look at Jesus and my Father. And I become overwhelmed with thanksgiving that HE is my absolute.

- Assuming you have truly laid everything that the devil's been doing down before God; and assuming you have stepped over into the reality that Jesus is the only thing that matters, now surrender your all. Tell God all that you are has come from Him and you give it all back to Him. Every hope, every desire, every ambition, every goal, every idea, every plan, and every dream. Give God your family and career, or lack thereof. If you still battle with lusts or have addictions, confess that you know He is your source of freedom to these and He will finish this deliverance in you - through your submission to Him. If you're full of or even acquainted with resentment, anger, dissatisfaction, fear, worry, discontentment, jealousy, self-defense, selfishness, or pride, confess this to the Father and ask Him to wash you clean. I know you already repented when we started, but this is a deeper level. Repent as you go along, as you come to understand where you've been out of line in your depths. Repentance is key.

- Now tell the Lord that even though you've been a wreck and vulnerable to the strategies of darkness, you know you are safe in His care. Thank Him for being there for you. Thank Him for showing you how to hide in Him. And rest in Him. Knowing He is with you through your journey into manifest freedom. Rest. If you do not feel peace, then you have not fully yielded to the above instructions. Go back and begin again. If you want His peace, you must follow His path to get there. Again, it's through humility, repentance, surrender, looking away from the darkness and basking in the only thing that matters. If you can't look away from the darkness, then it is bigger to you than the Wonder of your Creator. Your faith is in the darkness, not in God. And this is to your demise. You will remain dominated by the kingdom of darkness. Go back and begin again.

What we've just discussed is how to stay safe. Though you may still have particular agreements with darkness in your soul that you do not yet know about which has given the enemy legal authority over you, I'm telling you that by hiding under the shadow of the Almighty through continual humility, repentance and LOOKING AT HIM instead of the darkness, and REMAINING IN HIS PEACE no matter what stunt the devil pulls, **you'll be safe!** You'll be able to focus on this program and excel in your journey into the full stature of Christ wherein you'll finally see the enemy beneath your feet. Amen.

Before we pray, let's be sure to not take any of the following to the altar.

- Insecurity
- Fear
- Inadequacy
- Shame
- Worry
- Anxiety

Let's go to the Lord confident that, though we don't deserve to, He is excited that we did! Because He is so wonderful.

Dear Heavenly Father,

Thank you again for another day to praise you. Lord, I don't know what's going on with _____ right now, but you do, so I ask you to meet them right where they are. Father, we humble ourselves as we come before you, to repent for every known and unknown sin, and ask you to cleanse us by the blood of Jesus Christ, your holy Son. Father, you say you oppose the proud but give grace to the humble. Dear God, please show us if there is any pride in us, even hidden. Let us know so that we can repent. Help us to be humble. Father, you say our hearts are deceptive so we don't even realize sometimes when we're sinning against you, even in pride. So, help us with this. Bring it to light. Let us see it that we may repent!

Lord, thank you so much that you are still on your throne. Despite everything _____ is going through, you remain steadfast and certain. You are our "constant". Without you, we'd be completely destroyed! So thank you for being absolute!

But Lord, we need your steadfast hand to come in and make things right in our lives. We need to be delivered from the liar and even our own flesh. Father, apart from you we can do nothing. So please help us to be one with you, whereby we can do all things! Only you can make this possible.

Father, I speak to the lives of all the members, and every foul spirit that still attempts to thwart your work in them. I speak to every antagonistic and tormenting spirit working against _____, to cease and desist right now by the authority of Jesus Christ! Lord, let every trespasser be stifled now by the power of your Holy Spirit. Send in legions of holy hosts to contend with every power of darkness that's trying to cause any type of trouble in the lives of all these members! God, please reveal your manifest presence to them right now. Please confound and scatter the works of darkness. Father, I speak to everything that's dried up because of the deceptions and strongholds, to come back to life now. Dear Lord, please breathe onto every area of _____'s life, bringing everything to order. Where there has been loss or devastation, please restore! I speak holy kingdom life to prosper in each of the members right now, Lord. Blessed be your holy Name!

Thank you for your unfailing love, God. Please increase _____'s comprehension of your love and passion! Let it become a manifest reality deep in the soul, not just head knowledge! I speak life and perfect love into _____'s soul right now! Have your way, oh God!

We praise you, Lord. Now please give every member, including _____, *the wisdom of God and fresh revelation and understanding, helping them to see whatever it is they need to do to detach from old programming and submit to you like never before!*

Bless _____ *in every way, Father. In Jesus' Name, Amen.*

Before this next module...

Let me give emphasis to a scripture brought to point several times previously. It's important to meditate on this truth and get it down into your soul. When I "got" the revelation of this passage, it changed so much in me! It's one of the most powerful truths in the Word of God in my opinion! And here it is:

"You have been rescued from the dominion of darkness and transferred into the kingdom of God's dear Son!" Colossians 1:13.

If you don't already know this by heart, then it's time to. This is a reality that needs to become a part of who you are. It's your skin. Your identity.

Please memorize, meditate and chew on this reality day and night until it's a part of the very lining of the fabric of your soul. It's key to your victory.

Heavenly Father, Please help _____ to fully grasp this truth and to have the mind to grasp all the truths you intend to convey this week. Devil, get out of the way. You are forbidden from interfering. In Jesus' Name, Amen.

Again, **"You have been *completely* rescued from the dominion of darkness and transferred into the kingdom of God's dear Son!" Colossians 1:13.**

Now read and repeat the following: "I, _____, have been rescued from the dominion of darkness and transferred into the kingdom of God's dear Son!"

It doesn't take long for devout believers in Christ to realize that the moment you start pressing in to God, all hell breaks loose. So, since we know this, let's plan for it.

Make a list of your soft spots, soul issues, things that are easily provoked or hurt in you. Add to that list things that may still be temptations in your life. Add to that list the types of things that get you all worked up or discombobulated. And add anything else to the list where you are vulnerable. This list should comprise all the obvious ways the dark kingdom attempts to bombard us when we're trying to focus on the King. If we are mindful of the types of things the enemy will do to thwart us, we'll be prepared to not fall for it. Of course, if the enemy thinks he won't get away with the obvious because you're a step ahead of him, he will come up with a unique type of right hook to throw you off. But don't worry about this. The fact that you are in "preparation" mode keeps you on alert. So as things arise, you are not "as" shocked and you are quicker at getting your footing so that the devil's attempt is a fail. Even if you begin to falter and yield to the trap or snare, you'll be far more like to catch yourself. Now...

Once the list is complete, here's what to do:

- First, repent for everything in you that allows you to still be vulnerable to yield to these propensities. Don't fret over it, we all have this stuff. The idea is to face it and bring it under the blood and endeavor to truly put it behind us. But for right now, the primary thing is to repent for these tendencies. Something in you is not yet fully aligned with God, otherwise, these would not still be vulnerabilities. But for now, the first thing you can do is acknowledge them and repent. Get them under the blood of Jesus by virtue of sincerely choosing to put them behind you.

- After you've established that you do not want to continue being vulnerable in these ways, THANK the Father for making the way for you to be changed from these ways.

- Now understand, that deciding these ways are behind you doesn't solve the problem, obviously.

- Next, ask the Lord for His mercy and protection over you in these weak areas while you are digging deeply into this program and all else that you're doing to seek Him earnestly. Ask Him to ensure that you are not challenged in any of these areas UNLESS they are an opportunity for you to practice overcoming. Now embrace this in its entirety. You know God uses situations to teach us things. Many years ago when I faced an ongoing trial of pain and was questioning God over it, He said, "Trials are so that I can Teach you, Train you, or Toughen you up". So, it's time to learn to accept the trials that God allows. HOWEVER, as you also know, there are other times when devastations or injustice and such were strictly unnecessary assaults from the enemy. They are extra efforts to pummel you to keep you from growing closer to the Lord or get you off track. So, though you must not presume you can pray all problems away, you CAN entrust the details of your life to God, asking Him to not allow any unnecessary assaults! To deliver you from evil. And trust that He'll make sure of it. That's one thing we all have to learn - is to rest assured that if we ask for God's help with something that's His will to begin with, He WILL SURELY DO IT, NO QUESTIONS ASKED. (Perhaps you should talk to Him about your confidence levels right now if this is an issue. Because if you don't believe He'll surely do what you ask concerning this, then this gives the enemy rights!) But back to the point, in all CONFIDENCE, ask the Lord to protect you from all the devil's crap while you're trying to dig in and learn. And He'll put a shield about you - only allowing situations to occur to give you an opportunity to practice responding according to what He is teaching you or what you're seeking to learn at that particular time. And note: If you fail, no worries, He'll give you a new situation to practice handling yourself according to His truth.

- Next, be prepared to walk out the truths you are learning. Meaning, don't just read the Bible or a teaching and not chew on it and resolve to apply it. Make SURE to spend genuine time meditating on what you are learning. This is where we go wrong. We glaze over everything. Then when life happens, we're operating how we always have, totally unaware that we were just given new techniques to apply. So, take everything God shows you very seriously and deeply ponder and meditate upon it so you are full of it when the opportunities arise.

- And finally, prepare your mind and heart that it's okay to go through God permitted trials. Don't dread the songs and dances the devil does put on. It's time to be less devastated over the things of this life, even the bad! Trust me, I've been down some very painful roads. But I've learned not to get swept away by the terrible things of this life. Honestly, I can say that some terrible things have happened in my life this past couple of years that would have sent me into profound despair and hopelessness ten years ago. Because I now choose to walk in the truth of God's peace. Jesus truly is all that matters. True, the stuff of this life does matter but only to a point. ONLY to a POINT. It's all beneath Jesus. None of it is eternal. The only thing eternal is my response to it all. So please, stop being devastated by the devastations. Choose peace. Choose joy. Even despite them. Because you do, after all, still have Jesus.

Now how can we tell the difference between God-permitted trials and an unnecessary pummeling? Well, unless God reveals it, we can only suspect which is which. Sometimes you can just tell when it's just relentless and ridiculously evil. But I think when God allows trials, we sense God in the midst of them if we are abiding in Him. Bottom line, we don't know for sure. But if you'll take the approach of being prepared, all the while praying for God to protect you from the unnecessary stuff, then you can be confident that whatever happens as you begin digging deep into His truths is because it's something to practice overcoming.

You'll be surprised how taking this perspective and preparing in advance as to how you are going to deal with the devil's schemes seriously changes everything. I mean, you still have to go through it and you won't be perfect, but you'll see yourself growing in leaps and bounds! And, because you're praying, you'll see far fewer unnecessary assaults!

Now it would be good to create a list of:

- Your soft spots, pain areas in your soul where you're tender, sensitive, vulnerable or easily provoked
- Sin areas of weakness; temptations
- Things that throw you off, make you feel discombobulated

Remember, it's best to know ahead of time where or how the enemy is going to try to pull something in order to thwart your focus off what God is showing you and doing in your life. This isn't being focused on the devil. It's being aware of the systems at work. Being mindful of your vulnerabilities and asking for God's help with them is an excellent way to *not be vulnerable* to the enemy's tactics anymore. Since you know, now, that the minions assigned to you know which buttons to push to make you crack or spiral down and away from Jesus, you'll be on the alert and not fall for it so easily.

In fact, they're good at setting you up, reminding you of failures and stirring up old wounds before they strike via a new but similar assault. For example, say Jane Doe has been rejected all her life and moves to a new school or job to start over. The night before her first day, she dreams of something that stirs her rejection wounds, waking up hurt as if it just happened, carrying that throughout the day. While at school or work, at some point in the day, her demons successfully cause someone to reject Jane. Bingo. Two points for the dark kingdom. Now Jane Doe is in lock down, goes into her coping mechanisms, and worse, if she's trying to press into God, she is seriously struggling because her soul is in a whirlwind...again. That's how things go. Of course, for some believers, it may require a series of separate events to get them all discombobulated. But you get the point. The minions assigned to believers know which button(s) to push to keep them down, or send them on a downward spiral so they can't see or feel God. All we believers have to do is know our vulnerabilities, be on the lookout and use this knowledge to heal from what we now fully get that the DEVIL was behind with every assault that ever came against us.

And watch... Once you become wise to this, you'll pick up what they're up to while it's unfolding right before your eyes and you'll find yourself saying, "Yeah, right... Not buying it, devil. I know you're strategizing, just playing on old wounds YOU instituted throughout my life! And yeah, they still hurt. But now I know it was all tactical so I'm getting over it fast! Thank you, Father, for setting me straight on this!"

Again, realize the minions that are assigned to you know you very well and have been working strategically for years doing what they know works best against you. **So be sure to create your list of vulnerabilities in order to be wise to their strategies against you.** And keep it handy so that when they pull their stunts, you'll be prepared to not fall for them so easily. Things might sting but if you can quickly remember it's all a part of their system, you'll sober up from it far more quickly which is to THEIR defeat.

Please do not undermine this step in your journey! Please put deep thought into it and even ask God to let you know what you should include on your list. He'll tell you things you otherwise won't think of. Be ready throughout the day for the Lord to say, "X or Y is one of your vulnerabilities" and write it down on something immediately so you don't forget. Below is a list of potential vulnerabilities and history of wound types to help trigger your personal soft spots:

- not being understood
- being looked down on
- feeling inadequate, inferior
- failure
- being the bad guy / scapegoat

- being disliked
- being hated
- being rejected
- being bullied
- being scorned
- always criticized
- perpetual hardships
- always losing, anticipating loss
- and so on

Sin Areas / Temptations Examples:

- pride
- self-seeking, self-serving
- entitlement mentality
- taking matters into own hands
- needing to be right, heard, believed; defending self
- back-biting, jealousy, dissension
- worrying over money, kids, life
- resenting people, circumstances or self; hatred, bitterness
- unforgiveness
- fearing conflict, injustice, defeat, rejection, disappointment, etc.
- idolatry, obsession over things, relationships, even success
- pornography
- self-mediating, alcohol, drugs, cigarettes
- and so on

MY HISTORY OF SOFT SPOTS & VULNERABILITIES

_____

_____

_____

_____

_____

_____

_____

_____

_____

_____

_____

_____

_____

_____

_____

_____

_____

_____

_____

_____

_____

_____

_____

_____

_____

If you're anything like me, you've asked the Lord, *"Father, since your Word says we have the victory, especially over sin, why don't I?"*

Decades ago, while singing the old hymn "Victory in Jesus", I knew the bottom line meant that we who are saved win. That it's because Jesus SAVED us that we have the victory. And this was, as you may know yourself, so comforting; even exciting!

But as the years passed, I didn't feel so victorious. I saw myself operating in cycles of the same old sin - despite being a devout Christian. I had learned in the Word that I had power over sin through Jesus. But this power seemed lost to me. Where was it?

The truth is the power wasn't lost. It was still in me. But the clever kingdom of darkness knew how to push my buttons and influence my belief system so he could veil it. The reason the power of Christ in me seemed lost was because I listened to what the enemy had to say and was more concerned about his power to prevail against me which meant I didn't yet believe or KNOW the validity of the power of Christ in me. Therefore, though in me, it was lost to me. The seed was in there. It had even taken root. I know it did because of how thrilled I was in knowing that the victory was mine through Christ, when singing the hymn throughout the years before.

But that old serpent... Just as the devil snatches up the seeds that fell on the path, he still had profound influence over my soul to peck away at my belief system, at my sure confidence in that victory. Remember, the dark kingdom has had thousands of years to perfect their strategies. We may have been born recently, but the dark kingdom wasn't. They know what works and how to mess with believers just the right way to get them all discombobulated.

Though I knew that the victory through Christ was a sure thing... I didn't "know" it. Not when the circumstances of my life continued to look dark. Not when I remain defeated. And certainly not when I lived on a "sin-don't sin" seesaw for years.

Please understand it was my lack of assurance in the truth that hindered the power and victory from taking manifest form in me. It was in me, but wasn't able to manifest due to my lack of resolve for and confidence in it.

So what's a believer to do when the devil is so clever and is all up in our business when we don't even realize it?

That's what the Church is for. We're supposed to be there to mentor, teach and guide one another. And fortunately, many people are helped out of their discombobulation and into truth by the elders. But, sadly, the enemy has done so well to infiltrate the Church better and better over the decades that he's been quite successful at hindering the body from caring for, equipping, and raising up new believers soundly.

But no need to despair. God saw this day coming. It's all a part of how things go in the final hours. He speaks about how in these last days the Church will be a mess. Yes, that's what He said. People will be lovers of themselves. They'll chase doctrines that tickle their ears. The love of many will wax cold, etc. There will even be a huge falling away from the Church (2 Thessalonians 2)! So, it's all par for the course. All the mess in us and in the Church should not be this way, but it is this way because of the hour we are in. The antichrist is soon to rise...And Jesus is soon to return.

So take heart, everything is going to be okay soon.

Meanwhile, God is delivering the true Children of God from their mess. He's calling us out of our discombobulation and breaking the power of the devil off our minds and souls! He's showing us how to align with the truth so that His manifest power finally DOES TAKE OVER in us. We are rising up!

So where are you? Are you resolved in the knowledge of the victory of Christ in you? Or are you like I once was... defeated despite the power of God that is in us?

You can find the song, Victory in Jesus, on Youtube. Meanwhile, here are the lyrics if you'd like to chew on them awhile:

> I heard an old, old story, how a Savior came from glory
> How He gave His life on Calvary to save a wretch like me
> I heard about His groaning, of His precious blood's atoning
> **Then I repented of my sins and won the victory**
> Oh victory in Jesus, my Savior forever
> He sought me and bought me with His redeeming blood
> He loved me 'ere I knew Him and all my love is due Him
> He plunged me to victory beneath the cleansing flood
> I heard about His healing, of His cleansing power revealing
> How He made the lame to walk again and 'caused the blind to see
> And then I cried, "Dear Jesus, come and heal my broken spirit"
> And somehow Jesus came and brought to me the victory
> Oh victory in Jesus, my Savior forever
> He sought me and He bought me with His redeeming blood
> He loved me 'ere I knew Him and all my love is due Him
> He plunged me to victory beneath the cleansing flood, c'mon
> Oh victory in Jesus, my Savior forever
> He sought me and He bought me with His redeeming blood
> He loved me 'ere I knew Him and all my love is due Him
> He plunged me to victory beneath the cleansing flood
> He plunged me to victory beneath the cleansing flood

Notes/Prayers

Look, I know you may feel stuck. You may be full of your flesh, full of sin again, or in full-blown rebellion. You may feel completely apathetic, weary, and hopeless. Or maybe you're just at a standstill. You've tried to give your whole self to Jesus but fail, ending up back at square one. Believe me, I know all about this! But it's a LIE!

You are not defeated! Everything you've been living outside of Christ has been an illusion. By illusion I do not mean imaginary. Rather, it's all a result of deception. It's all the result of the dominion of darkness in your life. The kingdom of darkness is a literal kingdom that rules the earth. All those who do not abide in Christ's kingdom, even if they "got saved" remain subjects of the dark kingdom. But for those that did receive the seed of the truth of God's kingdom, who haven't really connected with it, their true reality is one of victory over darkness. But because they haven't connected with this truth, yet, their lives are byproducts of dark kingdom deception; hence, an illusion. That may sound ridiculous but it is true. Everything, the entire cycle of your life, has been because you simply have not connected yet to KINGDOM POWER! I don't care how "terrible a Christian" you've been with your flesh and sin, it's because you haven't truly connected with the truth. You know full well the Bible says that you will KNOW THE TRUTH AND THE TRUTH WILL SET YOU FREE! John 8:32. So, that's the problem. You really don't know the truth yet.

And how can I say this with certainty? Because that's my story. I'm living proof that coming into the truth for real literally does set you free!

For decades I was an avid Christian... following protocol, going to church, serving, giving, obeying, worshiping (I'm a big worshiper), praying, and seeking God. Though the Lord taught me numerous things one on one from 1989 through 2009 via dreams, visions and experiences, and though I learned all the prominent teachings routinely taught by the corporate Church, I was still STUCK. I remained defeated! Come September 2009 when, once again, my back was against the wall with injustice, I went head to head with the Lord. I needed answers or, as I told Him, I was NEVER going to speak of or defend Him to anyone again. Because I was done being a fool that promotes my God when He never shows up on my behalf. I was such a joke to everyone that knew me, especially and painfully, my children, because I always professed God was good. Yet all they saw was my defeat time and time again. Everyone I knew was far better off than I ever was, while I was the one that loved the Almighty. I was the one that was a daughter of the Most High God to (seemingly) no avail! I was tossed to and fro like a rag doll. My life was no testimony to the goodness of God which I faithfully (and seemingly foolishly in their eyes) proclaimed. I was nothing but a joke.

But suddenly, something broke! And God brought all the supernatural teachings He'd personally taught me together, and He gave me great revelation, and suddenly my life was finally on the upward spiral for the first time ever!

The bottom line is from 2009 forward, because of the revelation and new understanding, when I would study the Word of God, I began to see that I never really KNEW THE TRUTH of the Gospel. Not really. And so many aspects of what I did know via the popular teachings of the Church, were simply incomplete or off kilter. I began to see how the enemy has infiltrated so much of all that goes on in the corporate body. But as I dug in and grasped the REAL truth for myself, THINGS BEGAN TO CHANGE. And the kingdom of darkness lost its power over my life! **The more I aligned with the real truth, the more I saw the enemy defeated in his**

tactics against me! And the false reality I'd been living was dismantled, while my true reality took form!

I'm telling you, I knew what most everyone else knew about the Bible but didn't actually know the real truth of God's Word from 1989 to 2009. I didn't. My belief system was all messed up! And this is why I was defeated all those years. And now that I know that I know that knowing the truth really does make you free, because I'm living proof, I have set out to teach the real truth - to make my brothers and sisters in Christ free, too!

I don't care how defeated you think you are. The POWER of the truth is a seed inside of you because you took the first steps towards Christ. Now all that needs to be done is you need to get to know it and align with it, and you too will be free!

Forget what you feel. Forget it now! Disregard it. It's empty noise. It's all an illusion because your rightful reality is inside of you waiting to be aligned with via the truth. Everything you are experiencing now is a FALSE reality occurring outside of the TRUE reality. All you have to do is connect with YOUR TRUE REALITY.

Still think you're defeated? STOP! You aren't. It's your false reality! Take heart. You may still experience manifest defeat for a while. But don't worry about this. God told me once that today's circumstances are a harvest of the previous season's seeds of doubt. Meaning, what you see today is a harvest of what you've planted recently via your faulty belief system and sin. Don't fret over it because all harvests die! To the contrary, dwelling on it, complaining about it, or worrying over it, is sowing those same seeds for a new harvest to grow. So don't! See that your current harvest (all your circumstances) will die and your new quality seeds of truth that are being sown even this moment will indeed grow! But as it is with any harvest, you must give it time! KNOWING it will bear fruit! So I repeat, see your circumstances as a dying harvest and that it's all a byproduct of your false reality which is being usurped by your true reality - even now as we speak!

Please know that this program *will* align you with your true reality! Again, this is going to take a little while because there's a lot of aspects of your belief system that need tweaking; and it takes time for new harvests to replace current harvests of lack and problems. But for now, regardless of where you are, how addicted you are, how angry you are, how defeated you are, how depressed you are, or how stifled you feel, etc., it is IMPERATIVE that you know that it's all your false reality. Make this known to your soul! Give God praise right now telling Him how thankful you are that the mess or even just the apathy, confusion or lethargy of your life **is all false**. It's not your rightful reality! Thank God that the seed of His Kingdom Power is deep within you, waiting to be watered and brought to life! Amen.

Intro to Section One

If you're one that's been going in circles getting nowhere all your life, I understand that you're desperate for things to change and might be longing for a single teaching or two that will set you free in a snap, and be done with it. You may have been suffering for decades with dark clouds chasing you. Or you may just be on fire and zealous for serious Christian meat! I personally spent decades in both places simultaneously! But trust me when I say, my life changed because God straightened out my belief system which took time - many, many years, in fact. So that's why I'm starting from scratch with this program, regardless how many years you've been walking with God. The Lord showed me so very much that's off in us and in order to walk in truth, we must know the whole truth accurately. That's what needs to happen in order to come into the full stature of Christ as well as experience genuine, permanent, God-instituted deliverance from every level of oppression. And it needs to start with the bare bones of Christianity. Or you'll never truly be free. So be patient with the next few modules. We'll be getting into the heavy stuff soon enough!

Listen, whether you've been suffering or not, let me remind you that Christianity is not what it's supposed to be for most of us. And that's because the Word of God isn't readily taught and comprehended as it should be. In order to come into the full stature of Christ (and out of suffering at the hand of the devil) we must become one with the truth. That's what the Holy Spirit personally taught me to do - and it's working! Unity with God's truth is the key.

Heavenly Father, Thank you for your wonder. Though we cannot comprehend it fully, thank you for granting us the privilege of getting to know you. Oh Lord, I pray for every

ODJ member that you rectify all that's wrong in their lives. Father, please bless, elevate, inspire, and even restore hope and well-being where needed. Please do a deep work in every ODJ member's soul. I ask you to help _____ to fully grasp every truth you intend to convey this week. Please have mercy and forgive every member wherever they may still be aligned with the policies of darkness, knowingly or not. Satan, the Lord rebuke you. Back off from the Children of the Most High God, regardless of where they are in their walk or understanding of Him. Father God, in addition to the power of your Spirit, send in your holy hosts to protect, guide and help _____ in every possible way.

In Jesus' Name, Amen.

I'm not sure if you are familiar with the song called the Days of Elijah, but I'm going to reflect upon it here to make a point.

Though the writer of this song says his inspiration was to speak a message of hope during trying times, I believe it had far more of a prophetic purpose than Robin Mark could have possibly imagined as the song took form.

It was prophesied over me in 1998 that I would be a witness to the truth and the light, but I had no idea what that fully entailed. I probably still don't. However, what I do know at this time is that God has revealed that He has actually raised up many witnesses like myself - believers whose eyes have been opened as mine have been - in order to illuminate the **real truths of God's Word** in this last, very dark hour. We are called to prepare the bride for her Groom's pending arrival. You are called to this purpose yourself. I believe I'm called to help you.

A profound strategy has been at play through the ages; the Lord has all of the pieces in place. While I thought my mission was specifically to teach fellow believers how to overcome darkness and to rise up in Christ, I now understand that congruent to this is the call to *"prepare ye the way of the Lord"*. Amen.

As Robin's song conveys, *"These are the days of Elijah, declaring the Word of the Lord. And these are the days of Your servant Moses, righteousness being restored. And though these are days of great trial, of famine and darkness and sword, still, we are the voice in the desert crying 'prepare ye the way of the Lord'!"*

We think the song points to the gathering of the harvest of unbelievers, but this is only the half of it. Note that Elijah, Moses, David and Ezekiel (all referenced in the song) didn't minister, so to speak, *to the lost*, rather, their call was to Israel! To God's chosen people! **And the mission of the Old Testament prophets was to call an adulterous, pagan-ladened, self-serving people BACK to their God!**

Consider how in 1 Kings 18:21 Elijah said, *"How long will you waver between two opinions? If the Lord is God, follow him; but if Baal is God, follow him."* ~I'm afraid Elijah could say these exact words to the Christian 'Church' today. Indeed, some of us do follow the Lord, but we follow all sorts of other things, too.

You may be here to get a solid grip on your walk with Christ and to come into manifest victory over the powers of the air to which I say, "Praise God". **But please realize that the real reason you're here, whether you knew this or not, is because God sent you - to come into full alignment with truth so that your life can be a manifest witness of the kingdom of God for such a time as this.** You know the Word says in Matthew 5:14 that we are the light of the world. But the light of the Church is presently rather dim, isn't it?

I say all this to ask you to please recognize the necessity of becoming completely right with God; getting rid of all kinks, hidden deceptions, unbelief, and any other potential error of the soul. Note that I didn't bring up sin. Not because it's irrelevant, but because the primary goal is to get the kinks out of our faulty **belief systems** so that we can THEN overcome sin! Time is running short. You don't need to just overcome darkness for your own sake, but for the world's sake around you. Especially in the days to come! When great distress hits the entire planet. Please understand this and commit to seeking God with all your heart like never before. And please use the ODJ Program as a tool to help you along your journey. Be resolved to complete it in its entirety. There are many aspects of the truth of God that need to be understood by God's children, many things I had to walk through just so I could learn and receive various insights that are not readily taught 'at church'. And realize that I do not tout this program because I developed it, but because I know the Holy Spirit began this thing in me back in 1989 and that everything I've been through and learned ever since has been for this hour.

So please, no matter how well versed in the scriptures you are or aren't, no matter your credentials or lack thereof, no matter your background, please humble yourself to what's laid out in this program asking the Lord to give you a witness to it if the contents are, indeed, from Him. Allow Him to speak to you and shed light on anything that is in you that needs tweaked, corrected, and repented for. It's time to come into alignment. It's time to prepare ye the way of the Lord.

In case you're wondering if I've arrived, the answer is an emphatic no. Please understand I am learning even as I am preparing teachings! Holy Spirit just won't quit. When He finds a student that really wants to learn, He runs with it! Praise God. And I'm sure He's only just begun to teach me thus far. But all I have that He has given me, to the best of my ability, I work very hard to present in the most accessible and comprehensible ways possible - which happens to be this program. And I pray every word in this program that is not from God falls to the ground devoid of meaning. To the contrary, may every word in this program that is from God go forth mightily to connect with the seeds of life in the hearts of God's people, and bring them all into full alignment and the full stature of Christ.

Let me say that "The Days of Elijah" is not just a powerful worship song. No, this song is a prophetic rendition of the hour we are right now entering! It's straight from Heaven. Look how emphatically the Lord is trying to get our attention, to show us what's going on. Now let's respond and get ready. Let's do all we can to align ourselves with the kingdom of God and His truths. In Jesus' Name, Amen.

Find some time soon to color this heart and deeply meditate on God's love for you and who you really are in Christ. Block all negativity out. Lay all burdens down. Use this time to bask in God's wonder. Let every stroke of color carry you into the presence of The One Who Authored that very color. Gaze upon Jesus. Seek His face. Think upon all that is wonderful and true. Praise the King. Give Him thanks. Worship Him. Glorify His Holy Name.

Imagine that instead of being born as an infant without full mental capacity and awareness, you came straight from the Father into this life as a full grown adult, fully conscious from whence you just came.

And from where did you just come? Well, before the Father breathed your soul out from Himself, you were in a place of eternal love. You were surrounded by splendor, glory, holiness, and perfection. It felt so wondrously peaceful, so beyond words. You were completely safe, engulfed in the totality of the majestic, holy One who loved you beyond measure; never experiencing even an inkling of distress, worry, concern, or pain. The glorious One snuggled you closely in the center of His ancient grandeur. There was no such thing as failure and defeat, shame or distress there. What were such things? What was it to labor and toil? What did that even mean? What was it to be agitated or provoked? What was it to feel jealous, lonely, rejected or abandoned? What would having a thorn in your side feel like? These were all unknown, because there was no such thing in that eternal place. You were in perfect harmony with the Author of wonders, swimming in a sea of ecstasy, peace and divine love. This was your only knowing.

But suddenly, you were breathed into an earth body as a full grown adult, instantly made aware of the profound, unexplainable shift from eternal bliss into perpetual darkness. You see portals of the light of bliss from which you just came. You see shadows of the goodness of glory in the canvas of the earth. But apart from these random reflections of the eternal, the energy of the atmosphere is unstable and contentious. It's ladened with heaviness. Though you have no idea what it is, you smell the stench of rebellion and discord in the breeze. The offense of the liar and sin violently assaults all your senses and knocks you off your feet! You are completely stupefied! What is going on? Where is perfect peace? Where is perfect love? Where is the Author of Majesty? And what on earth will you do?

After some time, the shock wears off and because you KNOW what you KNOW to the contrary of this horrific illusion, you're determined to find your way back home! No matter what it takes. You must find it and enter back into that perfect place! And nothing can stop you because you know where you came from is real and supreme, and that where you are now just isn't right! You don't understand the why or the how of this alternate reality, but you do know beyond a shadow of a doubt... it isn't your home. It is not your destiny. And nothing will stop you from finding your way back.

You are quickly drilled on the requirements of living in this finite place where, if you do not work and acquire resources to care for yourself, you would die. So, you submit to the requirements of earth. You find a job and you go about the details of earth living.

But you've got something far more pressing on your mind. In your coming in and going out, you're constantly on the alert, looking for that way back. Looking for the glorious One from whence you came. You know He's out there. But where? And how do you get back to Him? Despite the number of days, weeks, years and even decades that pass, this is your utmost desire. This is what you seek more than anything. You do what you have to do in this life. You make the most of it. You put your best foot forward towards the best outcomes. You even acquire a spouse and experience carnal things that didn't exist where you came from. And it, along with other pleasures of this life, are good. But, they're just par for the course. What you *really* want is to go back to that place in that One, that glorious One from beyond the firmament. Because nothing else compares. You see the world's obsession over its riches and wonders thinking how it all pales in comparison. It's all

NOTHING. You're never concerned with the things of this world. You certainly don't obsess over them. You just go through the motions outwardly while inwardly, you're forever asking, "When will I ever go home?"

Unfortunately, we don't have the luxury of remembering where we come from. Otherwise, we'd be in hot pursuit of the Father and the things of this life would not take His place.

Instead, when the Creator breathes a soul out from His wondrous self, He sends it into a tiny, virtually mindless, body so that there is no shock to the new, very harsh, surroundings. So that it will gradually acclimate to the disturbing atmosphere. In the hope that one day, when the child begins wondering about the meaning of life and how all things began, it will hopefully begin its pursuit to find its way back home.

Unfortunately, the soul also took on the corruption of the darkness which could terribly hinder its subconscious knowing that there is, in fact, an Author over its existence. Plus, the soul is limited by its carnality. It cannot discern God very well because its spirit is dead. So rediscovering God is challenging, to say the least. Aligned with darkness, dominated by a sin nature, and only knowing how to pursue and satisfy the desires of its flesh almost forbid a soul from finding the truth. Is there any hope?

For the souls that say, "Wait... I just know there's something more!", yes, there's hope. Because deep inside of them, beneath all the corruption, is a knowing. Deep in the recesses of the subconscious, they remember the Father. And God, in such honor and tear-filled delight that they remembered Him despite the separation and inundation of a false reality, quietly responds to that soul's innermost being,

"Yes, my dear child, you're right. And how I've missed you so much. I sent you away to give you the choice to come back home. And, you remembered Me!

But though we must remain apart for a while longer, rejoice, because I sent the power of my spiritual government into your world for you to lay hold of. I made a way through the death of my Son to bring you back here to us. But... you must believe and seek to find me with all your heart, and you will.

And because you only understand the system and government of earth life and even the kingdom of darkness wherein you have been living, you must seek to learn the reality of my government and the truth of your real home and destiny. Don't remain compelled for your earth reality as you have understood it, but get to know your eternal reality. This must be your greatest desire now. Not the things of carnal life. Yes, you will continue to live and experience the things of the finite realm, but don't overly esteem them any more. They are temporary and don't compare to your eternal future. Therefore, with all your heart, keep your mind stayed on Me. Learn everything you can about me, including all the precepts, statutes and nature of My kingdom. Seek to understand and walk in your eternal identity. Discover who you really are and let my light shine in you unto all the earth. And I will put My Spirit and power in you to teach, comfort and guide you back into perfect peace and safety, with the authority of my Son over the darkness in the world where you live, until it's time for us to be together again forever."

Before we pray, I just want to ask you if you've been experiencing transformation in your soul. See, God tells us to love Him with all our heart, all our mind, all our soul and all our strength for a reason. And it's because our mind might be thinking one way while our souls are thinking another.

When I began to get to know the Lord in the 90's, it was mostly out of my head and heart. My mind and heart were zealous for God and would spend the next 20 years passionately declaring all the truths of His Word that I knew out of that zeal. It was real. It was genuine. I defended my God tooth and nail even in the face of injustice, as the people in my life refuted Him. Because my heart and mind were convinced of all the truths of God and His goodness.

But, unbeknownst to me, my soul wasn't on board. The abuse and torment of my past had programmed my soul to feel very alone, abandoned, rejected, etc. My soul did not believe in love; it had no comprehension of what it even was. My soul was very self conscious, and remained in self-preservation and self-protection 24/7.

Does this sound like the attributes of a Christian? Yet, because my soul could only go by what it knew, it was unable to see the light or comprehend the same truths that my mind and heart were so very passionate and convinced about. While my mind and heart rejoiced over how much my Heavenly Father loves me, my soul was blind to it, despondent, and hurt by His supposed lack of love. My soul was actually in hiding, afraid, on guard, and still separated from God.

After several years in this ministry, God showed me clearly that this was the case with most of His children, not just me. That this is a huge way the enemy interferes with our ability to connect with God and rise up in our faith and destinies in Christ. This is what I feel led to pray concerning it right now.

Dear Heavenly Father, First of all I ask you to forgive us for everything that's off in our soul, from not recognizing your truth and love on account of all the false programming we adopted because of the darkness we've endured throughout our lives. Lord, we ask you to forgive us for buying into the illustrations of darkness which made us blind to the truth; and we ask you to restore our soul's sight now.

Father, please illuminate the areas in _____'s soul where the enemy's policies have been yielded to, agreed with, bought into, and adhered to. Father, you know that _____'s heart is truly for you despite the confusion in the soul. Father, please undo the programming of Liar. Please go into the deep places and shed light on any darkness. Lord, we cannot do this ourselves, only you can do it. So I ask you to dismantle the lies that seem so real, and help _____ to see things as they really are even at the subconscious level. Let your love take over every department. Let truth take root and prosper. Father, you desire that we would prosper even as our soul's prosper. Please do a mighty work in _____'s soul right now. Do a complete transformation and begin to walk _____ into total prosperity in every facet of life.

Oh God, I praise you for being so eager to help us. I know you are calling us into your fullness - and into every purpose you had for each of us. I know you are on the move. I know you are the one that is zealous now. Praise you Father! Thank you for what you are doing in our lives. Thank you for the changes in us. Thank you for helping us to know how high and how wide, how deep and how long your love is for us. Because it is. Because it is; it really is.

Breathe now upon _____ a fresh touch. And I ask for your guidance this week in all matters. I pray you give _____ the spirit of Wisdom and Knowledge for every decision. Your will be done in all matters.

In Jesus' Name, Amen.

Aspects of God and His Truth that My Mind (and Perhaps My Heart) Swear By - But My Soul Doesn't Agree or Comprehend:

_____

_____

_____

_____

_____

_____

_____

_____

_____

_____

_____

_____

_____

Notes/Prayers

--------------------------Have Things Heated Up?---------------------
My Prayer For You

There's a good chance things may have heated up in your life since you began this program. If that's the case, I am sorry things go this way but please count it as a good thing. Remember, the dark kingdom does not want to lose its influence over you (be it big or small), because you'll become more of a threat when they do. The more truth you align with, the more of a threat you become to the kingdom of darkness. Whatever is going on in your life, take heart, Jesus has overcome it. That certainly sounds cliché but it is, in fact, our reality.

You have a wonderful future ahead of you! That may not take the sting out of current, crappy situations, but I'm here to encourage and remind you that your hope really should not be in this life. As you know, we have an astonishing future with the Great I Am ahead of us where the troubles and challenges of this life will never exist! We have an eternity of wonder to look forward to! And we're supposed to keep our hearts and minds fixed on this so that we do not get sucked into the drama of this broken world. Please keep this at the forefront of your mind ongoing. This is what really matters. Doing so aligns with God's kingdom and enables God's dynamics, such as peace, prosperity, and the power to overcome the darkness of this life, to manifest. I can only say this because I know it for a fact! However, the more I pressed in to ascertain this reality, the more the devil acted up trying to dissuade, discourage or distract me. But I learned to deal with it all God's way which changed everything! And you can do the same. Because Jesus really is for us. This is all that matters at the end of the day!

If things haven't heated up for you, I'm shocked. We have to wonder why the devil isn't afraid of you yet. Why he isn't trying to keep you from deeper study - including the teachings in this program.

The next module entitled "No More Struggling to Read the Bible" may not pertain to you or seem to have any relevance to things. I know, you're eager for meat! But bear with the nuts and bolts. Besides, you may get something out of it just the same.

Now before I pray, let me reiterate that if things have gotten somewhat chaotic, or the waves of life have kicked up a notch since you began the program, you already know that it's because you're trying to press into deeper truths that will absolutely bring you into cleaner alignment with God - which terrifies the enemy. So do not be alarmed or bow to any of the ruckus. Do not meditate on who did what or anything negative. The enemy is behind it! Take all burdens to Jesus and ask Him to help you deal with things, without dwelling. Focus on Jesus and do not let circumstances control you. Center yourself on truth. The chaos, injustice, insults (etc) DO NOT MATTER despite how terribly they hurt. The only thing that matters is Jesus. Know that the devil just needs to act out or poke at you to keep you off course! Do not allow it. Stay focused. Keep going. Be steadfast.

Dear Heavenly Father,

If things have heated up in _____'s life, I ask for added protection, increased wisdom and understanding, and increased guidance as to how to deal with it all. Lord, you say you have overcome the world but that doesn't mean living in it is a piece of cake. In fact, we cannot do this life apart from you and your help. So, please do help. Your will be done in every matter going on. Again, please give _____ wisdom to see what's really going on and to not get caught up in the drama of this life. Let us remember our eternal destiny and that it is all that really matters in the end. Meanwhile, Father, I call all deceptions and strongholds to be dismantled. And may your truths ever expound deep in _____'s soul this week and onward, Father God! In Jesus' Name, Amen!

This may not be your struggle, but please bear with me...

After being born again and baptized in 1988, I was given a King James Bible. As it is with most, reading something written in the language of the 1600s just wasn't workable for me. But the bigger reason reading the Bible was such a challenge was because I still operated under the perpetual demands and aspirations of my flesh.

The flesh does not have any real capacity or aspiration for the Word of God. Indeed, scholars can read the Bible from their flesh because their intellect is a prominent strength within all the skill sets of their flesh - craving knowledge - but not revelation. Therefore, they won't connect with the spiritual insights of the Bible because they are veiled to carnal minds (despite how brilliant) unless their soul humbly and whole-heartedly seeks these incomprehensible things of God and His truth. Meanwhile, the majority of mankind, including many of the souls truly seeking Him, have a hard time picking up the Bible because the flesh which still dominates them does not resonate with it - and it's too overwhelming. Even after being born again, if the flesh is allowed to maintain dominion, the believer will subconsciously continue to resist the Word of God because it's the antithesis of the flesh system. This goes the same for those who are born again who also have the minds of scholars, able to read difficult material within the confines of their flesh. If they aren't transformed by the Word they're reading, their flesh remains in dominion as well.

That's why there's such emphasis, after you are born again, to commit to a genuine Bible-based, Holy Spirit-filled church. Because the things of the flesh that most of us are entangled with upon entering new life will choke the life of God right out of us if we don't connect with a support, accountability, and solid, truth-based guidance system (and hopefully a good one, which is hard to find these days).

I understand now that those who dive in deep, genuinely searching God and His Word passionately at the get-go and being transformed by it, had to be good soil to be able to begin consuming God's Word and its revelations right off the bat like that. Unfortunately most new believers aren't good soil, so learning God's ways via Bible study, sermons and things like Sunday school are crucial because this begins the transformation process whereby the flesh is put down, and the spirit grows in Christ - as the kingdom truths are yielded to and applied, that is.

This steadfast alignment with truth, even in its beginning stages, brings the spirit into dominance and, with more of the flesh out of the way, the spirit's desire for understanding and revelation of God takes over. This is when the desire for reading the Bible, though it may still be challenging, increases. But without training in the truth, without connection to accountability and support of other believers, the flesh is allowed to remain in charge. Therefore, unless the decision is made to put the flesh under, any reading of the Bible is minimal at best. Unfortunately, for me, it would be a couple of years before I was involved with a church to begin learning to put my flesh under. But when I did, the Word called out to me; inviting me to feast.

Concerning the dominance of the flesh, do you know how in the parable of the sower (Matthew 13, Mark 4 and Luke 8) some seed fell on the good soil and some fell on the path, some fell on rocky soil, and then some fell on soil among thorns? Well, we know that for the seed of truth that is planted on 'the path', the devil comes quickly to steal it (talk them out of it). The reason these people are referred to as a path is because nothing in them received the seed. Their hearts weren't really interested. Therefore, the seed lays at the surface where the devil can come snatch it away easily before their hearts do take interest and receive it. Then, the seed of truth that is planted in rocky soil is zealous for God and quickly grows a bit. But when troubles or persecution occur on account of their new faith (people insulting or rejecting them for it), the truth dies in them because they care more for being accepted than the truth of reality. They are rocky soil because their hearts were rocky, not able to receive the truth down deep where it could grow with vitality and resilience to persecution or rejection. And finally, we know that the seed which is planted in soil among thorns does indeed grow, too... but it desperately struggles to thrive because, as I discussed earlier, their flesh and all its aspirations and burdens for this life, choke out their spirit's longing for the truth of the Word. The seed does take root because the person is resolved and fully received it deep in their heart. But as it grows, it's all entangled with its desires for, cares for and issues of this life. This was my problem. The soil of my heart was tremendously tangled up with thorns. This, I believe, is the most common reason believers struggle to read the Bible.

In my case, post traumatic stress, depression, and the massive chaos my soul was in - all its issues of pride, self-preservation, stubbornness, rebellion and idolatry, desperations, lusts, fears and longings - constituted a mega thorn system that polluted the life of Christ in me. And after working with countless people over the past decade, I see that these are the most common thorns in the lives of believers. If you relate to this, you'll find great insight and help with it in other teachings in the program. Just be sure to complete the entire program! It's imperative.

Meanwhile, what I'm telling you is that if you struggle to read the Bible, it's because your flesh is still dominant. So, if you are connected with other believers, a solid truth-teaching church or Bible Study, and if you are receiving these truths that are taught and you're applying them with all your heart, yet you still struggle to read the Bible, then your flesh is likely still dominant on account of hidden thorns in you. And you must avidly work with God, desperately seeking Him to expose the thorns so that they can be burned up. Again, make sure you complete this program. Otherwise, you'll remain full of thorns which will continue to be the biggest reason you not only can't read the Word of God, but can't grow up in your kingdom of God identity. On the contrary, the sooner you identify the thorns and get rid of them through your submission and cooperation with the Holy Spirit, the sooner your flesh will be hushed with your spirit increasing. At which time you'll instinctively be compelled to seek and find God by reading the Bible.

NOTE that if the compelling for deeply knowing God and learning His truths ever diminishes or disappears, then realize that your flesh may be peaking and if you aren't on watch, this could lead you into a downward spiral.

Now, based on my personal experience and AFTER the issues of the flesh are addressed (though these are an ongoing battle), there are some additional tips that will help. Because even while the flesh is out of the way, the Bible can be rather intimidating or overwhelming:

- Start (obviously) with an easily understood version like NIV or NLT. But always ask the Lord to put emphasis on verses that may be mistranslated so that you can check into things. You can do this through a website called Scripture4all.org. It may not be perfect, itself, but has been a tremendous help to me. I have seen many things mistranslated in every version of the Bible, including the KJV. So, always ask the Holy Spirit to put a check in your spirit if what you are reading is not what He meant.
- Don't be locked into the idea that you have to read the Bible from cover to cover, or book by book. Don't be legalistic or ritualistic about it. It's supposed to be a source of life, not a system. So don't make a huge deal about "what" or "how" you read. At least not in the

beginning. I found the way the Holy Spirit got me into the Bible was by enticing me concerning specific topics. He'd put things on my heart that I wanted to understand. So, what I'd do is go search out that topic to find answers all throughout the scriptures. I wanted to know what the entire Bible had to say concerning the subject. I used a concordance back in the day to look up specific terms (now I just search online) and searched all the scriptures relating to the subject. One thing would lead to another and before you knew it, I was reading all sorts of things in the Bible. Topical studies have been the primary way I read the Bible - in conjunction with what God is speaking to me about. As I matured, I did select random books without a topic in mind and began reading the Bible that way, too, to saturate myself and let the Lord show me what He wanted me to meditate upon.

- If you're not a "reader" because reading anything has always been a challenge due to focus struggles or something, there are plenty of audio Bible sources. Biblegateway is what I've been using for years. I even pull the passages up in multiple versions at once so I can compare. But some versions, such as NIV and KJV, have audible recordings so you can listen to the Bible. This is such an awesome thing! There are also MP3 players specifically loaded with the Bible - as well as CD's and DVD's. These were all very helpful to me during the years where my mind struggled to focus via "reading".

- Do not be legalistic about the idea that there has to be a set time to read the Bible. Certainly, if you are wired to follow a routine, by all means, do so. But I have found that when I'm seeking God with all my heart, I actually spend the days (be it locked away one on one or throughout the day in my coming in and going out), all over the place, back and forth, praying, worshiping, studying a topic, meditating on specific truths, etc. I have no system or structure to it whatsoever. One day I might worship God all day, or glean here and there from solid based teachers online. Another day, I might get caught up studying something specific in the Bible for hours and even into the next day, trying to understand something like the "Full Armor of God" for just one example. Meanwhile, other times I might spend the day fasting and praying, meditating and listening to what God wants to tell me, writing it down, and then searching it out. Then still other days I might soak in full audio books of the Bible and talk to God about them, even searching specific things out more deeply as He highlights them. Then another day I might do a smorgasbord of all of the above if I have time. The point is... Seek God, submit to His Spirit and He will guide you. You'll consume His Word all sorts of ways. It doesn't necessarily have to be a scheduled practice. It merely happens by default of wanting to know God and following His lead.

Keep in mind if you are struggling to comprehend, it is strictly by the power of the Holy Spirit you can do so. He is the one that teaches you and gives the understanding. So simply humble yourself and pray to the Father, asking for guidance believing you'll get it and you will! And also asking what is more pressing on your heart that is actually quenching your thirst, thereby replacing your thirst for Him.

Baptised in the Holy Spirit

On a side note... If someone is telling you that you need to be baptized in the Holy Spirit before you can comprehend the Bible, the fact is if you were born of Christ, His Spirit was born into you. The baptism of the Holy Spirit that happened in Acts at Pentecost, ten days *after* Jesus ascended into Heaven, happened because Jesus had told His disciples to stay in Jerusalem and wait for the power of God to come on them (Luke 24:49). They obeyed this, hanging together in the upper room, praying for ten days. Then, when the various Jews from all over came into Jerusalem to observe a holy day, that's when the Holy Spirit endued the 120 with power. Later, however, other converts were endued with the Holy Spirit instantly, upon being born again (Acts 10 & Acts 19). There's no explanation why the 120 required a specific baptism of the Holy Spirit while others did not. But I speculate that it's because the 120 were born again while Jesus still walked the earth. He'd always said the Holy Spirit (the comforter) cannot come unless He leaves (John 16:7). So, these believers weren't able to receive the infilling of the Holy Spirit til after Christ's ascension - which is what occurred at Pentecost.

The point being, if you were born again by believing that Jesus Christ is the Son of God who came in the flesh, and that through His death and resurrection you have remission of sins and eternal life, then the Holy Spirit was given to you in that moment. If you are struggling to sense Him, His guidance, or His comfort, simply talk to the Father about this from your heart. Be real. Hold nothing back. Ask Him why you do not feel His presence. Trust me, He'll show you. That is, the Holy Spirit will. Just listen to that inner voice which promotes Christ. Press in. Be determined to experience what the Bible says you now have and who you are. Stop at nothing. Go after it. And I assure you, the wall between you and the Holy Spirit will be torn down and you WILL hear Him. And He WILL help you with all things. Including reading the Bible! Amen.

Notes/Prayers

Defining the Gospel

If someone were to walk up to you in the street in an attempt to preach the Gospel to you, they'd likely convey that Jesus loves you and died for your sins. Perhaps they'd offer to pray for a healing miracle and lead you to Christ. Or, if you were to ask people in the streets what they understood the Gospel of Jesus Christ to be, most would say that it's the message of salvation, made possible by Christ's death and resurrection for the remission of sins, for all those who believe in Jesus Christ. In fact, perhaps the number one message preached by the true Christian Church is salvation by faith through Christ. But the truth is, the gift of salvation is a result of the Gospel, not the Gospel itself. So, just what is the Gospel, then?

"Now after John was put in prison, Jesus came to Galilee, preaching the gospel of the kingdom of God, and saying, 'The time is fulfilled, and the kingdom of God is at hand. Repent, and believe in the gospel'." Mark 1:14-15.

And, "From that time Jesus began to preach, and to say, 'Repent, for the kingdom of heaven is at hand'. And Jesus went about all Galilee, teaching in their synagogues, and preaching the gospel of the kingdom, and healing all manner of sickness and all manner of disease among the people." Matthew 4:17 & 23.
Note that Jesus Himself preached the Gospel. If the Gospel was the message of salvation which wouldn't occur for another three years, how could it already be preached?

What Jesus *did* preach was:

- The Kingdom of God is at Hand

- Repent and Believe this Good News

The good news, then, was that the kingdom of God that had been long anticipated, had finally come into the earth. It just didn't come in the fashion the Jews had expected. Israel was looking for a king to deliver them from oppressive Roman rule, to bring the nation peace. Instead, Jesus came and introduced His invisible kingdom wherein its constituents could have supernatural peace - despite Roman rule, despite *all* dark rule in the earth. Though His physical throne had yet to come to earth (and still does), Jesus made His government and reigning authority accessible to our realm *through us*. Jesus came to teach about the system, policies and dynamics of His kingdom, whereby all who submit and believe could be carriers of and partake of its supernatural, manifest reality, authority and benefits right here in the earth.

Now, to be thorough, let me point out that after Jesus rose from the grave and revealed Himself to His disciples, He said, "This is what is written: The Messiah will suffer and rise from the dead on the third day, and repentance for the remission of sins will be preached in his name to all nations", Luke 24:46-47. Note that, though this message in and of itself is great news and absolutely a profound message all its own, Jesus Himself never referred to it as "the" gospel.

Soon after He said this, before ascending into Heaven Jesus told His disciples to teach everything He'd taught them to all nations. Matthew's account says, "Go therefore and make disciples of all the nations, baptizing them in the name of the Father and of the Son and of the Holy Spirit, teaching them to observe all things that I have commanded you", while Mark's accounts says, "Go into all the world and preach the gospel (good news) to every creature. He who believes and is baptized will be saved; but he who does not believe will be condemned. And these signs will follow those who believe...", Mark 16:15-17.

Note how neither of them reported that Jesus said to specifically preach that the Kingdom was at hand any more, rather, Jesus said to teach *everything* that makes up the sum total of all the good news. In other words, Jesus commanded them to teach the nations:

- to repent because
- the kingdom of God (which is SUPERNATURAL, MANIFEST peace, righteousness, joy, love, kindness, patience, self-control, authority, well-being, wholeness, etc) is now available to mankind in the earth
- to learn, apply, obey and operate in all the statutes, policies and dynamics of His kingdom (which are all taught throughout the New Testament)
- to be born again through believing, repentance and being washed by His shed blood; and baptized
- to submit to, love, and seek Jesus as King above all else
- to adhere to the fact that He is the only way, the only truth and the only life
- to learn all truths concerning what happens to those that believe verses those that do not
- and to know what to expect in the last days concerning the antichrist, the impending wrath of God, and His soon coming return to earth to reign.

You can see how that's a lot of important stuff that, all together, constitutes **the total reality and teachings of all the good news**.

However, in Matthew 24:14, Jesus explained to the disciples that the last sign before the end would come is, as He put it, "When this Gospel **of the kingdom** is preached to all nations, then the end will come." Isn't it interesting that He commanded the apostles to teach everything, the entire spectrum of the good news, yet He points out that a final sign before the end is when, specifically, the Gospel **of the kingdom** is preached! Not the specific message of the remission of sins, not the entire spectrum of the good news, but specifically, the MESSAGE OF THE KINGDOM! And why? Because HE'S COMING! The physical REIGN of Christ is about to come down to earth! That's a big WOW to me because I see that this last sign is NOW happening! Have you noticed the theme of the teachings across the board have suddenly become far more "kingdom" focused? Watch! You'll be hearing talk of the kingdom of God increasingly and without end until Jesus returns. And as the teaching increases, SO WILL THE POWER and MIRACLES OF SAID KINGDOM INCREASE! Because "the last sign" is unfolding right before our eyes. This very journey program is part of this last sign!

But more importantly, at least for the moment, is we need to realize Jesus Himself put the emphasis on the ARRIVAL of His kingdom in the earth 2000 years ago because this meant **God's power, government and rule could dwell with man in the earth finally, that people could have access to the Father, and that people could come out from the rule of the dark kingdom immediately! Not just when they die.**"For God has rescued us from the dominion of darkness and transferred us into the kingdom of His dear Son." Colossians 1:13. Yet we don't get the big picture because, for centuries, we haven't really been preaching the full Gospel. And we've been suffering for it!

See, we're quick to comprehend that the wages of sin is eternal death and Hell. But we're somewhat clueless that Satan is a legal, reigning prince over all the systems of earth. The devil literally has a kingdom himself, and he rules in this world - whether people realize it or not. Whether they're nasty wicked, or not. If a person does not belong to the kingdom of God, they are under Satan's reign. Regardless of religion, nationality, or culture, or even how nice people might be, Satan has had legal authority over the world ever since the Garden of Eden incident. Until Jesus came to give mankind a way out from dark kingdom rule, that is. Yet, we just don't get all that very well.

So, do we see the error of primarily preaching that the Gospel is the message of salvation? Because **the real message begins with separation and deliverance from the rulers of the air.** Where God made His joy, peace, power and authority available to us while **we're still here** dealing with darkness, sickness, disease, demonic spirits, oppression, all of it! And then, at the end of the day, those who believe and **abide in God's kingdom** will ALSO have eternal life.

We've done ourselves and God a great injustice by not following Christ's example. The Lord's first and primary emphasis was to preach the good news that the kingdom was here for us. Instead, we lead people to Christ through the sinner's prayer, teach them a few dos and don'ts and how to follow the system of the Church, **but provide no solid concept of the realm they've entered**. Though they hopefully at least understand that they're citizens of Heaven and will go there someday, do they know that God's kingdom has, likewise, come down to them? Though they have eternal hope, do they also have ever-present hope? Though they know they've been delivered from eternal damnation, do they also know they're delivered from the dominion of darkness on earth? Because if they don't know all this, then it cannot be their reality! And they cannot submit to and operate according to these dynamics! So, you see that centering Christianity around salvation is a dangerous misrepresentation of God's Word. And this isn't just an injustice of the truth, it's a huge problem because the emphasis of the message of salvation is to make Jesus your savior while the true Gospel says to **make Jesus your king**, and in so doing, you will, thereby, be saved.

If we don't grasp the full concept of the kingdom, we'll act like long-distant heirs to a mighty king that we only ever hear stories about, who we never get to know. We'll potentially feel that our savior is more of a dictator than a deliverer, controlling our lives with all His rules from a distance. We'll possibly never experience His kingdom's manifest reality - of supernatural peace and joy throughout the storms of life, for example. We'll likely fail to overcome sin. And we'll likely fail to grasp that we could and should be contending with the darkness - healing the sick and casting out demons. That all these benefits and gifts are not just meant for a Christian minority or the five-fold ministry, but for all.

For three solid years, Jesus preached and demonstrated the aspects of the Kingdom of God that were to be imparted to anyone that believed in His kingdom. Then, after three years of training His disciples how to be administrators and carriers of His realm, He completed His mission and gave Himself up for our sins, to shed His blood for our redemption so that we TOO might enter in and be carriers of that same kingdom. Not just be 'saved'. What an assault on the TRUTH that is!

Romans 1:16 says, "For I am not ashamed of the gospel of Christ: for it is the **power of God unto** salvation to everyone that believes." -**It is the power of God unto** salvation. The good news of the kingdom of Christ, God's very government here in the earth which trumps Satan's for all them that believe, **is also the power of God unto** eternal life. In other words, **"I am not ashamed of the good news that Christ's kingdom is here in the earth to rescue mankind from the dominion of darkness and give them power over it, even over sickness and demons, because it is this very power that also brings salvation to everyone that believes".** So we see then, that the message of salvation is a result of the good news. You actually cannot have the latter (salvation) without the former (believing in, submitting to, and being subject to Christ's realm and its system).
Is the Gospel, then, to only believe that Jesus saves you from your sin? Or is it to believe in the reality of His kingdom power that's here?

Remember, in preaching that His kingdom was here for us, Jesus always emphasized repentance. His point was to turn from self-rule, dark rule, and worldly rule, and submit to His kingdom's system and rule; aligning with its principles, precepts, and power. Believing in your new identity and acting like it. Becoming administrators and implementers of the kingdom of God. Becoming the salt of the earth. Becoming the light of the world. Putting the power and reality of God's kingdom to good use and helping others come out of the rule of darkness, too, by healing and delivering them.

That, my brothers and sisters, is the Gospel. And that's what needs to be the primary message of the Church. That's what needs to be believed and lived. Paul told the Thessalonians, "Our gospel came to you not simply with words **but also WITH POWER, with the Holy Spirit** and deep conviction." 1 Thessalonians 1:5. In other words, the Gospel, the very message of the kingdom of God being here in the earth, is the power of God and His Spirit. So you see? Believing the message of salvation, if that's all one believes, would hopefully be enough to get them to Heaven. But believing the message of the kingdom is what puts God's power and Spirit to flight in our lives, in the here and now!

What would our world look like if, instead of making the gift of salvation its foundation, Christianity followed the example of Christ and taught the message, policies, dynamics and power of His kingdom? We need to realize that the measure of the preaching, believing and submitting to the actual Gospel (as opposed to its end result) would unleash an unprecedented increase in kingdom power, healings and miracles in our world - like nothing ever before seen in history!

Yet, the preaching of the good news that the kingdom of God is here has taken a back seat to the message of salvation. This lack of understanding in the corporate body is a huge reason why, today, many are defeated or just plain powerless. And it's why so few acknowledge, learn, abide and operate in the reality of the kingdom of God. Worse yet, some "believers" even deny the reality of God's realm and supernatural power here, all while proclaiming Jesus as Savior! This will prove to be eternally fatal come Judgment Day when those who believed for salvation through Christ find out they never acknowledged and submitted to the reign of His kingdom. At the end of the day, those that didn't submit to God's kingdom and reign in this life... might just not get to be a part of His kingdom and reign in the next. Amen.

Put Your Spiritual Sunglasses On

We know full well that Ephesians 6:12 tells us that we wage not against flesh and blood, but the powers and principalities of darkness. Yet we still deal with and perceive the circumstances of life, how people treat us, violations and injustice, and everything else, through the understanding of our flesh. We know there are dark powers ruling the air, yet, we can't see past our carnal senses. As a result, we perceive that the family member that's rejecting us is strictly their heart towards us. Or the boss that's underestimating us does so strictly because of their perspective of us. Therefore, we're easily hurt or offended, devastated that they think, feel, or act the way they do towards us. Completely disregarding what Ephesians 6:12 tells us.

Whether you're a person that's lived a life of hell, with injustice and mistreatment at every corner, perhaps rejection or abandonment, or more, or whether you've been fortunate to not have been born into a life of abuse, everyone needs to come to respect the truth of Ephesians 6:12 once and for all. Because if we continue dealing with or perceiving the situations of life from a carnal perspective, having no regard for what's going on in the spirit realm, then we're not "seeing" from the eyes of our spirit which means we are not operating in the kingdom of God. And this is wrong. If we believe Jesus is God in the flesh, if we believe Jesus is the King of Kings, if we believe that the kingdom of God is here in the earth and that we have been born into it, then we must act accordingly which means realizing the issue isn't that so and so rejected you. The issue is there's a platform of work behind so and so rejecting you. There's an organized system of trouble makers assigned to your life to work through usable sources to stunt you, stifle you, paralyze you, squash your spirit, and more.

Understand that the devil and his minions do not have their own bodies to operate through (at least they don't at this time), otherwise, they would! But since they don't, they must influence humans to do their bidding. They whisper in their ears "Isn't he stupid!" Or, "Look how great she thinks she is". Or, "Don't give her the promotion, she just wants your job!" Need I go on? No. You get the idea. The enemy works tirelessly striving to use people to work against each other. Most people are gullible and have no idea the hatred or disgust, twisted perspective of or critical spirit that they have towards someone is because they're being fed ugly ideas and thoughts. Unfortunately, because they are inclined to or approve of such evil, they quickly bend their knee to the enemy's every suggestion and act out as per the inspiration.

So it's time we put on our spiritual sunglasses and look to see what's REALLY going on in a matter behind the scenes. Then we'll not be as hurt or offended. I mean, violations still sting. Even if you can see the demon whispering something into someone's ear and then experience the person yield and belittle you, it still hurts that they would listen to the devil and choose to be cruel. But at least if you can see the reality that the person is obviously vulnerable to be so usable, it's easier to choose to respond according to the ways of the kingdom of God - which is forgiveness, patience, peace, joy, kindness, and love despite their ugliness.

Make it a point to put on your spiritual sunglasses everywhere you go. Ask God to help you see what's going on behind the scenes in the spirit realm. Literally ask Him to show you where He is standing, where your angels are, and what particular demons are present and what they are up to. Scan the premises. You most likely won't see things right away but this will establish your resolve that you want to know, and God will begin to give you understanding. You might never actually see exactly where the demon is standing but God will reveal what's going on in your knowing. You'll discern there's a demon up to something and what it is. This will help you not fall for its stunt or be so hurt as things play out. And as time goes on, you'll become more knowledgeable as to the details, so much so that if someone comes against you, you'll be filled with the Spirit of God, discerning their broken heart or something and will be compelled to pray for them right there while they're still vomiting all over you. Not always, but the point is when you truly get to the place of respecting Ephesians 6:12, you'll deal with things so much differently. And you won't carry the baggage, "Why did so and so say that? How can she treat me like this? What's wrong with me? Why does she hate me?" Please remember that everyone has their issues. And the bigger the holes are that people have in their hearts, the more usable they are to offend people of God. So, you truly do not have to wonder whatsoever why someone hates you.

The bigger question is why does the *devil* hate you so much to be giving you such a hard time every time you turn around. And the answer is... because he needs to mess you up, get you all out of whack, so that you won't be who you are called to be in Christ. Because the devil is terrified of who you are meant to be in Christ Jesus.

And here's something to keep in mind... If you do have a history of being rejected, bullied, abused, abandoned, defeated, insulted, or belittled from various sources all your life, it's because there are demons assigned to continue inciting these situations against you. But here's the deal: They're able to keep doing it because it works. You've been receiving the abuse, so to speak. Meaning, if they insult you, you believe what they say. And if you don't believe it, you wonder why they believe it, giving the garbage merit. This empowers the enemy to continue doing the same. But what will happen if you'll be diligent to look at every matter through the eyes of your spirit, seeing what's really going on, you'll stop engaging with the garbage. You'll stop taking the abuse or injustice to heart. You'll stop wondering why this and why that. You'll stop believing what they say. All because you know there's an agenda to shut you down - and because you'll know who is really behind so and so's perspective of you. And what will happen is these age old strategies that used to trip you up no longer will. So, eventually you'll put these particular demons out of commission. They'll see their missions aren't being accomplished. Their efforts will become futile. So, they'll eventually stop. And where there has been a lifetime of rejection or whatever, you'll see God's love manifesting instead.

Something to consider... If you are able, get yourself a pair of sunglasses from the dollar store and set them in a place where you will notice them regularly, so as to remind yourself of Ephesians 6:12. Or do something else to help you begin looking at every situation conscious of the spirit realm and always inquiring of the Lord, "What's really going on here, Father? What's this all about? What do you want me to see? Open the eyes of my spiritual understanding!" In Jesus' Name. Amen.

Intro to the Great and Greatest Commissions

Remember... it's our alignment with truth that raises us up in Christ. And Christ is all powerful. That's who we are supposed to be, then! So if maturing into the full stature of Christ is important to you, or more pressingly, if you're tired of seeing the dark kingdom exhibit more power than God in the world around you, then do please buckle down and dig into these next modules. In fact, the Greatest Commission teaching is one that, if you do not digest it and live it, you'll not excel in Christ; I assure you.

Please don't be intimidated or offended at my straight-forwardness. I try to be loving but to never water down the truth. Yes, I'm laying it on thick but that's because alignment with God is paramount, won't happen by accident, and especially because we're complacent otherwise. Coming into the full stature of Christ requires an alert, sincere submission on our parts.

If you're overwhelmed or feeling like the program is a mountain too big to climb (as one dear sister recently helped me to realize), because you've just been dried up or have practically given up trying to move forward in Christ, let me encourage you this way: Instead of looking at this program as some big task to commit to that you have no strength or ambition to do, look at it as though an angel of the Lord just appeared to you and said, "Jesus wants to show you some things that will help you. He's given your sister, Paula, some words that will help you. Take a listen."

If an angel showed up right now and said that, would that feel as overwhelming as "taking a program"? I hope not. Because that's all this program is. It's just committing to listen to me for 15 minutes here and there or in so much as you desire. And what you'll see happen is the truth will do a beautiful and intense work inside of you. Light bulbs will go off.

You'll dream dreams. You'll hear the Holy Spirit better. You'll get revelations. You'll connect dots. Your soul will prosper. You'll begin to rise in faith, endurance, and strength. The TRUTH will do the work. Not you. All you have to do is listen.

Father, I lift _____ up to you. Please do what only you can do. I speak to the mountain(s) that stand between _____ and your truth. The Lord rebuke every foul spirit that continues to strive to dictate the destiny of this blood-bought child of the Most High God! Praise you God, that you don't give up on us even if we do! Father, please deliver _____ from all evil, discouragement, sickness, lethargy, despondency, injustice, lack, deception and plots right now. And I pray that more of your truth and light will take root, that false ideas, beliefs and perspectives will shrivel up. I speak that all unknown alliances with dark kingdom policies will be exposed so that _____ can repent and detach from them. Thank you for your wonderful grace, Father. You are a mighty God!

Thank you! In Jesus' Name, Amen!

"All authority has been given to Me in heaven and on earth. Go, therefore, and make disciples of all the nations, baptizing them in the name of the Father and of the Son and of the Holy Spirit, teaching them to obey all things that I have commanded you." Matthew 28:18-20.

The Christian Church has been told for hundreds of years that Jesus commands her to spread the Gospel, either as one sent forth to the nations, or as one sent into our own neck of the woods. It was coined as the "Great Commission" in the 1600s, is based upon Matthew 28:18-20 (above), and frankly has been causing confusion ever since. Many sincere Christians fear they're in disobedience because they don't verbally share the good news with others. But unless they are defying the call to the field, they are not in disobedience because Jesus never commanded this of them. The "Great Commission" is not their commission.

We know Jesus was speaking specifically to the eleven Apostles, but because Jesus had previously sent not only the twelve but 70 other disciples out to preach the good news (who weren't necessarily ordained as apostles), this is one of the primary reasons people believe that Matthew 28:19 was, therefore, directed to all believers. But this just isn't so. Let's look at the 70 men Jesus selected to send out.

According to Luke 9:51, Jesus knew He was soon to be crucified and began heading to Jerusalem. Many of his disciples were with him but He apparently picked up some new followers along the way. Because,

"As they were walking along the road (en route to Jerusalem), a man said to him, "I will follow you wherever you go." Jesus replied, "Foxes have dens and birds have nests, but the Son of Man has no place to lay his head." To another man, however, Jesus said, "Follow me." But he replied, "Lord, first let me go and bury my father."Jesus said to him, "Let the dead bury their own dead, but you go and proclaim the kingdom of God." Still another said, "I will follow you, Lord; but first let me go back and say goodbye to my family." Jesus replied, "No one who puts a hand to the plow and looks back is fit for service in the kingdom of God."

After all this is when Jesus appointed the 70 and sent them out two by two.

Now why the emphasis on the conversations Jesus had with these three men? It's because, in them, Jesus established what such a "commission" demands.

First, when the one man offered to follow Jesus, the Lord discerned this man's dependence upon the comforts and stability of home. So He had to point out to him that he might not be a good fit for this sort of assignment. Jesus established that He's strictly looking for people who can let go of all that, and be willing to deal with no longer having the typical comforts of home.

As for the second man, Jesus is the one who invited Him to join the ministry. Consequently, the man presented his intent to take care of a personal family matter. The Lord's response, "Let the dead bury the dead" suggests a couple of things. First, that this man's Jewish family wasn't on board with his opinion of Jesus, so what more does he have to do with them now that they are divided like this? Why put people who are no longer your real family above your call into the service of your true kingdom family? The second suggestion might also be that being called to the service of the kingdom requires that life as is typically lived, is no more. The needs of the kingdom of God take precedence; and this changes everything.

And finally, for the third man that said he'd join Jesus once he says goodbye to his family, Jesus took the opportunity to, again, point out that such a call is strictly for those who can put their lives of service to God above their personal lives without distress. Serving the Lord in this fashion is not for those whose hearts, while out in the field working for Jesus, are constantly looking back and longing for home. Not that Jesus meant they would never see their families again or get to spend time with them. That's not the point. The point is for those times that they are in the field, which may be a lot, it's a cross to carry. It requires an unusual strength. Few can handle it. That's why Jesus says those who cannot are not fit for this extremely sacrificial type of service.

The point of this entire passage was to establish that such a commission is NOT for everyone. If it was, why would Jesus lay such deterrents before them? So there is no doubt that the 70 men that Jesus did choose needed to fit a specific criteria. This alone debunks the idea that the "Great Commission" is for all.

However, the next argument in favor of the Great Commission being a mandate to all, is that part of the instruction the Lord gave the Apostles was to teach the new disciples to obey the very commandments Jesus had taught them, which would, therefore, include even this commandment to make disciples. Meaning, the Lord telling the Apostles to go and make disciples includes teaching all of the new disciples to also go and make disciples, and so on and so forth until the end of the age - which they never did! There's no record anywhere in the New Testament of the original twelve Apostles commanding their new disciples to go make new disciples!
As if all that's not enough, consider how, via his rather lengthy "training manual" to his protege, Timothy, in his service to Christ, Paul specifically instructs Timothy to devote himself to preaching and teaching both in 1 Timothy 4:13 and 2 Timothy 4:2. Yet, nowhere else in all the books written by Paul, does Paul instruct believers to preach or teach the Gospel! No. In

fact, the only commands given for anyone to preach, teach, or make disciples, throughout the entire New Testament are given to very specific people.

Next, take Romans 12 and 1 Corinthians 12. Both of these speak to the fact that there is one body, but many parts. Everyone has a unique purpose and mission in this life. Everyone has specific gifts and strengths, both in the natural and in the supernatural. Therefore, not all are called to go out and make disciples because there's much to do after the disciples are made! Consider how in Acts 6:6, the twelve Apostles stated that they don't have the ability to tend to the issues of the Church, and they appointed seven others to take care of such things. Frankly, there're many things the Apostles cannot do, not just because they're too busy with their own call, but because it's for others to do, for those who have the gift and talent for it. Because there are many parts to the body of Christ - to accomplish all the various needs and services of the kingdom of God.

Paul specifically asked, "Are all apostles?" in 1 Corinthians 12:29. This is additionally relevant because the call of an apostle, "a delegate, messenger, one sent forth with orders" (see apostolos G652 at blueletterbible.org), is to, essentially, start new churches. To go out and introduce the good news to the nations with the intent to teach them to receive the kingdom of God and its King. This is precisely what Jesus expected in His saying, "Go and make disciples", that they'd start churches (not religious clubs, mind you, but groups of holy kingdom carriers) as a result. And we know this because that's exactly what happened. The Apostles traveled abroad making disciples which, inevitably, started church groups. And they trained them, got them rolling, and then moved on.

Since this was Christ's obvious intent in commanding the Apostles to go make disciples, so that the Church would spread throughout the nations, suggesting anything else dangerously misrepresents the passage. It's dangerous because it causes many believers to feel guilty for being uncomfortable teaching or preaching the good news to those within their reach. Though they obey God's commands and serve the kingdom of God in ways conducive of their gifts and callings, they wonder if they're in sin for not fulfilling their part of "The Great Commission". **This false doctrine** is a yoke Jesus never intended to place on the necks of kingdom carriers. And the false teachers will be held to account for it even for their negligence to not clarify what's true and isn't true before imparting to the body.

Indeed, another argument that the Great Commission does apply to all Christians is because, in the Greek, the only imperative was on the "make disciples", not on the going, baptizing, or teaching. That these were somehow peripheral to the primary instruction for all Christians to simply spread the Gospel right where they are - in their own neck of the woods. But the error in this line of thinking is that though the "going" has been eliminated from the equation, the very nature of making disciples still has to include teaching and baptizing the new converts. Just because the imperative wasn't placed on teaching and baptizing doesn't remove the necessity of doing it. But, here again, teaching and baptizing are specific gifts and calls. Not everyone is a teacher. Not everyone should baptize.

All of the above scripture provides ample evidence that the emphasis placed on Matthew 28:18-20, known as the Great Commission, is wrong. Though the commission to very specific believers is indeed "great", it's not for the entire body of Christ. It's also wrong to infer that everyone should be sharing the Gospel if even in their own area. This simply is not so because it would still require the specific gifts and drive. So, if you are a Christian that often feels guilty for not being comfortable verbally promoting Christ or His kingdom as a way of life, you're off the hook. Now, this doesn't mean the Holy Spirit might not inspire you once in a while in a special situation to share your testimony or give an answer as to why you believe what you do (1 Peter 3:15). And it doesn't mean the Holy Spirit won't randomly, perhaps, give you a Word of Prophecy for someone, or use you to bring healing to someone since you may be the ONLY person around that He can use to help someone the way they need. But you'll have a knowing and inspiration to do it. Which is completely different than taking on the false yoke of being called to witness or preach the Gospel every chance you get, everywhere you go - if that's not you! So be released from this false doctrine that says every believer has a part to play in the "Great Commission".

However, there is a mandate concerning the spreading of the Gospel that does include *all* Christians. Though not given through a single directive, rather, through the whole of the Gospels, it's the greatest commission of all. And it's that all believers should, in fact, be spreading the Gospel. Only... not with preaching, teaching, or sharing; not with any words at all, in fact.

Notes/Prayers

Bearing Fruit

"The Greatest Commission"

John said to the crowds coming out to be baptized by him, "You brood of vipers! Who warned you to flee from the coming wrath? Produce fruit indicative of your (so-called) repentance. And do not (presume) that you have Abraham as your father. (So what!) The ax is already at the root of the trees, **and every tree that does not produce good fruit will be cut down and thrown into the fire.**" Luke 3:7-9.

Later, Jesus shared the following parable with some people: "A man had a fig tree growing in his vineyard, and he went to look for fruit on it but did not find any. So he said to the man who took care of the vineyard, **'For three years now I've been coming to look for fruit on this fig tree and haven't found any. Cut it down! Why should it use up the soil?'** 'Sir,' the man replied, 'leave it alone for one more year, and I'll dig around it and fertilize it. If it bears fruit next year, fine! If not, then cut it down.'" Luke 13:7-8.

At another time, Jesus declared, "I am the true vine, and my Father is the gardener. He cuts off every branch in me that bears no fruit, while every branch that does bear fruit he prunes so that it will be even more fruitful...Remain in me, as I also remain in you. No branch can bear fruit by itself; it must remain in the vine. Neither can you bear fruit unless you remain in me. I am the vine; you are the branches. If you remain in me and I in you, you will bear much fruit; apart from me you can do nothing. **If you do not remain in me, you are like a branch that is thrown**

away and withers; such branches are picked up, thrown into the fire and burned. John 15:1-6.

The Lord makes it clear that believers **must bear fruit**, otherwise, they'll be thrown into the fire. Indeed, the Lord is patient with us, even working to fertilize us, giving us more time to bear fruit. But in the end, those who have none are destroyed. This is very sobering and should have every one of us on our toes, seeking God on this issue; making sure we are, in fact, bearing fruit. Making sure that we are in the kingdom of God and that His kingdom is, in fact, in us. Note in the previous illustration of the tree - that the tree itself had Jesus, the Word, and the Kingdom in it. This is the first necessity in order to be able to live in supernatural peace, righteousness and joy. And the reason I say "supernatural" is to put emphasis that only in the kingdom of God is there the eternal, kingdom TYPE of peace, righteousness, joy, etc. Not the worldly type, but the kind that can only come from the eternal kingdom of glory. And AS trees of the kingdom of God, we are capable of bearing these supernatural attributes.

But I'm not writing this to emphasize what we already know, rather, to declare that bearing fruit is actually the **greatest call or commission of all believers of all time**. As we saw in the previous lesson concerning the error of the Great Commission, which wrongfully suggests that "all" believers are called to preach the Gospel, I shared that it's true, nonetheless, that all Christians are in fact supposed to impact the world **with the Kingdom of God**. Just not according to the supposed 'great commission'. Rather, it's through the bearing of the LIVING, ETERNAL, SUPERNATURAL fruit of the Spirit that all Christians are to expand the Kingdom. So let's take a look at what this entails in depth.

Now realize concerning the Matthew 13:23 illustration tree shown previously that the tree is the kingdom of God and the SOIL is the person that the kingdom is planted in. Note that if the soil (the person) is a shallow path by the wayside, rocky, or full of thorns, the kingdom will struggle to grow and manifest in this person. However, if the soil is good, it is able to receive the water and nutrients of the Word of God and grow up into a mighty eternal kingdom tree. Consequently, even in the face of adversity or strife, they are strong and have selfless love, patience, joy, unexplainable peace, self-control, and more. They are no longer tossed to and fro by this world or any false wind of doctrine - because the mighty kingdom of God reigns inside of them. They are upright and genuinely kind. They are meek and resolved in their faith and convictions for Christ. And scripture tells us that **because they bear this fruit, the Kingdom of God which is in them will multiply as new seed - and spread**, taking root in any other good soil within their circle of influence; some a hundredfold, some sixty, some thirty. Wow! This is how the GOSPEL IS SPREAD!

We can deduce that a believer who produces a hundredfold likely bore a higher level of fruit than a believer who produces thirtyfold. Clearly, the more a believer seeks and applies the ways of the Kingdom of God and His righteousness, the more prominent their spiritual attributes (fruit) will be, which means the greater their impact on the world. Jesus doesn't break it down as to *how* a believer's profound growth in unexplainable peace, for example, ends up producing up to a hundredfold's worth of new believers. Yet, that's what He says happens.

Moving on, let's look at how, in Matthew 22:37, Jesus said, "You shall love the Lord your God with all your heart, with all your soul, and with all your mind. This is the first and greatest commandment. And the second is like it: You shall love your neighbor as yourself. On these two commandments hang all the Law and the Prophets."

We see that "love" is the basis of each commandment - and that these two "love" commandments sum up all the rest of the commandments. Therefore, love is the epicenter of Christ and His Kingdom.

But what exactly is love? According to modern culture, love is tolerance and acceptance of all whims, practices and ideals. Today's world pridefully demands that love approves sin. Meanwhile, the world's love itself is strictly conditional, requiring that everyone jump on the unity-of-sin bandwagon, or they shall be the object of scorn for their supposed *lack* of love. Relationships and marriages are often plagued, if even minimally, with selfishness, entitlement, unforgiveness and conditions. When the romance and surface appeal wanes, they split up because they believe they fell out of love - when they never completely loved each other in the first place. Because the world does not know what love is.

As you know, the Bible says, "Love is patient, love is kind. It does not envy, it does not boast, it is not proud. It does not dishonor others, it is not self-seeking, it is not easily angered, it keeps no record of wrongs. Love does not delight in injustice, but rejoices with the truth. It bears all things, always trusts, always hopes, always endures". 1 Corinthians 13:4-8.

Unfortunately, although the Church has a far better grip on the truth of what love really is, she sometimes gets caught up in the world's version. There's almost as much pride, entitlement, compromise, tolerance, selfishness, discontentment, anger, and impatience operating in the Church as the world. When that driver with road rage cuts the believer off in traffic, for example, many believers retaliate. Anger and resentment rise up. We all know this is how we can be at times. Because we do not fully walk in love even as children of God, despite how much we'd like to think we do. We justify our hatred because the offenders are 'wicked'. But Jesus was our example on earth. He told it like it was, but he never responded with hate, rage, self-defense, resentment, vengeance, arrogance, entitlement, or anything of the sort when He was mistreated - even unto death.

Note how Galatians 5:22-23 says the fruit of the Spirit is love, joy, patience, kindness, meekness, peace and self-control, etc. But, how 1 Corinthians 13:4 says that love "IS" patient, love "IS" kind, not boastful or proud, not easily angered, etc. In other words, all the fruits of the Spirit are the embodiment of the initial fruit of love - which is Christ!

But there's more. Remember how the 'seed' which the good ground received was the Word of the "Kingdom of God"? Well, Romans 14:17 says, "For the kingdom of God is not a matter of eating and drinking, *but righteousness, peace and joy in the Holy Spirit*". So, the Kingdom of God is peace? The Kingdom of God is joy? Yes! Therefore, the kingdom of God is one and the same as the FRUIT of the Spirit. The attributes of the Spirit in a believer - which are all of divine love - "IS" the Kingdom of God, even Christ, in them. And we can substantiate that the Kingdom of God is, indeed, "in them" because in Luke 17:20-21, Jesus said, "The coming of the kingdom of God is not something that can be observed, nor will people say, 'Here it is,' or 'There it is,' because **the kingdom of God is in you**". *[Note that "within you" is the most accurate translation because the Greek term, entos ἐντο`ς, Strong's G1787, is defined: within, inside; within you i.e. in the midst of you; within you i.e. your soul.]* Thereby, confirming that the fruits of the Spirit are one and the same as the Kingdom of God "in" us. For example, peace in us IS the kingdom of God. LACK of supernatural peace is a lack of God's kingdom in us.

Now, let's look at how Jesus said, "The kingdom of heaven is like yeast that a woman took and mixed into about sixty pounds of flour until it worked all through the dough." Matthew 13:33. If the Kingdom of Heaven is one and the same as the fruits of the Holy Spirit, such as righteousness, peace and joy, then Jesus is saying that mixing righteousness, peace and joy into and working (developing) it in a believer, spreads like yeast into an entire batch! Just like in the parable of the sower!

But that's not all. Jesus also said, "The kingdom of heaven is like a mustard seed, which a man took and planted in his field. Though it is the smallest of all seeds, yet when it grows, it is the largest of garden plants and becomes a tree, so that the birds come and perch in its branches". Here again, just like in the parable of the sower, when the believer received the seed of the Kingdom, in this case, a mustard seed, when it grew to full maturity, it became the largest in the entire garden and was a blessing to everything around it - including the unbelievers. Because just as God rains down on both the just and the unjust, a believer that becomes a mighty Kingdom of God tree won't be able to prevent the world around him from benefiting from him, or even relying upon him somehow.

But back to the point, we're seeing a running theme, that the Kingdom of God always starts out small in someone. But if it grows to maturity in a believer, it is massive and quite beneficial to the world around it. All from one seed; from receiving Christ. From one person truly believing and understanding the Word of the Kingdom and maturing in God.

And there's even more: After Paul teaches the Corinthians about the supernatural gifts and even exhorts them to seek them in 1 Corinthians 12, he proceeds to inform them that what's far more important than these amazing supernatural gifts is...FRUIT (love). He explains that if he can do all these supernatural things such as prophesying and healing others (which anyone can do by merely believing, John 14:12), but has not fruit (love), he's nothing. Paul is emphasizing that if we are operating in supernatural gifts outside of the divine attributes of the Spirit, we are big fat zeros at the end of the day. Paul even closes the passage saying that the day will come where there will no longer be a need or a place for the gifts of the Spirit (because we'll be in Heaven). But that while these activities cease, the Kingdom of God and all of its attributes, namely love, are eternal.

As if all that is not enough, look at these passages as well:

- "In the same way, let your light shine before men, that they may see your good deeds and praise your Father in heaven." Matthew 5:16.

We know that light will only "shine" in the darkness. Believers don't automatically shine in the darkness by default of receiving Christ. If after receiving Him, they do not develop the fruit of Christ in themselves, working it and causing it to grow (by sowing to peace, patience, love, joy, kindness, self-control, etc), it remains dim. But, if they do develop that seed of light, it will shine when, in the face of darkness, they respond with divine attributes (fruits). While everyone else responds with panic, fear, terror, distress, anger, worry, frustration, resentment, violence, looting, and more, those who developed Christ in them respond with peace of mind, self-control, selflessness, and assurance because of the strength of their faith. In other words, no fruit, no shine.

- "Wives, in the same way submit yourselves to your husbands so that, if any of them do not believe the Word, they may be won over, without words, by the behavior of their wives." 1 Peter 3:1. Wives have a hard time submitting at all if they don't develop meekness, unconditional love, patience, joy, selflessness, and self-control. How much more these fruits are required to submit to an unbelieving husband! She will fail to do so if she does not develop the fruit of the Spirit. Note that an insecure wife that submits out of fear of her husband is not what's meant by this verse. This type of submission is not out of the fruit of the Spirit. How she "wins the unbelieving husband over" is because of her fruit of stability and security in God exhibited by healthy submission. And note that this is how she spreads the Kingdom of God. By her attributes; her fruitful behavior; without words.

- "There is no fear in love; but perfect love casts out fear... He who fears has not been made perfect in love". 1 John 4:18. In other words, he who fears does not have the resounding, unexplainable peace, assurance and faith of perfect love.

So then, with all that said...

If, without bearing the fruit of the Spirit, we will be cast into the fire... and, if the fruit of the Spirit constitutes how we must expand the Kingdom of God in the earth... and, if the two greatest commandments are to walk in the fruit of the Spirit (LOVE)... then, would not the greatest commission of all time be to develop the fruit of the Spirit?

There's no doubt about it. Jesus said the two greatest commandments were to love. Therefore, the two greatest commandments are to, likewise, bear fruit. Because you cannot love God with all your heart, soul, and mind, and you cannot love your neighbor as yourself, unless you develop, or grow in, divine love and all that it encompasses.

If you're wondering what exactly you can do to bear fruit, you're doing it. Seeking God, sowing to the Spirit, digging into the truth, seeking understanding, learning it, meditating on it, and applying it which is what develops Christ and His fruit in us. Remember, Jesus said that He is the vine and we are the branches and that if we remain in Him, we'll bear fruit. Remaining in Him doesn't just mean calling yourself a Christian. It means seeking and sowing, digging and applying which is remaining in Him.

So we can see, then, that Christ's overarching mandate is that believers are to grow up in Him and His attributes. God's children are to be walking temples of divine peace, righteousness, joy... of the kingdom of 1 Corinthians 13:4-8's love. This is clearly the Lord's greatest mandate or, "Greatest Commission".

Unfortunately, there are more believers that look like this: "Now he who received seed among the thorns is he who hears the Word, but the cares and anxieties of this world, and the seduction of riches (spring up) and choke (stifle) the Word, and he becomes unfruitful." Matthew 13:22.

Before reading any further, please jot down any and all thoughts and prayers that came to you so far concerning what the greatest commission is and where you are:

_____

_____

_____

_____

_____

_____

_____

_____

_____

_____

_____

_____

_____

_____

_____

_____

_____

_____

_____

The following picture is an attempt to illustrate what this actually looks like in the spirit.

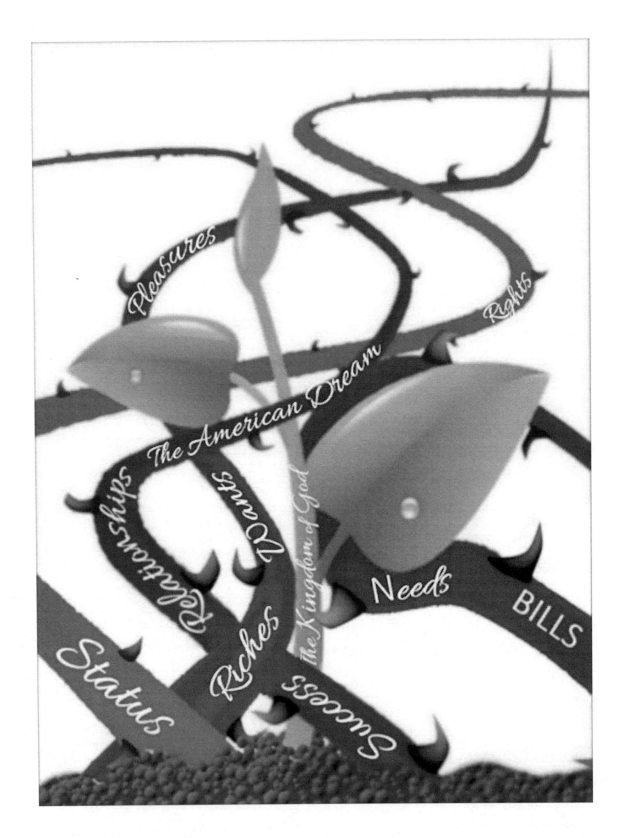

Note how in the illustration that because the kingdom of God was planted in soil (the person is the soil) that was full of worldly aspirations, anxieties, namely the cares of this life, it isn't growing very well. This person will therefore not have supernatural peace, joy, righteousness, self-control, kindness, or love in the face of adversity. If this person doesn't remove these thorns, and begin cultivating the Spirit, the thorns will very well overtake the kingdom of God and completely choke it out. Either that, or the kingdom of God will simply dwindle and never prosper in them.

Things that constitute the cares of this life would be: status, success, our wants and needs (spouse, children, financial stability, even the 'American Dream' and our perceived rights) are all things that can take over us. These certainly are a part of living on this earth, the problem is when they are the meditations of our heart and longing - when they take precedence over eternal hope. When we look at them intently, catering to them, striving after them - worrying about them - instead of being primarily concerned about Jesus and His business, and pursuing after God with all our hearts.

This is where so many of us go wrong. We believed and received the initial Word of God, so the seed of truth, the seed of the Kingdom of God, Christ Jesus, took root. We experienced and perhaps exercised some of its fruit such as peace, joy and righteousness. Unfortunately, because our lives are filled with other passions and even anxiety over them, these things are what grow. And the more we look on them, the more we fret over or chase them, the more we despair of the lack of them, the bigger they become. And the bigger they become, the more the Word and the kingdom of God is choked out. **We cannot and will not have manifest, divine love, peace, joy, etc., unless and until we stop catering to our thorns.** If we would fervently submit, seek and sow to the Word and crucify the meditations of our hearts for these non-eternal things, we would grow vibrantly, and the thorns would begin to die off, becoming obsolete. We'd find that our anxieties and compelling for the things of this life will become insignificant. Our involvement with and even pursuing such things would become a part of our relationship with God, instead, **remaining balanced and underfoot**. The end result being the thorns are overpowered by the Word and kingdom of God, where we're now walking in the divine, supernatural fruits of the Spirit, no longer full of anxiety or desperation for the things of life. No longer lacking the joy of the Lord and needing the carnal things of this world to satisfy us. No longer lacking in self-control and enslaved to things of the flesh. No longer lacking in faith or trust in God to set the course of our lives straight. The end result being we walk and look so much like Jesus that we spread the kingdom of God and become a massive blessing to the world around us.

To the contrary, if we continue to yield to the thorns, that's what will grow. The cares, anxieties and seductions of this life will dominate our passions. We'll not care so much about the Word of God, and we'll have trouble meditating upon it even when we try to out of knowing that we should. And we'll see whatever fruit of the Spirit we did have begin to dwindle. We will find ourselves becoming short fused with the people in our lives, impatient with situations, and easily angered. We'll even find ourselves being more selfish, adamant about getting what we want and not being slighted. And if we keep catering to the thorns, thereby neglecting the kingdom of God, we'll begin to slip into great sins of addictions, lust, adultery, and more. Because the attributes of Christ in us have, by then, dwindled to nothing, leaving us with little to no self-control. And this is dangerous. "Therefore I tell you that the kingdom of God will be taken away from you and given to a people who will produce its fruit." Matthew 21:43.

Fortunately, until we leave earth we have the ability to repent and get right with God. **Just always remember that being right with God is evidenced by whether or not we bear His fruit.**

"By this everyone will know that you are my disciples, if you love (are patient with, are slow to anger with, are kind with, are faithful with, are meek with, are upright with, and are self-controlled with) one another."

John 13:35. "For the fruit of the Light consists in all goodness, righteousness and truth." Ephesians 5:9. Therefore, "Live a life worthy of the Lord and please him in every way: bearing fruit in every good work, growing in the knowledge of God." Colossians 1:10. Amen.

_____

_____

_____

_____

_____

_____

_____

_____

_____

_____

_____

_____

_____

_____

_____

_____

_____

_____

_____

_____

I love you, Lord.

You rescued me!

You are here with me now and always were.

My cares and desperations have cloaked Your presence.

Forgive me, Father.

My offense allows the cloaking, but You haven't left me!

You LOVE me so much!

Show me Your MAJESTY that I might forget this world.

Consume me, Lord.

I love you,

———————————————————

Okay, so if we didn't already, we surely ought to have a better scope as to the fullness of why Jesus brought His invisible Kingdom to earth by now. And, we should be compelled more than ever to be true disciples of Christ. We should be eager to thoroughly develop the truth of the Kingdom in ourselves, so that we can finally excel in the attributes of God's Spirit. In fact, we should now be able to tear out all the thorns and weeds in our lives that compete with and choke out our love for God's Word, and hinder our pursuit of His Kingdom once and for all! But...

If only it were that easy! Unfortunately, there's no switch to flip to instantly love God above everything that competes with Him, to truly regard and esteem Him above all else. There's no button to push to shut off all that we lust after, long for, that we're acclimated and even addicted to.

If you recognize that God's not truly first in your heart but you're not sure that you care enough to change this yet - because you're so entangled with and even attached to your thorns, you've come to the right place. You may feel stuck. You may lack resolve. You may even lack conviction. **But you will move forward. Just watch, you'll see.**

We know that the thorns constitute both the anxieties and the longings for the good things of this life. I know the Bible says "riches" but God showed me this encompasses all the aspects of life; at least the things that someone may find "enriching" to them personally. I used to think this part of the passage didn't apply to me since I never longed for 'riches'. However, as the years passed, God showed me how, in my pursuit for financial stability (as a single mother on welfare), I may as well have been longing for riches. Because, though all I longed for was to not be on welfare, and though it is right to work and earn which is what I esteemed, what's wrong is when we *idolize it* - which is what I did. During the times when God held first place in my heart, however, my pursuit for financial well-being came from a place of peace, with submission and working *with Him* concerning it. When He wasn't my highest priority but I was instead driven and desperate for financial stability, it was more important, it wasn't out of peace and working with God, rather, it was idolatry. Fortunately, through a very painful course of discipline which I share about in other writings, I found out that chasing and striving after **good things** - *even the things that God wants for us Himself...* is idolatry. It's all about the excessive value these things hold in our hearts. So, I assure you, when Jesus speaks about the riches of this life choking the Word in us, it has to do with esteeming them higher than Him.

Let me reiterate that God made the good things of this life for us. It is His pleasure to give us pleasure! The problem is we let these things take His place and they become more important than Him. Things like measuring up to the Joneses is a perfect example of the deception of riches that Jesus was talking about. Not to mention the obvious longings for pleasure, excessive sensuality, comfort, entertainment, and "things", big and small. Whether we need them or not. And don't forget about status or being worried about how others perceive you, including family. Now there's a tricky one! Because it is more than the obvious error of seeking the praise of man from employers, employees, fans, colleagues, etc. What's tricky is it seems right to be driven to make sure our family members, especially our spouses, are "happy" with us. Even if we have to compromise a bit to do it. We put their opinion or desires above God and then justify it by saying we need to submit or that we do it out of love for them. But what about loving God first, above them?

Beyond worrying about the bills or obsessing over if we'll be able to take that vacation finally, we place our relationships with other people before God, too, especially our spouses, like I said. Again, it's difficult to recognize because we're supposed to be making the most of our marriages, being kind and selfless. Yet, we are more concerned with pleasing our spouses or having their approval or love, than pleasing God. Even in bad marriages where one spouse puts up with a lot of unkindness - to put it mildly, you can bet that they struggle to focus on God because of the pain of the marriage. Why? Because their marriage or spouse "changing" or healing may just be an idol - something they're desperate for, more than God. They love God, but their longing for their situation to be made right may be more important to them than God Himself. Trust me, I've been there and I see it all around.

And it's not just marriages. Singles who live in pain for lack of a mate often struggle to focus on God first, too, because their desire for a mate is greater than their desire for the kingdom of God. Again, not that this desire is wrong! Just that it's bigger than the desire for the Lord and knowing Him intimately. God's *"just not enough"* or *"the same"* because He cannot meet a human's physical needs. Believe me, I know. I spent years as a single woman. What makes it so hard is when you "know" God has someone for you and you have no patience! (Low fruit.) You're desperate for your destiny to happen yesterday! Why? Because you love the notion of having your mate (or whatever) more than loving God Himself (which is why the kingdom of God in you may be so minimal to begin with - which is why you may be so weak and vulnerable to the demands of the flesh and your thorns.)

Though the Bible clearly establishes that loving anything more than God as idolatry, I believe Jesus referred to the normal desires in life that we sometimes idolize (mates, healthy marriages, financial stability, success) as thorns to help us hone in on the fact that they are naturally occurring, as opposed to man-made false god type idols. This type of idolatry, therefore, is very sneaky and deceptive, which is exactly what He said. Because these are normal desires so there seems to be nothing wrong with craving them, or loving them more than God Himself.

Yet, despite how tangled up we are, we must CHOOSE to get rid of these naturally occurring idols! We MUST put God first! We MUST get to the place where He is the meditation of our heart - our focus - our preoccupation - not the thorns! Where we not only focus on Him and deeply seek Him out of duty, but we WANT to! Of course, I know it's not as easy as flipping a switch, but the necessity remains! Please, do not leave Section 1 without dealing with this!

And here's how...

Since we can't just turn excessive love off, especially for things that even God desires and HAS for us (financial stability, a healthy marriage, a mate), what we need to do is:

1. Start with Confession: **Confess our sin of loving things above God and repent**. Even if you don't feel like turning from it. Just declare that it is flat out wrong and offensive to God. Call it what it is. Don't sugar coat it or make excuses. Even regardless how right it is to desire God's destiny for yourself, it is WRONG and DANGEROUS that it's more important than knowing God Himself.

2. Now **cry out for great hunger and thirst for God's Word**. Passionately ask God, and I mean passionately, to give you pure hunger and desperation to know and understand the Word of God; not just as head knowledge, but in a way that actually *changes* you finally. You're not doing this because you "feel" the passion necessarily. Do it passionately even for the lack of having passion. Make the decision to focus on and chase it even if you have zero desire for it. Gradually, your buried desire for God will break forth.

3. **Ask God to woo you**. Tell Him you want to love Him first, but He's got to give you something to go on, considering you're already in love with other things and can't just turn it off like a light switch. Plus, He's invisible and all which makes it hard to fall in love with Him. Tell Him that you will gladly give up your excessive preoccupation and desperation for your physical needs, and your extreme dependence on the hopes of this life, if *He'll appeal to your spirit, tantalizing and invigorating your invisible senses.* Ask Him to let you experience the ecstacy of having spiritual intimacy with Him so that the physical stuff will lose its seduction!

4. Now this may be all you can do right now. You may be struggling to stay on top of this program, even. Fortunately, you may manage to praise God each day, you may even manage to pray little prayers for help or for needs, even for family, here and there, each day, and you may even have it in you to read a two minute devotional or the Bible for a few minutes here and there to glean from Him. If so, great! But, depending on how much your thorns are choking you, this is why you may not be able to dig deep into and meditate upon the Word of God in a life-changing way, yet. You may not be able to spend time pursuing God intimately, praying at length and worshiping Him, either, because you just don't have the desire or focus for it. But it doesn't have to stay this way. For now, however, continue to do everything you have managed to do, but add the above three instructions to it; that's all. **But do these continually, every day, with passion!** Even if it's all you can accomplish in your pursuit of the Lord. Even above doing this program! In fact, there's far less benefit to doing this program if your heart still isn't able to truly and completely put God first. So before you continue, make sure God is in fact first in your heart! And like I said... **Do the three instructions above non-stop until you experience an intimate touch from God that begins to impact your heart**. And continue even still, asking Him to give you even more hunger and thirst for His Word as well as an intimate understanding of His presence that will knock

your addiction to carnal reality out of the water. Like I said, if that's all you do, DO IT PASSIONATELY non-stop, every day for the rest of your life on this earth. You must establish that you want your heart to change. You must demonstrate that you don't want to put anything else before God any more. Again... If that's all you do, do it with great fervency and resolve until you experience a most wondrous, intimate moment with God. Then go after more, forever.

Notes/Prayers

_____

_____

_____

_____

_____

_____

_____

_____

_____

_____

_____

_____

_____

_____

_____

_____

Now that we've clarified that eternal salvation is a result of the Gospel of Jesus Christ and His kingdom, and not the Gospel itself... And now that we have clarity concerning the false aspect of the "Great Commission"... And now that we've wrapped our brains around what the greatest commission of all time is, let's close out Section 1 of the ODJ Program by examining and refining our perspective of what a disciple actually is - and isn't. Though we all have the basic idea, there's a lack of clarity to it just the same. And this lack of clarity, to whatever degree it is, colors the believer's comprehension of the entire New Testament, and hinders their capacity to truly understand their kingdom of God identities.

The general perspective is that a disciple is a pupil who devoutly adheres to and practices the doctrines of the teacher they follow. But there's the added perspective that disciples also spread the doctrines of their teacher and recruit new followers, such as the twelve disciples did. This right here is what we need to sort out. Because, since this is the general outlook, that spreading doctrine and recruiting is something which defines a disciple, the inference, then, is that all the disciples of the Bible were required to spread the Gospel, which then implies that all Christians today are to do likewise. But as we have clearly established in the previous teaching concerning the false aspects of the "Great Commission", this isn't the case. Yet, though we've established the difference between disciples and apostles, my concern is we can still fail to keep them distinguished. Because if our brains have been programmed that "disciples spread doctrine", then every time we see "disciple" in the Bible, that may be where some of our heads automatically go. That may not be the case for everyone, but it is for many, so it's important to drive the difference between "disciple" and "one who spreads doctrine" home.

If you're already clear on this and are not in the habit of thinking of disciples as "doctrine spreaders", please indulge me and continue reading just the same.

The term "disciple" comes from the Latin word "discipulus" meaning "a learner". And in the Bible, disciple is translated from the Greek term mathētē´s (μαθητής)[1] which means means "one who engages in learning through instruction from another; a pupil, an apprentice"[2] Whereas, apostle comes from the Classical Greek word ἀπόστολος (apóstolos) (as we previously discussed), meaning "one who is sent off". So by definition, then, we must conclude that disciples are devout learners and adherents, while apostles are the ones that spread the doctrine and recruit new followers.

In the New Testament, what you find, for the most part, is there are two primary audiences: those who are trained as to what it is to be a citizen of the kingdom of God; and those who are trained for the service of training the citizens of the kingdom of God. Making it a deliberate point to distinguish which group is being addressed throughout each passage in the entire New Testament makes all the difference in how we interpret them.

For example, we know that when Jesus addressed the crowds, He spoke in parables. But that He spoke far more plainly with those he sent into His service. Now with that in mind, let's review what Jesus said it is that's required to be His disciple:

1. Mark 8:34-35, Matthew 16:24 & Luke 9:23, "Then Jesus called the crowd to him along with his disciples and said: *Whoever wants to be my disciple must deny themselves and take up their cross and follow*

me. For whoever wants to save their life will lose it, but whoever loses their life for me and for the gospel will save it."

2. Luke 14:26-27, *"If anyone comes to Me and does not hate his father and mother, wife and children, brothers and sisters, yes, and his own life also, he cannot be My disciple. And whoever does not bear his cross and come after Me cannot be My disciple."*

3. Luke 14:33, *"So likewise, whoever does not forsake all that he has cannot be My disciple."*

4. John 8:31, *"Then said Jesus to the Jews which believed on him, 'If ye continue (know, obey, abide) in my Word, then are ye my disciples indeed'."*

Now, these are serious depictions of what it takes to truly be a disciple! It sounds like if we don't stop and drop everything, lay every aspect of life down, including our families, and forsake EVERYTHING to 'follow' Jesus, as in going out and doing things exactly as He did, then we are not true Christians! But hold on... Let's pay closer attention as to WHO is being addressed and go over each passage, one at a time:

1. Mark 8:34-35, Matthew 16:24 & Luke 9:23, *"Then he called the crowd to him along with his disciples and said: 'Whoever wants to be my disciple must deny themselves and take up their cross and follow me. For whoever wants to save their life will lose it, but whoever loses their life for me and for the gospel will save it.'"* We're clearly told that Jesus is speaking to both the disciples and the crowd. Knowing Jesus never spoke plainly to the crowds, but in parables, then, we know these words were an analogy. He didn't mean we have to give up everything in our lives to be a true Christian. Rather, since following Jesus was a big no-no for Jews, doing so would be extremely problematic. Choosing to follow Jesus at that time was literally asking for big trouble. Therefore, what Jesus meant was, "Look, I know following Me will cost all of you (Jews) dearly. You will

be sacrificing so much to accept the truths I tell you, and follow My teachings. And this will be a heavy cross to take up. But, whoever wants to be My disciple must deny themselves, and be willing to suffer to follow Me and My kingdom. For whoever refuses to believe in Me and my fulfilling of the law, in order to avoid conflict with family and friends, will actually lose their life in the end. But whoever is willing to deny themselves and face the painful hardship believing in and following Me brings, will actually save their lives".

2. Luke 14:26-27, *"If anyone comes to Me and does not hate his father and mother, wife and children, brothers and sisters, yes, and his own life also, he cannot be My disciple. And whoever does not bear his cross and come after Me cannot be My disciple."* Again, Jesus is speaking to the crowds here. His words are an analogy. I'm sure you know He wasn't saying to literally hate our families. But remember, Jesus was strictly addressing Jews whereby following Christ could get them put out of the family and community, or even killed. So, He had to be straight with them concerning the cost of following Him - and the cost of *not* following Him. He knew that choosing Him is likewise rejecting their families if they don't also choose Jesus, and abandoning the only lives they've ever known. So, the Lord was telling them that choosing Him is no different than hating your family even though you don't. And that it could be the hardest thing they would ever have to do. But if they are truly His disciples, they would choose to bear the drudgery of that cross. Living for and unto the King of Truth is what's right and necessary, though dangerous in this world; while choosing to stick by our unbelieving families over Him is ETERNALLY dangerous. You may have peace with your family/friends for the remaining time you have on earth, but you'll not taste eternal life. So, choosing Christ, for them, was the same as hating their family if their family hated Jesus. But although this was directed to Jews in the Bible, the same principle applies to everyone else in the world. That, no matter your background or religion or lack thereof, choosing Christ may mean losing family, friends and the only

life you've ever really known and held dear, if they don't approve of your faith in Christ. But if you truly want to be His disciple, you will deny yourself and take up this cross. You're willing to face whatever terrible things may occur for choosing Jesus.

3. Luke 14:33, *"So likewise, whoever does not forsake all that he has cannot be My disciple."* This is a continuation of the previous passage which is still addressed to a completely Jewish crowd. Here, Jesus is reiterating that if those who have a lot to lose by choosing Christ who, after considering the cost, are not willing to do so, they have no place with Him. If they weren't willing to forsake all, as in forsaking everything that opposes Christ, then they could not be His disciple. Likewise, to the rest of the world, if we're not willing to forsake the traditions of our upbringing and anything or anyone that tries to stop us in our newfound faith in Christ, then we aren't really His disciples.

4. John 8:31, *"Then said Jesus to the Jews which believed on him, 'If ye continue (know, obey, abide) in my Word, then are ye my disciples indeed.'"* This is obviously to a group of believing Jews, but there's no analogy here. Jesus straight up conveys that those who abide in and adhere to all His teachings... are truly His disciples indeed.

So, what we see, then, is Jesus isn't literally saying we have to hate our family in order to follow Him, or that we must drop everything and forsake all to follow Him like apostles often must do. Rather, Jesus was saying the people in your life might flip out on you for following Him, might forbid you from following Him, they might even reject or kill you. But if you aren't willing to endure such hardship if this is your predicament, then you cannot be His disciple. That's it in a nutshell.

Therefore, though these passages SEEM to suggest that true disciples must walk completely away from everything, much like what He told the new followers in Luke 9:51-62, that wasn't what Jesus meant. To the contrary, we should clearly see, now, that being a true disciple has nothing to do with being like how some apostles are called to a deeper baptism for the sake of their calling - while it has everything to do with the propensity of suffering for your newfound faith if your family, friends, colleagues or religion opposes it. **The bottom line being, if you aren't willing to forsake all false belief systems and idols, life style, positions, etc., and give Jesus preeminence over all who might reject you for following Him, then you really aren't His disciple.**

We need to close this section clear on the matter that every Christian, then, is supposed to be a disciple. I say supposed to be because, unfortunately, most Christians are not devout learners or pupils of the kingdom of God. That is, after all, the real definition of a disciple. Plus, most Christians blend in with the world, not forsaking heretical teachings and the false goings-on in both the world AND the Church. Because, just like the Pharisees, who knew the *history* of scripture and the letter of the law but didn't really know the heart and principles of scripture, Christians have minimal comprehension of the heart of the Word or understanding of the reality of the kingdom of God as well. Meanwhile, as we saw, Jesus boldly established that only those who *truly know and abide in His Word* are His. After all, a true disciple, a true Christian, is one who is a devout student, steward, executioner and exhibitioner of the Word of God.

As we know, there are billions of "Christians" in the world. But you tell me... How many of them fit the true, Biblical description of a disciple of Christ?

"By this everyone will know that you are my disciples (my devout students who intimately learn my ways and follow them); if you love one another (in peace - by being slow to anger, in joy, patience, kindness, selflessness, goodness, self-control, in humility, and gentleness)." John 13:35.

"This is to my Father's glory, that you bear much fruit (that you develop my attributes, are transformed and emanate my ways, my divine love,

and my light), showing (demonstrating and proving) yourselves to be my disciples (my true, devout "Christian" Children)". John 15:8.

_____
_____
_____
_____
_____
_____
_____
_____
_____
_____
_____
_____
_____
_____
_____
_____
_____
_____
_____
_____
_____
_____

The Overcomer's Checkpoint

Section One

Despite walking with Jesus and being raised up in the Church for 30 years, I've discovered (as you'll most likely agree) that most of us Christians have barely scratched the surface as effective representatives of Christ. Though Section One of the ODJ Program outlines where we're "off" concerning what the Gospel is, *the overarching goal was to align us with the truth of our foundation and what being a true Christian is supposed to look like.*

Hopefully Section One has helped us to PUT OFF the following FALSE beliefs:

- that all Christians are mandated to **verbally** share as in preaching or teaching the Gospel, if even in their own neck of the woods
- that the Gospel primarily reflects salvation
- that only some believers are also disciples
- that when it comes to reading the Bible, we have to feel guilty if we don't read it religiously the same time every day, a specific portion every day, read it cover to cover, thinking of it as an obligation that makes us right with God, etc.

To the contrary, hopefully Section One has instead:

- helped us realize that the Gospel is actually that **God's Kingdom is right here with us**, even in us, so that (in addition to the redemption of our sins and eternal life) we can live in supernatural peace, supernatural joy, supernatural power over the devil, supernatural power over sin, and prosperous in every way while still on earth
- helped us realize that being a Christian means we are also disciples - that it's one and the same - which means we are to be **devout learners, adherers, practicers and executioners of the kingdom of God** and His government and policies
- helped us realize that the Greatest Commission ever is actually that we grow in the attributes of Christ (supernatural peace, joy, patience, kindness, self control, meekness, righteousness, faith and love) by loving God above all else with all our heart, mind, soul, and strength
- and helped us realize that the thorns of this life can be anything, even good things, and are sneaky and that the only way we can be true Christians is by putting God first, above all, and killing the thorns

If we are going in circles, or worse, just going through the motions of Christianity, not *really* exemplifying Christ, or worse, if the devil has a field day wreaking havoc in our lives, **being out of alignment (as most of the Church is) with the above foundational principles will keep you going in those same circles.** Things will continue as they always were. Hopefully Section One establishes that we honestly don't know the Word of God like we think we do which is why the Church has not been very effective representatives of Christ and His authority. So please make sure you understand Section One before moving forward. Ask God if your mind, heart and soul have all received the facts and done away with the false perspectives.

Now, what's equally important is taking action concerning overcoming your thorns so that God's attributes (fruits of the Spirit) can soar in you. I've found that as I have grown in the fruit of the Spirit (though nowhere near to perfection), the devil has far less ability to mess with me because, **when you're in true peace, for example, you aren't as vulnerable to the devil's tactics**. You may get knocked down for a moment but you get back up much faster. Your reaction may be a startle but not devastation. When you're truly secure in God where joy is constant, even on a bad day, you can't be tossed about like a rag doll anymore. See, it's when we fail to apply these truths and grow in the attributes of Christ (love, peace, joy, etc) that the devil can mess with us so much more easily.

But we haven't really understood what a true Christian is let alone being one. When the going gets tough, there's minimal demonstration of the Kingdom's attributes in the corporate body as a whole. True, we all start as babes in Christ and aren't going to rock the fruit of the Spirit overnight. But when years go by and we're still just getting by, not growing up, this is why. It's because we haven't understood what the Gospel is, what a Disciple is, and the greatest commision to grow up in Him.

I'm preaching to myself as much as anyone. Just because the Lord releases insight and wisdom to me doesn't mean I've mastered applying it. I'm still a major work in progress. But, I repeatedly see the drastic impact that practicing what I preach has had on my life! The Word is true! It is power. It transforms! But...

We can't just "casually" listen to solid teaching and walk away not applying it with all our heart anymore. That's not a true Christian. If you're a medical student, you need to search the instruction out and meditate on it to get it inside you so you can apply what you've learned when the time comes. Not just listen to lectures. Yet, we do not have the same regard as stewards of the Kingdom of God.

We know the emphasis of the Church has been how much God loves us. And the focus has been His grace. But this has allowed us to become a very spotted bride that bears minimal fruit, clueless of what we're capable of, and failing to spread the Kingdom of God by virtue of our life example, fruit, and authority.

Again, I hope Section One served to correct the error of the Great Commission, the NECESSITY to bear fruit, the totality of what the Gospel is, and the meticulous clarification as to what a disciple is and ISN'T, so that we'll have a far better grasp as to who we, the Church, really are; and what we should be doing.

Section One Checkpoint

Questionnaire:

Please review the checkpoint questions below to assess where you are. Be honest with yourself and God. Keep this with all checkpoint reviews for future reference. Down the road you may want to revisit this section and redo this assessment. You'll discover how much you've improved. Simply rate the following from 1-10 as to the degree of strength, 10 being maximum:

_____ I understand that the Gospel isn't centered around the gift of salvation, rather, it's centered around Christ bringing His invisible, supernatural Kingdom into the earth which includes the gift of salvation.

_____ I understand that salvation is a result of being a genuine recipient, believer and exhibitioner of the invisible, supernatural Kingdom of God that Jesus brought into the earth.

_____ I understand that the Great Commission was addressed to the fivefold ministry such as apostles are, and that the Greatest Commission of all is that all Christians are to grow in the attributes of Christ in order to spread the Kingdom of God by virtue of their example.

_____ I appreciate the reality now that a true Christian is someone that literally loves the Lord with all their heart, mind, and soul... and that the key to growing in His attributes is by putting Him first.

_____ I understand that the cares and lusts of this life, including things like "the American dream" trip up many Christians and that this chokes the Word of God in them, which means they are more committed to this life (with all its issues and splendors) than God.

Now, we must live life on this earth which, let's face it, keeps us busy. But we are to love the Lord more than this life, more than this world and the things of this world; He truly must take priority in our hearts. This means that in our coming in and going out, whether we're working, on vacation, having dinner, showering, enjoying hobbies, and all else, we are to be living for God through it all. This means abiding in Christ's Kingdom policies and attributes and remaining submitted to Him in all that we do, forever mindful of our King and His ways. The following is a list of habits mature, devout Christians walk in. Of course, none of us are perfect in these, but we do want to assess where we are. Please determine on a scale of 1 to 10, 10 being maximum perfection, where you are with the following:

1) Despite being busy with life (work, family, the house, school, shopping, ministry, projects, etc.), I...

a) _____ talk to the Lord constantly, always seeking His approval or input

b) _____ am continually mindful and reverent of His presence

c) _____ always want to please and obey God in all I do

d) _____ walk in humility, love, peace, joy, patience, self-control, kindness, etc.

e) _____ maintain a positive, grateful, and thankful heart no matter what

f) _____ continually find myself giving God thanks and praise

g) _____ continually choose to be selfless and helpful to others

h) _____ am quick to repent if I get off track, disobey, or offend the Holy Spirit

i) _____ am quick to obey Holy Spirit if He instructs me to do something

j) _____ trust God with my life, my finances, my needs, my family, etc

2) Though you love God, there are many aspects of this life that you're passionate about, many things that are quite important to you. Rate the following between 0 – 10 as to how passionate

you are or how important they are to you. Now pay close attention to the things that you have extreme passion for – giving those a 10+++. And be honest with yourself. This is for your good.

a) _____ Achieving career or ministry goals / destiny / success
b) _____ Achieving social status / reputation
c) _____ Making money / acquiring wealth
d) _____ Knowing, studying and truly understanding God's Word
e) _____ Taking care of family (housekeeping/care/maintenance/providing)
f) _____ Acquiring a mate / spouse
g) _____ Having children
h) _____ Overcoming addiction / sin / habits / flesh / self
i) _____ Overcoming illness / defeat / poverty / oppression / depression
j) _____ Blessing my family/kids with what they want
k) _____ Measuring up to the Joneses
l) _____ My hair, nails, looks, physique, looking great/hot/sexy
m) _____ Feeding / Helping the poor, hungry / widows, orphans
n) _____ Taking a vacation
o) _____ Taking regular, extravagant vacations
p) _____ Growing into the full likeness of Christ, in His power and authority
q) _____ Representing and reflecting God's light & love to the world
r) _____ A "fancy" car
s) _____ Spending quality, personal time with the Father as much as possible
t) _____ Spending quality, personal time with loved ones or friends.
u) _____ Drugs, alcohol, cigarettes or other chemicals and substances
v) _____ Leisure time: hobbies, music, entertainment, social media, lounging
w) _____ Other:_____

Now please honestly assess where your heart is. Most of these are okay to love. But if these get more devoted focus, passion and pursuit or feel **more pressing** than being close to God, then these thorns are idolatry and will choke out your affections for God. Be honest, if you had to choose which to chase, the item(s) you rated 10+++, or God, which would you find yourself chasing? Again, it's okay to love the good things God made possible for this life. After all, He's the author of talent, skills, and even wealth. But as for letters b, k, l, o, r and u, these things, as you know, should not have high ratings, if any rating at all. So, please be honest with yourself as to how much the things of this life, be it good or bad, take precedence over your love and passion for God. Do some sincere soul searching and talk to God about this before you proceed with the devotional in Section One. It's important to know where you are before we pray about it, so that we can do so far more effectively. Continue to the next page.

3) Finally, please circle all that apply:

A) I realize that I want Jesus to be first in my heart, but I am very tangled up with my thorns
    a) and it feels impossible to give them up
    b) and I don't want to give them up
    c) and I desperately want to give them up but I just need help!

B) I realize that for as much as I love and want to obey Jesus, I am negligent and unfaithful because this world still sucks me in
    a) so, I'm hoping what I learn in this program will help me to overcome this
    b) and I'm desperately eager to see this program through and overcome
    c) but I'm honestly still not 100% resolved to press in with all I am

C) I am fed up with not walking in the full authority of Christ; and I realize I must and want to fully surrender my life to Jesus once and for all for it all to change!
    a) Yes, totally
    b) Not Quite
    c) Not really, no

D) I love Jesus and have actually grown up in some of His attributes. I'm no longer a babe in Christ. You might say I'm a teenager in the Lord. Because just like a teen, I know, at times, certain things tug at my heart strings and I'll drift off and go my own way! Because I'm still my own first priority and am overconfident in myself. But I'm ready to lay my whole self down and grow up once and for all.

  a) *This is so true*

  b) *Not Quite*

  c) *Not really, no*

E) I know it takes laying this life and all its "thorns" down and loving God with all my heart to be a disciple, to overcome darkness, and to come into Christ's authority.

  a) *But as much as I esteem this, I am still intimidated & feel I will never make it*

  b) *But as much as I esteem this, I honestly don't care enough, I'm not resolved*

  c) *And I'm nervous, but going to keep plugging away with all I am*

Your Prayer Devotional Instructions

Once you complete the checkpoint questions, if you find that your answers demonstrate that you are ensnared with thorns, struggling to love the Lord with all your heart, and feel overwhelmed at the notion of overcoming, then complete S1 Prayer Devotional Option #1.

However, if your answers demonstrate that you are resolved and ready but that there are still things that distract you or compete for your devotion at times, and you're fed up with it, then complete S1 Prayer Devotional Option #2 .

S1 Prayer Devotional Option 1:

Heavenly Father, Thank you for all you have done to bring me back to you, to deliver me and call me into alignment with your reality. But Father, I'm struggling. You know the challenges in my life, you know my habits/addictions, you know how discouraged I get. Father, it feels like I may never actually come into the fullness of who you are and all you've done for me. I see what you're saying in the things you teach me, but it hasn't taken a solid root! And now I know more clearly why - which is because there's so much about this life and my history that rules me. I don't want it to, but it does!

This program has shed plenty of light on where I am, how, though I love you, I confess, you aren't my highest priority. There's so many things in my life that my heart gives greater focus to. I'm so entangled in these thorns, Lord, and I feel (somewhat or completely) hopeless about it. A (small/huge) part of me doesn't even want to bother trying anymore.

But here I am, Father. I come before you, once again, desperate for your forgiveness and the cleansing power of the blood of your Son. Oh God, wash me clean now of all unrighteousness and forgive me for the pollution of my soul. Forgive me for my love affair with and obsession over the things of this life, be it the good things, bad things, or issues. Forgive me for not understanding your Kingdom and all of your ways. Forgive me for carrying the cares of this life instead of bearing Kingdom Peace, Kingdom Joy, Kingdom Patience, and Kingdom Self-Control.

Father, though it feels hopeless, I concede right now that YOUR WORD IS TRUE. I have confessed my sin, you forgive me so your power is within me to move forward and overcome. Not by might (my will)... not by power (my own strength)... but by your Spirit! I declare unto the depths of my soul that you are great in me and YOU are capable. Thank you, Father! Thank you for making the way in me. Because it's hopeless outside of your power in me. REGARDLESS HOW I FEEL, YOU ARE IN ME AND YOU ARE CAPABLE. PERIOD. I believe this now Father. Therefore, you can prosper in me now! Your truth can now take flight in me and help me overcome these thorns!

My life belongs to you, the Author of all life. Have your way in me. I choose you first. True, there's other things in this life that still have their hooks in me, but I confess right now that...

THEY ARE NOTHING COMPARED TO YOU!

Father, I choose to lay them down. I choose to declare they are sub par. They are all finite. They are all secondary to my existence. They may need to remain a part of what I am involved with on this earth, but they are subject to you. They do not rule me. I no longer grant them my allegiance. No matter how dependent upon them I'd always been, it's no more. I'm dependent upon you alone. You are my hope, Father, not the things of this life.

And I lay down all the worrying and distress I've had over things like the bills or other things that are important to me that haven't worked out. I confess that walking in anxiety or obsession over anything is not a holy Kingdom policy, but is the way of the dark kingdom! Forgive me, Father. I choose your peace in all these things now, Lord. I choose to trust you. I lay all this false programming down and choose to walk with

159

you on all the matters of this life from this day forward. Please hold my hand tight, Father, yanking me back into reality if I begin to operate out of these false ways. Please stop me in my tracks. Please, no matter how compelled I am to operate out of my old ways, please BOLDLY address me. I know you are gentle, but SCREAM at me to cut it out. I'm asking you for this help, Father. I'm giving you permission to do whatever you have to do to pull me back in line - and to do so as quickly as possible. Please do not allow me to entertain my thorns and get away with it. You say you discipline those you love, then prove your love. Discipline me if I refuse to listen to you, Your Majesty! I need your help in this. I do not want to be stuck here, caught up in all the stuff of this life and unable to keep you first. Father, I want these thorns gone. YOU are what really matters. My being just doesn't get it yet. HELP my entire being to recognize this truth, that you are all that really matters! Stay close to me like white on rice and boldy address me every second that I'm loving or catering to or worrying over this life above you. I know I will still esteem things here which is normal. But please don't let me OVER esteem them to where they are choking the life of your Spirit and Word out of me! Father, I plead with you to do whatever it takes. My flesh is too bossy, too demanding, and too selfish. I confess this. I repent for this. But I also know that without your intervention, I will remain this way.

Father, I choose to stand on the TRUTH that "I have been crucified with Christ. It's no longer I that lives, but Christ that lives in me. The life I live in this body I live by faith in the Son of God who loves me and gave Himself for me". Galatians 2:20. And "I can do all things through Christ who strengthens me", Philippians 4:13.

Father, those scriptures are fact, I just haven't made them my truth. I have, instead, made false things my truth. My soul has believed this is my life. My soul has been (desperately) chasing things like comfort, satiation, vindication, vengeance, recognition, fulfillment, and even love. But now I see, Father, I'm not in this earth for my soul to get all these, rather, I'm here for you. So I lay my whole self down once and for all. I surrender everything I've been running to or relying on to complete me in place of you. And I surrender my anxiety over the trials of this life including my finances, relationships, and all else. I will trust you. Take my life. Have your way, Oh God.

In Jesus' Name, Amen.

S1 Prayer Devotional Option 2:

Heavenly Father, Thank you for all you have done to bring me back to you, to deliver me and call me into alignment with your reality. Father, you have been first in my life for quite some time. I have laid myself down for you on many levels, because I know this life is not about me. You purchased my life with a heavy price and I am fully submitted to your will. I have made it my resolve to love you more than anything else in this life. But Father, I'm struggling. You know the challenges in my life, you know where I'm still vulnerable to become distracted. Sometimes I still get sucked into things that divert my passion away from you. Sometimes I get caught up in things that feel more important than you. I know in my mind it's not true, that they aren't. Yet my soul is still inclined to drift! Father, I hate this and want to overcome this once and for all! But it feels like I may never actually come into complete victory over these thorns in my life. I see what you're saying in the things you teach me, but it hasn't taken a solid root! And now I know more clearly why - which is because there's still aspects of this life that I actually do esteem as much as you.

This program has shed plenty of light on where I am, how, though I love you, I confess, you still aren't always my highest priority. There's still some things in my life that my heart and soul are vulnerable for. I feel somewhat entangled with them, Lord. I need your help to get past this once and for all.

So here I am, Father. I come before you, once again, desperate for your forgiveness and the cleansing power of the blood of your Son. Oh God, wash me clean now of all unrighteousness and forgive me for the pollution of my soul. Forgive me for my love affair with and obsession over the things of this life, be it the good things, bad things, or issues. Forgive me for not yet fully understanding your Kingdom and all of your ways. Forgive me for carrying the cares of this life instead of consistently bearing Kingdom Peace, Kingdom Joy, Kingdom Patience, and Kingdom Self-Control.

Father, though it sometimes feels hopeless, I concede right now that YOUR WORD IS TRUE. I have confessed my sin, you forgive me so your power is within me to move forward and overcome. Not by might (my will)... not by power (my own strength)... but by your Spirit! I declare unto the depths of my soul that you are great in me and YOU are capable. Thank you, Father! Thank you for making the way in me. Because it's hopeless outside of your power in me. REGARDLESS HOW I FEEL, YOU ARE IN ME AND YOU ARE CAPABLE. PERIOD. I believe this now Father more than ever before. Therefore, you can prosper in me now! Your truth can now take flight in me like never before, and help me overcome these thorns!

My life belongs to you, the Author of all life. Have your way in me. I choose you first. True, there's other things in this life that still have their hooks in me, but I confess right now that...

THEY ARE NOTHING COMPARED TO YOU!

Father, I choose to lay them down. I choose to declare they are sub par. They are all finite. They are all secondary to my existence. They may need to remain a part of what I am involved with on this earth, but they are subject to you. They do not rule me. I no longer grant them my allegiance. No matter how dependent upon them I'd always been, it's no more. I'm dependent upon you alone. You are my hope, Father, not the things of this life.

And I lay down any worrying or distress I've had over things like the bills or other things that are important to me that haven't worked out. I confess that walking in anxiety or obsession over anything is not a holy Kingdom policy, but is the way of the dark kingdom! Forgive me, Father. I choose your peace in all these things now, Lord. I choose to trust you. I lay all this false programming down and choose to walk with you on all the matters of this life from this day forward. Please hold my hand tight, Father, yanking me back into reality if I begin to operate out of these false ways. Please stop me in my tracks. Please, no matter how compelled I am to operate out of my old ways, please BOLDLY address me. I know you are gentle, but SCREAM at me to cut it out. I'm asking you for this help, Father. I'm giving you permission to do whatever you have to do to pull me back in line - and to do so as quickly as possible. Please do not allow me to entertain my thorns and get away with it. You say you discipline those you love, then prove your love. Discipline me if I refuse to listen to you, Your Majesty! I need your help in this. I do not want to be stuck here, caught up in all the stuff of this life and unable to keep you first. Father, I want these thorns gone. YOU are what really matters. My being just doesn't get it yet. HELP my entire being to recognize this truth, that you are all that really matters! Stay close to me like white on rice and boldy address me every second that I'm loving or catering to or worrying over this life above you. I know I will still esteem things here which is normal. But please don't let me OVER esteem them to where they are choking the life of your Spirit and Word out of me! Father, I plead with you to do whatever it takes. My flesh is too bossy, too demanding, and too selfish. I confess this. I repent for this. But I also know that without your intervention, I will remain this way.

Father, I choose to stand on the TRUTH that "I have been crucified with Christ. It's no longer I that lives, but Christ that lives in me. The life I live in this body I live by faith in the Son of God who loves me and gave Himself for me". Galatians 2:20. And "I can do all things through Christ who strengthens me", Philippians 4:13.

Father, those scriptures are fact, I just haven't made them my truth. I have, instead, made false things my truth. Though I've known and lived by the fact that this life is not my own, my soul still strives to live for me. My soul still chases things like comfort, satiation, vindication, vengeance, recognition, fulfillment, and even love. But now I see more than ever, Father, I'm not in this earth for my soul to get all these, rather, I'm here for you. So I lay my whole self down once again, completely. I surrender everything I've been running to or relying on to complete me in place of you. And I surrender my anxiety over the trials of this life including my finances, relationships, and all else. I will trust you. Take my life. Have your way, Oh God.

In Jesus' Name, Amen.

"You Give Thanks"

This is a very embarrassing story to share but I must be transparent if I really want to help make a difference...

During a season of rebellion where I had left my church to make life happen the way I wanted, I was living with the father of my children out of wedlock. Without going into details, I'll just say things were extremely dysfunctional and ugly. During this time, I was not praying, reading the Bible, worshiping or anything because I was angry at God for not giving me what I had been waiting for.

Months into this rebellion and during a very bad time, as my boyfriend walked past me in the dining room, I began cursing, even snarling at him, under my breath. Now, I have to tell you I have always been considered a loving, gentle person. Some would even say I was a Miss Goody Two Shoes. While everyone drank, smoked and cussed, I didn't (for the most part). I didn't like any of that. I had always hungered for righteousness even in my rebellion. Yet, there I was, full of disgust for my boyfriend. I was so appalled with his behavior that I took on this wicked attitude and found myself snarling with full-blown hateful contempt saying, *"You are such an #@%*&x!"* under my breath as he walked past.

Instantly I heard the Lord say as clear as day, "Stop it!" He did not shout it, it was a very calm but authoritative, "Stop it!". However, because I felt justified for my critical perspective, I made my defense right away saying, "But Lord! LOOK at him!" And to that the Lord just as quickly replied, "You give thanks!"

I was stunned. Give thanks? For WHAT? As far as my human understanding could assess, there was NOTHING to be thankful for. But I knew that I knew that God had just scolded me. Though I did not understand what I was to give thanks for, I submitted on the spot and began to do it just the same! -And I realized later... My behavior was more dispicable in that moment than the "disgusting" behavior I was judging my boyfriend for! Who do we think we are to be so disgusted with anyone! We're all sinners.

Now this was very early on in my Christian walk. I had only been actively seeking God for three years before my rebellion, so I didn't understand the principle behind giving thanks. But this day proved to teach me exactly what it was all about.

For the most part, we are taught in the Church how giving thanks is powerful. It's a way to connect to God. But what I learned first-hand in this very horrible situation that I'd gotten myself into is that no matter who does what, no matter how terrible someone is, no matter how ugly the circumstance, no matter how unjust, no matter the violation or cruelty, bending the knee to hatred like I did is WICKED. It's not the way of the kingdom of God. To the contrary, giving thanks despite the horror is precisely the way of the kingdom of God. I learned that day that God passionately stands behind 1 Thessalonians 5:18, "In <u>everything</u> give thanks: for this is the will of God in Christ Jesus concerning you.

That means EVERYTHING. I never would have imagined that God meant even in the face of totally disgusting, despicable circumstances that we were supposed to... give thanks! But that's exactly what we're supposed to do!
I share this because this is but ONE key truth that we believers should live by. But we don't because we feel justified snarling, complaining, and being angry or sore with our offenders. And it's so wrong. It's wicked and it is bowing to the kingdom of darkness! So please keep this in mind. NEVER

allow yourself to rise up in such bitter contempt for anyone or anything no matter how terrible it is. Nor to even the slightest degree!

Instead, do what God told me to do in place of being disgusted: Give thanks. For what? Well, for whatever comes to your mind. God will give you the words if you yield in submission to His correction. He gave me the words, He'll do the same for you.

Do please take heed to this. Never ever presume the right to snarl in hatred for anyone or anything in your heart, because it's extremely offensive to God and puts a barrier between you and His kingdom. It grieves the Holy Spirit and stifles His breath in you. And worse, gives a greater platform to the system of darkness in your life if you stay in that place! So please do what God says. Give thanks. And if you fail to, repent as quickly as possible. Amen.

"After 6 Months I slipped back into Pornography"

As I've shared previously, and as you have probably experienced time and time again, whenever you press in to God, the dark kingdom has to kick things up a notch to hinder you from chasing God. Since you've begun this program, the enemy has been working more adamantly against your excelling in Christ and overcoming dark kingdom influence in your life. The powers and principalities of darkness must diligently work to stifle your progress.

After the first two weeks of starting the program, one of the members wrote to me to report that they were struggling to do week three. They proceeded to say that simultaneous to being stifled, they fell back into pornography as well, despite successfully resisting for six months, and became quite discouraged. They expressed they are fed up with this sin and want to move on.

The following, as per their approval, is my response:

"Hello John/Jane Doe,

Thank you for sharing what's going on.

Okay... The most important thing to God is your heart and what I discern in your heart is that you hate this problem that you have. Your spirit wants to be one with Christ. This is a repentant heart. This is right standing with God. Knowing you are corrupt and need His blood to cleanse you to make you righteous is what makes you right with God. Which is your situation. Even right now!!! Even though you fell into this sin again. No, I'm not making excuses for you. True, it is wrong and it shows that the dark kingdom does have power in your life via some deep *soul allegiance within you. And it's not good for the enemy to have any authority, true. But this is what you are working to change as we speak. Meanwhile, the most important thing is you <u>do not want</u> to be submitted to dark kingdom policies. Though something in your soul is still addicted, your mind, heart and spirit are against it! This is your heart. So this is why the devil does not have full authority and influence over you anymore! Because, ever since the first time you yielded in repentance to God and submitted to the reign of Christ, the devil lost significant authority over you! The only authority he has left is where your soul is still out of alignment with truth which makes you vulnerable to his tactics and suggestions. And he capitalizes on these. But that's why he is not able to control you with this sin all the time. That's why 6 months could go by with you successfully resisting. But because the minions assigned to your life know you VERY well, they know how to set you up to fall still. They know how to work on you, pushing just the right buttons at just the right time, even down to influencing your hormones by tempting you with foods that will make you vulnerable to the temptation. And of course, you know that because you signed up for the program, they had to work triple duty to ensnare you.*

I'm not saying you are not responsible because you are the one (just as I am, too) that bows to the devil. But the point is that your soul and belief system is in a whirlwind still. You know and believe some of God's truths, yet your soul only knows what it has experienced, so it has a mind of its own. This is why God had me make the program, to help people at soul level, where the devil still dominates. God showed me that for most of His children, including me, though our hearts are 100% for God, our souls are controlled by darkness based on all the past influences and charades of the devil. Plus all false programming, false teaching, even subtle false things in the Church, also keep our souls from aligning with the Father in order to experience His manifest reality, power and goodness in tangible ways in our lives.

So realize that what's going on with you is only because of all this discombobulation that is in your soul. And that you fell again because the devil is working VERY hard to hold you back, to keep you from pressing in, discouraging you because he knows he can do so by making you fail. So the best thing you can do for yourself and against the devil right now is rejoice that God knows how disgusting we are in our sin but that He loves us anyway! Rejoice that God is working hard to deliver your soul far more passionately than the devil is working to keep you down. That's what's happening right this very moment. He woke me up just so I could answer you. (It's 3:33 in the morning in the USA right now as I am typing this second!!! WOW!!!)

Okay, so, do NOT feel discouraged, that was the whole plan of the devil!!! Know that the disgusting aspects of our sin, and even the lusts of our flesh, do not shock God. What He sees more than anything with you is your HEART to PLEASE Him. He feels so very loved by you because of this! Because of how badly you do not want to have this sin or any other sin! Being both loved and believed by us are the two prominent things that God desires from us, above all else. Well, you have both of these - to whatever degree, right now. True, sometimes you bow to your flesh and evil. But other times you resist them and bow to the Spirit. This is the very war going on in us that Galatians 5:17 speaks about. But here's the thing: as you come into more alignment with truth, as you get more rooted in Holy Kingdom reality, namely at soul level, you will love and believe God more and more! And then the power of the devil to lure you into pornography or any other sin will be defeated. Once your soul is put into order, you'll not be controlled by this sin and lured into it so easily any more! The only vulnerability that will remain is if you do not remain centered in and abide in Christ.

So don't focus on your failure, focus on the extent God has gone to deliver you from it (at the cross)! And focus on the extent He is still going to, to raise you up out of it all! And in so doing, it will play a role in defeating the devil!"

I am sharing this response to this person with you, the reader, because if you have regressed back into sin recently, it's because the devil has to keep you tangled up because he is afraid of your coming into more alignment with truth - which becomes a problem for the dark kingdom. I know how horrible it feels to fail. I've shed plenty of tears over my own repetitive sin. But I've learned failure, even disgusting gross failures which make us feel so ashamed, are merely who we are apart from Christ. And I'm not mortified or devastated by this reality any more which has played a huge role in my experiencing manifest victory! The devil cannot use this against me because the tactic no longer works.

So please... Chin up. Face the truth so the devil can't use it against you anymore, either. Accept that, apart from Christ, you are dirty dust. Even if you don't do dirty things, you are. And if you can fully acknowledge this, you won't be so mortified and controlled by it. Drive it into your soul that God loves you despite how terrible you can be at times! Look at all He's done for you despite it! Focus on that and get over your shame. Don't let the minions assigned to hold you back win. Tell them you know you're a sinner but that Jesus loves you. Tell them what God has done for you far outweighs how disgusting you could ever be. Meditate on the reality that God is constantly fending you off, working to deliver you from evil, to give you a way of escape, to teach you truth and draw you out of the pit. Rejoice in this and be passionately conscious that God is for us. Seeing God for Who He truly is and what He truly does is one of the most prominent aspects to nullifying the power of the dark kingdom. So start today, refusing to allow your "failures" to continue to be tools the enemy can use against you, to control you and your pursuit of the kingdom of God and His righteousness. Simply repent, yes, for the 9,473rd time, for slipping back into pornography or whatever other sin. This repentance does count, don't doubt it for one second. Know that your repentance shuts down the dark kingdom on the spot. Amen.

Once again, the following heart coloring is provided as a tool to meditate. While coloring, forbid any thoughts except truths concerning who you really are, God's love for you, His presence, His passions for you, His plans for you. Praising Him, worshiping Him, going on and on and on about ALL that is right, good, and true. Cleanse the toxicity of the day by meditating.

Anxiety
Your Prayer to the Father

You know, as much as we know scripture tells us to not be anxious about anything, but in everything, by prayer and petition with thanksgiving, to present our requests to God (Philippians 4:6), so many of us are full of anxiety anyway.

PART of the reason that this is so, in all honesty, is because we live in a day and age where external factors impact our bodies, causing disturbances or imbalances in the systems of our body which lead to the propensity to be anxious. With our electrical, hormonal, neurological, chemical imbalances and more, we are far more prone to anxiety. Not that I want to blame the external factors. I just want to establish they are relevant. And there are ways to isolate if and what factors may be contributing to your having anxiety - if you have it - and ways to counter these factors. Unfortunately, I can't get into all that here.

Beyond the natural factors, however, are the spiritual factors. I've discovered the deeper reason for anxiety is a lack of security in God. Something in the soul is unstable, afraid, or in unbelief. Something in the psyche and belief system is not aligned with truth. The result is we respond to life circumstances from this place of spiritual imbalance, vulnerable and unable to cope very effectively with life without being anxious. The ODJ Program is designed to help undo all this, bringing balance and solidification to the soul with truth, so that things like anxiety will no longer plague children of God.

Meanwhile, the Bible does teach us to simply CHOOSE to not be anxious (Philippians 4:6) but to trust God, giving thanks despite whatever is going on, and in so doing, the peace of God which transcends human understanding comes upon us, guarding our hearts and minds in Christ Jesus. It's amazing. But this is an act of obedience, in choosing to say,

"No, I will not be anxious about this. Father, you got this. You've got me. Give me your wisdom how to deal with this. I don't know how things will turn out, things could get quite ugly for all I know. But I'm not going to worry about it because my life is in your hands. In the end, I'm with you in Paradise, so all this is temporary and has no eternal relevance to my existence. By letting go of this worry, Father, I'm taking the matter from the devil's control and putting it into your hands. And I trust that however you decide this to turn out, it's cool. Whatever you say. One way or another, you are taking care of me, I just know it! I need to trust that. Because that's the fact. You care about me and WANT to help me in every way. That's just who you are. So, no, I will not fret over this. It's in your hands. Your will be done, Father. In Jesus' Name, Amen."

"Where Did All These Ghosts Come From?"
~You Are Not Alone

In 2010 I had finished writing what I thought would be my first book, Operation Python, Dethroning the False Prophet. Just as it was about to be published, the Lord told me to put it down - which was quite upsetting. But I knew He'd spoken and I was afraid to not listen. So I laid the endeavor down in February 2011 and it wasn't until January 2012 that God told me to pick it back up. Long story short, He had me rewrite more than half of the book, taking it to a whole new level. And I saw how I'd gained depth of insight over the course of 2011 which impacted the new manuscript. It was clear that God was intricately involved with this book.

Now, what's interesting is in 2011 while the project was dormant, I had this dream...

I was in the middle of a large, old school cafeteria full of tables from wall to wall. Nobody was in the cafeteria but me. I wondered what was going on so I exited through the double doors into the corridor outside the cafeteria. To my left was this massive set of stairs, like you'd see in very large schools. The steps were about twelve feet wide. And they were filled with students from ages 12 up to about 21. All of the steps were covered with students, shoulder to shoulder, and they all just kept coming down and proceeded into the cafeteria.

What's strange was every single student was despondent. Their heads hung low, and they all had blank, empty stares on their faces. They seemed to be dead like zombies as they all stoically made their way into the cafeteria. All I could think was, "Where are all these ghosts coming from?"

Why I asserted that they were ghosts, I have no idea. It's not like they were transparent. They were as real as humans can be, just so despondent that it looked like death, somehow.

The next thing I knew, I was standing in the middle of the cafeteria again. This time the tables were filled with all the stoic students, and they were all looking at me. Meanwhile, all I continued to think was, "How can I see these ghosts?"

Suddenly, an Asian or Indonesian girl that looked to be between 18 to 20 years old walked up to me. Again, all I could think was, "How am I able to see you?" as she approached. And then, as we stood there face to face with her staring deep into my eyes, saying absolutely nothing, I understood that in her mind, too dead to ask out loud, she was asking, "Well, are you going to help us?", Meanwhile, guess what I was thinking? That's right. All I could do is reach out, touch her arm and say, "How can I see and feel you if you are a ghost?" And that's when I woke up.

My husband woke up, too, so I told him about the dream and how all these kids were ghosts, even though they didn't look or feel like ghosts. Holy Spirit spoke through him quickly, saying, "Those weren't kids, Paula, and they weren't ghosts. They were adults whose spirits were the age when something traumatic took place and shut them down. It's as if something in them died in their childhood, and they came to you to help them come back to life. What you were seeing is the part of their spirits that were dead."

Wow, I understood right away. God was showing me the nature of the ministry that would develop out of the book that had yet to even be finished. And that's exactly what happened. When the book was finally published, I began receiving countless emails from people who were severely oppressed, even dead inside, hopeless, and defeated, just like I had once been, and just like the dream. Suddenly God's anointing was upon me in a way I'd never experienced and He began using me to enlighten fellow brothers and sisters as to the truths that they'd not yet seen, in order that they could break free from dark kingdom dominion and live full lives in Christ.

Interestingly enough, a few years after the dream about the dead people coming to me for help, still remembering the cold, blank, despondent looks in their faces, God spoke to me one day that Satan succeeds at continuing to dominate children of God... *through their souls.* That, as I explain elsewhere and repeatedly throughout this program, Satan sets up shop in the lives of children who will one day become born again. He sets systems into place to train their souls to respond to and continue to yield to him and his suggestions even after we give our lives to Jesus. And that he does this through many different tactics such as abuse, negligent parents, rejection, bullying, repeated trauma, and so much more - to gain control of their souls. The plan is to fashion a person's soul's understanding and perspective according to defeat and, especially, doubting God and His love, by shutting them down via ongoing adversity (which is beyond the "trials" the Bible says are to be expected). Then, when the negatively indoctrinated person finds Jesus, no matter how much their mind believes Jesus died for their sins and that God will never forsake them, their souls don't get it. Their souls will have a perspective all their own. And THIS would keep the believer partially in allegiance with the devil's kingdom, giving him legal authority.

These are the people from my dream who love God but are stuck because of how the inundation of darkness from the enemy has stifled their souls. Though they are alive in Christ, yet, a part of them is still dead.

Not everyone that wants to come into the full stature of Christ that signed up for this program has been as adversely affected as the believers in my dream. But I have learned that the "ghosts" are the severe cases of the body of Christ who help us to recognize the reality of the corporate body at large. Because, though not severely debilitated as these stoic souls were in my dream, the majority of believers are in the same boat, just to a far more subtle degree. Remember, as I shared earlier, even the non-severely oppressed believers are oppressed one way or another if we're not excelling in the truths of God's kingdom and Word.

Whether you were one of the believers in my dream or not, please know, the devil is not creative. He learns what works and runs with it. If he didn't have legal jurisdiction to pummel you throughout your childhood in order to brainwash your soul into submission to fear, defeat, and despair, he still did all he could to twist your perspectives and influence your belief system somewhere along the road. This explains why you still have yet to soar in the truths of God the way you long to.

But for those who were in my dream, part of the programming you've taken on is you feel alone. Not as in completely isolated, necessarily. But as in you feel different, perhaps like an outcast, odd, and like you don't fit in anywhere. You especially find it difficult to connect to other believers. (This is because you're coming from a deeper sense of things because of what you've been through that most don't get or care to.) But, the truth is you are not alone. And understand that though you may not find where you do, in fact, fit in, there are countless people that feel exactly the same way for exactly the same reasons. I talk to them almost every day. I guarantee, the believers of this program are the people you would connect with in that way that you can't seem to connect with most everyone in your immediate circle.

And I also hope you'll understand that part of the reason you feel so odd is because of the crafty work of the dark kingdom that has been avidly working to program you this way all your life. You know, it doesn't take rocket science to know that if you continually manipulate or even badger a person from their infancy all the way up into adulthood, that person will be programmed accordingly. Consequently, they might become insecure, afraid, feel unlovable, inadequate, needy, desperate, and more. And they might subconsciously anticipate and have confidence in (and even fear) the works of darkness more than they have confidence in and fear God, because that's how they've been trained. Regardless how many mind altering classes they take to learn how to be positive, to believe in themselves, to be confident, or whatever, something deep in their soul is stunted; stoic. And until their SOUL engages and connects with God's light and truth, they'll continue to operate in the same cycles, getting nowhere fast.

As for the not-so-severely stoic, the same applies to you. Until your soul engages and connects with God's light and truth more succinctly, you'll continue to operate in the same cycles, getting nowhere fast.

If you've been reading my books or teachings and have thought, "Wow, what she is saying is the story of my life!" *(I've heard that too many times to count)*, the message I want to emphasize to you today is that you seriously **are not alone**.   Sure, we're scattered around the globe and can't get together for tea or a movie, which stinks. But, I've taken great comfort in seeing time and time again since 2012 that, despite there being almost nobody in my neck of the woods that relates to me in the things I teach or share with you about, I have countless brothers and sisters out there who do! Like you! The members of this program prove this.

On a side note, I created an exclusive member's blog for those who actually want to connect with like-minded believers. I hope you'll take the opportunity to post something if you're eager to connect. Just be patient with the blog because many of you will feel trepidation about it at first. In the meantime, I just hope that if you don't have anyone in your world that gets you or relates to you in this regard, that you'll remember from this day forward that most everyone taking this program **actually would get you** in the way that's hard to find! All everyone has to do is make themselves known via the member's blog.

Panic Attacks

As per the time of this writing, this past week, THREE people have brought up that they have severe anxiety so the Lord has led me to speak to it (as this is a subject I'm all too familiar with). I actually wrote an extensive reply to one of the ODJ members that mentioned their panic attacks and I'm just going to copy and paste it below.

After this member mentioned her panic attacks, I asked if she also has these other symptoms:

- startle easy
- excessive emotions at times (hurt, joy, anger for minor reasons)
- obsessive compulsive
- feeling overwhelmed more than average
- foggy mind
- feeling frazzled
- wanting to space out a lot
- perfectionism
- headaches
- mania & hyper minded one day, low and reclusive the next

She responded yes, naming seven of the symptoms, just as I'd suspected. If you or someone you know has the majority of these symptoms, too, please read my reply to her and feel free to share this email by forwarding to others that could benefit from the insight:

"Dear Jane Doe,

As per your symptoms, just as I suspected, you have almost all of them.

Now of course, I am not a doctor or specialist of any sort. I'm only sharing based on experience and research over the years. I've begun to see trends and can sometimes spot what's potentially behind these issues.

I'm discovering anxiety and panic attacks are on the rise. As well as many other things on account of several factors:

- DNA breakdown (body not performing functions such as eliminating toxins as well), breakdown of the gut (leaky gut, poor nutritional absorption)
- EXTREME Increase in environmental toxins in past 50 years, especially past 10 years: chemicals in air (chemtrails), products, foods, on skin; heavy metals in water, VACCINATIONS!, tooth fillings, toothpaste; **EMF radiation, RF, etc (rampant)**

People that are more vulnerable to the influx of toxins, including EMFs, have the weaker DNA genes (this can be tested) and they are the ones getting weaker and sicker faster. Jesus is definitely going to have to return soon because with the newly added 5G wifi on top of everything else, people are going to begin to get far more sick far more quickly than EVER in the next decade. Even healthy people will begin saying "Despite eating healthy, exercising, etc, I'm just so tired. I'm just not myself anymore. I just don't feel that great!"

That's how it starts. But anyway, those with weaker DNA have already begun getting sick. **Symptoms** from the influx of all the above toxins vary depending on which genes are weak in the individual AND which factors they are exposed to AS WELL AS other factors in life such as stress, abuse, Post Traumatic Stress Syndrome, etc., **can be any number of the following:**

- allergies
- foggy minded
- anxiety

- startle easily
- panic attacks
- depression, low, reclusive, overwhelmed
- bipolar, mania, low
- anger/emotion issues/major mood swings
- hypothyroid
- heart disease
- cancer
- diabetes
- autism
- fibromyalgia
- anemia
- seizures
- SIDS
- Teeth Decay / Problems
- Alcoholism, drug addiction, self medicating
- Schizophrenia, Psychosis
- Obsessive Compulsive Disorder
- Oppositional Defiance Disorder
- ADHD
- Skin disorders
- Alzheimers
- headaches, migraines
- And more

I know it sounds like I just listed a bunch of random diseases, but these can all be linked to weaker DNA and toxic influx - especially chronic overexposure to EMFS!!! Please re-read "Do This First" to get a better grip on how to reduce exposure. [And if you are holding an electronic smart wifi device right now that is currently plugged in and charging while you read this, **PUT THIS DEVICE DOWN AND WAIT TIL IT'S CHARGED! NEVER HOLD A CHARGING DEVICE.** Go outside and step on the ground barefoot or touch a tree to discharge right away. And unplug the device from the wall before you finish reading this!]

Now, the good news the Lord has been teaching me three solutions to all this. This breakdown on health is a deliberate assault on mankind as per Satan's intent to become god over all the earth. But God always provides the truth and an answer. I've been personally coming into this over the past few years due to a SEVERE sensitivity to EMFs. Wow, what an education.

You know... the one thing I hate about the ODJ Program right now is that for some people, there only access to this program is via the internet which means higher exposure to EMF and wifi radiation for those that don't know how to minimize exposure. I hope the paperback is a relief where necessary. Meanwhile, I'm determined to share all I know re: devices and internet use. I use the internet constantly but my exposure has been drastically reduced.

But yes, I've learned there's a three part solution to what's going on, because we can't escape it for the most part.

1. Get educated and take measures to reduce exposure to things as best as possible (i.e., use ethernet cables to hardwire internet to computer/laptop and turn off wifi signal which constantly travels through air, don't sleep next to devices, etc. Again, please read "Do This First" for more tips.)

2. Take plenty of antioxidants to help the body eliminate these toxins. Nowadays, with the increase in toxic exposure, we need tons of antioxidants such as **vitamin C, green tea**, and others. Taking a quality multivitamin with METHYL Bs MIGHT be super necessary for people with symptoms such as yours (although IF YOU FEEL WORSE AFTER TAKING METHYL FOLATE, THEN IT'S BAD TO TAKE AS A SUPPLEMENT AND YOU MUST MAKE EVERY EFFORT TO EAT LEAFY GREENS, EGGS, AND MEAT INSTEAD - it all depends on your personal methylation pathways. I repeat, folate might be a must - but it might be a big fat NO. The only way to know

is to test with small doses and do research). These various nutrients help detox the body big time. Also, other nutrients most of us **DESPERATELY** need are **magnesium (not oxide, rather, l-threonate or glycinate or transdermal especially)** and **selenium** (magnesium must be taken with selenium to work best as I found out the hard way). And for some people (many) they are also low on **vitamin D3 and Iron**. These levels should be checked by a doctor or lab, but get the actual results in front of you and look at them yourself, don't just let them say "it's normal" because they say the bottom of the range is normal when it isn't. My D3 was 34 and the range was 30 to 110 for normal, but doc said it was normal meanwhile I felt horrible. Had I not looked at the result and researched it, I would not have known that was part of why I still didn't feel well. And this after a year of supplementing 2000 IU/day of D3. Yet, it was okay? No. Experts say anything below 70 is getting too low for optimum well-being. So, get the labs yourself and do your research. Same with iron. And if these are in the LOW QUADRANT of the range (especially if you have pain in the body like fibromyalgia) you likely need a higher dose of IUs/day. Try increasing for a month or two of D3 and **get retested after two months to make sure it's not going too high, because that can be very bad, too**. And for iron, make sure it's ELEMENTAL iron, if your iron is in low range. ALSO, take a good fish oil (but I don't recommend Salmon oil, could be a problem). All these make such a difference when your body is struggling to fight off the modern day influx (and lack of nutrient rich foods).

3. And the third part of the solution is to rise in faith that you do not accept the inundation of the environmental toxins which are beyond your ability to control or avoid. There's so many that we don't even know. But tell your body to refuse to embrace them but instead, because of Christ in us, we repel and resist the devil (all corruption including toxins are of the devil), and they will flee. It's essentially a state of mind, a confidence, a security in your identity in Christ's

kingdom, a state of faith, living in the choice to not accept invisible influx. (You'll understand this better throughout the program.) Meanwhile, don't be cocky and deliberately negligent by purposely allowing excessive exposure saying, "Oh, I don't have to accept this". No, it's all about believing for protection from that which you have no control over. Like fire. You avoid it. If it's out of your control, you trust God for His help "through" it."

So, that's what I wrote to her. I know it's a mouthful but this is an abbreviated summation of the past 7 years dumped all in one email. I hope it helps.

Taking the antioxidants and supplements will help you deal with the influx, but remember to address your excessive exposure to EMF radiation. Anxiety and panic attacks are a SURE SIGN your body needs support and that you are overexposed. Follow the 3-step solution and watch yourself improve dramatically. (Although, you might feel crappy for a week or two while detoxing. But that's a whole other discussion.)

If you are one that has panic attacks and anxiety, trust me that reducing your EMF exposure is a MUST and take care to address it. Then get on antioxidants (and especially magnesium if you get headaches, leg cramps, etc). Vitamin C, magnesium spray and selenium are the most important. And finally, take the position that you do not accept the invisible influx you have no control over. This will surely help.

Update:

----------BEWARE OF----------
5G Smartphones & Towers!
---------PLEASE AVOID!---------

Food For Thought

Saw this posted on facebook and just had to share it here! It's so true! And it lines up with the Word of God in that we are to take thoughts captive and bring them into the obedience of Christ. Allowing negative, pessimistic, contrary-to-light thoughts is operating in dark kingdom policies, not God's! And it's to our detriment.

I thought this would be a wonderful stepping stone into the next two modules where we'll be discussing the two supernatural kingdoms.

Wish I knew who the author and creator of this post was so I could give them the credit for it. It's powerful!

Notes/Prayers

Good VS Evil - And the Wicked Good

Section Two 1

The world sees that we've got the good, the bad and the ugly. But from a spiritual perspective, we've got the good, the evil... *and the wicked good.*

It's no great revelation that we are in the last days. And that in the last days, that which is evil is counted as good, while that which is good is counted as evil (Isaiah 5:20). For example, a woman's "right" to kill her unborn child is an evil policy. Yet, the world counts it as a good thing... and counts those that believe abortion to be evil, as evil.

But this module is not about establishing the obvious. Before we go much further into the program, I felt it necessary to identify where we personally, as individual Christians, are in the scope of this whole perverted twisting of good and evil. And then from there, delve into an aspect of Christian culture that I refer to as the "wicked good" and how it relates to us. Because, remember, this program is meant to bring us into full alignment with truth in order that we come into the full stature of Christ, and we cannot do that if we do not recognize the areas where we personally compromise even unwittingly - counting evil as good. Nor can we thrive in Christ if we fail to recognize or become enmeshed with the "wicked good".

Let's first consider where we believers may be prone to calling evil good. Though you most likely (hopefully) already know loud and clear that abortion is evil, there are other things we neglect to count as evil with the same resolve, such as:

1) Public Attire: Though most would not admit this, many believers are somewhat okay with themselves or others dressing in appealing ways; immodestly, even provocatively or scantily, in public to one degree or another, since everyone else does. It's become normalized and somewhat accepted by the corporate body. I was "unfriended" on facebook once by a seemingly strong Christian female friend who actually has a ministry. She had posted, *"Which is your favorite Little Black Dress?"* with three images of very skimpy, form fitting black dresses that cause people to "look". I had expressed that the Lord doesn't want His daughters being all sexy out in public. I shared how I personally had a history of being immodest in my public attire, and that God showed me how wrong it is. I was not judging, just sharing the truth with a sister in Christ. In fact, it's still a habit for me to be a bit careless and buy an outfit that ends up drawing eyes to look my way. This is not right but I confess, due to being sexually twisted in my childhood, I learned that this was "my value" and was programmed in my soul to rely on looking appealing to the public to have any sense of self worth. This was one of the many lies that I adopted that needed to be corrected in my soul with truth. And I confess that I still have the propensity to yield to this lie if my eyes aren't on Jesus. God has to bring me back into line from time to time, though I'm nowhere near as negligent as I used to be. So, I sincerely wasn't judging my friend from church on facebook. But she took offense and said just because God told me it was wrong for me, didn't mean it's wrong for all. That God wants us looking sexy for our husbands during a romantic night out. And she unfriended me. Since she was such a passionate, outspoken believer, I was stunned she was so resolved for this, even resorting to being unkind - which is dark kingdom fruit, contrary to the fruit of love, kindness and forgiveness (had she perceived my sharing as a violation). But all this to show... This is one way we can be deceived thinking something is good when it is displeasing to God. In fact, it doesn't have to be a little black dress. Any clothing that draws eyes to look, even tight jeans and a t-shirt if form fitting or full of holes is evil because it's willfully inciting people to look upon you lustfully. It's also evil because something in you desires to be perceived in a specific

way. And it doesn't have to do with clothing only, but with hairstyle, shoes and makeup - and even excessive physical fitness, cosmetic surgeries or enhancements and such which all boils down to idolizing how we want to look for others. Plus it sends out subconscious messages of wanting to be sexy; wanting to be seen, wanting to be admired, etc. I know, I was there! There's no denying it. It's a problem in the Church as much as it is in the world. Perhaps to a more subtle degree and not as blatantly in your face, but it's definitely an evil in the Church that the corporate body turns a blind eye to.

2) Catering to Self: The idea that you're supposed to take care of, pamper and reward yourself is everywhere. Especially in the commercial market. *"Buy this, you need it... you deserve it!"* The world constantly promotes self. And we, the Church, are as guilty as the non-believers for yielding to this false ideal. Even if we say it's wrong, we're still inclined to cater to ourselves because it's our nature. And it's very difficult not to when we're surrounded by a million things and ways to do so. And, it's seemingly impossible to escape the temptation! Our only refuge is to stay in close proximity to the Father and to keep our eyes on Jesus, and the truth. And even that's hard when we're running around like chickens with our heads cut off dealing with this life. We get lost in the dynamics, ideals and protocol of the world. Both God and the devil know we are vulnerable to this. But at the end of the day, catering to ourselves is of the dark kingdom and we are to resist it. This goes along with the teachings of section one, that we're to bear fruit, growing in the attributes of Christ, not chasing ourselves or getting caught up in the thorns of life. We are to love God above all else, not revolve around our "selves".

We need to appreciate the truth that counting it okay to dress immodestly or cater to self is just as evil as killing innocent children. Indeed, murder is far more grotesque and horrific, but evil is evil. Just as an apple is an apple. One apple may taste bad while another tastes horrible, but they're still both bad apples that you aren't going to eat.

If we want to grow up in Christ, one very important thing we need to do is be wholly reverent for righteousness, remaining firm that evil is evil and what's good is good; not undermining anything like being immodest or desiring to be looked at or look good, or compromising in other areas like catering to self just because it's the way of the world. We are so resolved to not compromise with obvious evils such as murdering an unborn child. **But we need to be equally resolved concerning God's policies that we aren't to look and act like the world as well.**

The other thing we need to do in order to grow up in Christ is to identify the "wicked good" among us and stay away from them - *as in not becoming enmeshed and in unity with them.* Though we know this already, there is a profound mix of wheat and tares in the corporate body of Christ. We need to remain mindful that not everyone that believes they're a Christian, not everyone sitting next to us at church, actually walks with Christ.

The reason it's important to discuss this isn't so we can sit around and point fingers, judging who is and isn't really a Christian. No, the importance is to simply be aware for the sake of our spiritual well-being. Being blindsided about this makes us more vulnerable to the tactics of the dark kingdom, and we can get entangled with false Christians and taken down dangerous, problematic paths. We need to be wise and sharp; not gullible. And we need to start dealing with things accurately, not from a place of ignorance.

The day is coming when the wheat and tares will have been separated. It will be clear who is truly submitted to God as Lord, and who isn't. But for now, we're all still mixed together for the most part. So it's important to discern the good (those cleansed by the blood for real) from the wicked good (those who have a form of godliness but were never cleansed due to lack of repentance and/or literal submission to Christ the King) so that you will not get entangled with them. This matters. We are warned to avoid them.

"But if they have a form of godliness, how can we tell that they are not genuine believers? Especially when they are convinced they are Christians themselves?"

The best answer is if we stay close to Father God, He will give us discernment. **It's time we respect the Holy Spirit in us, knowing He is MORE than eager to warn us with red flags in our discernment.** I mean, seriously! He's in us speaking loud and clear constantly. We're just too boogered up to hear Him and it needs to stop. Let's just trust and respect Him already. But even more than Holy Spirit telling us straight up to proceed with caution, Matthew 7:16 says we will know them by their fruit. And what fruit is that? Well, do they truly submit to truth and have a heart for what's right? Do they have a heart like Jesus or just have a form of godliness? Do you see the light of Christ in their eyes, despite their flaws?

! Not to mention... "A time is coming when people (in the Church) will no longer listen to sound and wholesome teaching. They will follow their own desires and will look for teachers who will tell them whatever their itching ears want to hear. They will reject the truth and chase after myths". 2 Timothy 4:3.

! And, "In the last days there will come times of difficulty. For people (in the Church) will be lovers of self, lovers of money, proud, arrogant, abusive, disobedient to their parents, ungrateful, unholy, heartless, unappeasable, slanderous, without self-control, brutal, not loving good, treacherous, reckless, swollen with conceit, lovers of pleasure rather than lovers of God, **having the appearance of godliness**, but denying its power. Avoid such people." 2 Timothy 3:1-5.

Now these are "church members" these passages are referring to! They are the tares that are mixed in with genuine believers in the Church. So what the Bible shows us is that tares think they are saved because they are religious, follow outward rules, traditions and regulations - which is their form of godliness. On the outside they are serving God but inwardly, they are in charge and unrepentant because they chase and/or cater to self even when doing for others. They can also be prestigious but self-righteous, prideful, unyielding, and unkind to those not in their class. Their love is conditional and they aren't concerned for the needy, widows and orphans unless it's to their benefit. Their interest is in watered down messages which never ruffles their feathers. They do not respond to messages of conviction. Correction and transformation are not their forte. They prefer mellow teaching, just enough to soothe their conscience, and even chase false, self-serving doctrines. They typically do not want to acknowledge the reality that Jesus is returning soon for a spotless bride. Rather, they only care that God wants to bless them.

That's not to say genuine Christians won't exhibit some of these behaviors as well, so we cannot hastily judge anyone! **We must simply stay close to God, remain humble and submitted to Him, and seek discernment.** We should be able to recognize the light of Christ in those who are redeemed right away. If something feels off, we need to take it up with God and use caution to not get entangled with them. Be wise and use discernment, being careful to not connect with false things, including false Christians. Again, please, don't take this as an invitation to be paranoid or judgemental. But do be on the alert in not assuming that all Christians are really your brothers and sisters. 2 Timothy 3:5 says to avoid such people. Do not yoke up with them because it will serve to hinder your life. It gives a legal place to the enemy when you come into agreement with anything false - including false believers. It enables the enemy to lure you into deeper deceptions!

What's ironic is genuine believers are so full of grace that we're inclined to not assume the worst but instead, give everyone in church the benefit of the doubt, presuming they must belong to God. And worse, because they tend to be strong in their countenance, and because the enemy capitalizes on their giftings in order to give them high positions or draw others to admire them, we fall for it and esteem them. **Sometimes we may even be jealous or hurt that we aren't in similar shoes, coveting their greatness or position.** And what's worse yet is many of us want to connect with them to hopefully experience some of the favor that the wicked good tend to attract to themselves (with the help of the enemy).

That's just a generalization, but you get the idea. The point being the wicked good among us seem so noteworthy that we are sometimes drawn to them in ways that can only hurt us. --So, in so much as this applies to you... Stop esteeming them. Stop being jealous of them. Stop feeling inferior to them. Stop seeking their approval. Stop approving their worldliness. Stop catering to their demands and ideals. Stop pandering to their every whim. Stop idolizing them. Just stop. **See them for the wicked good that they are and be set apart.** Sure it may be lonely for now but you have an ETERNITY to be with your real family! Get perspective on this! You don't need their approval. It's only to your demise if you chase it. **Come out of this and don't aspire to be connected to anyone that doesn't plainly exhibit the light and fruit of Christ.** Be watchful and proceed with caution, being sensitive to the Holy Spirit instead of catering to your soul's longing to be accepted, elevated, esteemed or even useful. Put your whole self into God's care and let Him show you the path He has for you. Realizing He can only do so if you lay all this down. God cannot show you your path if you're choosing to chase all this other stuff for your soul's sake. It will only hold you back. Amen.

Questionnaire

1) Is there anything you feel you might be lax about in counting it as evil? If yes, list and write about them here. Seek God as to *why* this is your propensity. Perhaps there's something deeper going on in your soul which influences your apathy or negligence concerning it. Spend time working this out with God, repenting and making necessary changes. ***Seek greater reverence for God.

_____

_____

_____

_____

_____

_____

_____

_____

_____

_____

_____

_____

_____

2) Are you reminded that your love for the world and catering to self competes with the mandate to love God first? If yes, that's a cue to spend more time talking to God about this. Repent but don't be condemned. Repentance requires turning, not self-loathing or beating yourself up. Remember, we're all messed up and our walk with Christ is a YIELDING to

Him, not a situation of instant perfection! So, repent and ask God what you or He can do to increase your reverence and passion for Him so that you'll be driven for Him and not self or the cares of this world.

_____

_____

_____

_____

_____

_____

3) How do you look like the world? Ask God to reveal ways that you may not even realize yet. Meanwhile, what changes do you know off the bat that you can make in your life to not look and act so much like the world?

How I look like the world: _____

_____

_____

_____

_____

Changes I can make right now to not look like the world: _____

_____

_____

_____

_____

4) Are you cautious about who you mesh with? Or are you more interested in being accepted, in fitting in, and connecting with someone supposedly 'great' in yours or the world's eyes, etc? Are you jealous of their charisma, abilities, looks, or position? Are you hurt that you don't have or can't do what they can? Do you desire their approval or for them to esteem you? Ask

the Lord if your heart is clean concerning what motivates you towards relationships. Ask if you are attracted to the tares. Again, spend time dealing with this. These are the types of things that hinder our ability to prosper in the kingdom of God.

Notes & Prayers on this: _____

_____

_____

_____

_____

5) Do you KNOW beyond a shadow of a doubt that the Holy Spirit is eager 24/7 to speak to you, warn you, and show you things? If your confidence in this is lacking to any degree, repent and ask Him to forgive you. **Lack of confidence deafens our ears from hearing God**. So, you see, it's not that He is as quiet as you think, it's that your lack of confidence in Him blocks your reception to His voice that's right inside you! Repent and make this right. And watch how much more you hear the Holy Spirit!

Yes / No, I do / do not know beyond a shadow of a doubt that the Holy Spirit is eager 24/7 to speak with me: _____

_____

_____

_____

_____

6) Just curious... Are you eager for messages that tickle your ears, or for truth that teaches you how to be right with God? Ask God if there's even a hint of this in you, where you desire feel-good teaching over truth. This is definitely something you don't want to mess with. It's a profound gateway

to darkness, even if your appeal for it is minimal. Again, repent but don't beat yourself up. Just face it and ask God to change your heart, to fix what's wrong in your soul that makes you vulnerable to this. Ask Him to shed light on where the error is and what it is about, so you can get to the bottom of it.

Dear Lord, despite how much I may have preferred my ears to be tickled, I tell you now that I choose your truth above all else and reject all things false. In fact, Father, _____

_____

_____

_____

_____

Other notes or prayers: _____

_____

_____

_____

_____

_____

_____

_____

_____

_____

_____

_____

_____

_____

_____

_____

God's Last Will & Testament

"Are they not all ministering spirits, sent forth to minister for them who shall be *heirs of salvation*?" Hebrews 1:14.

Question: Do heirs automatically receive an inheritance? Or do they need to lay hold of it? Indeed, one must claim an inheritance to actually receive it. More so, sometimes conditions are attached to the will which must be met in order for the heir to claim the inheritance.

Such is the case concerning the Creator's will, which is found in the New Testament of the Bible, or rather, what I'm referring to here as "*God's Last Testament*". You know... the OT was God's first covenant or testament. This means the NT is the new covenant or testament. And since it's throughout the NT that God establishes the conditions to inherit eternal life, this makes the NT God's Final, Unchanging, Permanent, Signed, Sealed & Delivered via Christ's Blood... Last Will & Testament.

As we know, the NT reveals that, via the death of the Son of God and submission unto His kingdom through repentance and faith, people could inherit eternal life. But just as it sometimes is with an earthly inheritance, heirs to salvation could potentially forfeit the Father's will for them to inherit eternal life, by failing to adhere to the conditions of His will. **God's last will and testament outlines how we are made heirs of Christ unto eternal life by grace, adopted as sons into His Holy family.** But it additionally outlines how we must *remain* as heirs by abiding in Him in order to not forfeit His will for us.

Indeed, believers grasp that God sent His only begotten Son to die for us because He passionately loves us. And we know that God's will is that none should perish, 2 Peter 3:9. And we know that, "It is by grace you have been saved, through faith—and this is not from yourselves, it is the gift of God, not by works, so that no one can boast", Ephesians 2:8-9.

But that's not all God's last will and testament conveys.

If we thoroughly study God's last will and testament, especially looking at the original Greek to understand the intent, we see that there is definitely the potential for born-again believers to thwart their eternal destiny with Christ. We're going to examine this in depth. The following are many excerpts from God's last will and testament which clearly outline His conditions for salvation:

1) Philippians 2:12 says, "Wherefore, my beloved, as ye have always obeyed... **work out your own salvation** with fear and trembling". In other words, continue on in your obedience reverently. Failing to do so, to the contrary, is *not* working out your salvation with fear and trembling (reverence and honor). This establishes that salvation is not guaranteed just because you're adopted into the family. One must demonstrate via their convictions and actions that they are a legitimate member of God's family, committed, submitted and loyal to the holy family and its values.

2) Hebrews 10:26-29, "If we willfully (continue in habitual) sin after we have received the knowledge of the truth, no sacrifice for sins is left, but only a fearful **expectation of judgment and of raging fire** that will consume the enemies of God. Anyone who rejected the law of Moses died without mercy on the testimony of two or three witnesses. **How much more severely do you think someone deserves to be punished who has trampled the Son of God underfoot, who** (as believers!) **has treated as an unholy thing the blood of the covenant that**

sanctified them, and who has insulted the Spirit of grace?" Big stipulation here! If we sin, we are forfeiting grace! Though our works (obedience) aren't what gain us salvation, a life of willful sin without repentance and faith negates the will of the Father that we should have eternal life with Him.

3) John 15:1-6, "I am the true vine, and my Father is the gardener. **He cuts off every branch** (believer) **in me that bears no fruit**...Remain (abide) in me, as I also remain (abide) in you... **If you do not remain in me, you are like a branch that is thrown away and withers; such branches (believers) are picked up, thrown into the fire and burned**.

4) Colossians 1:21-23, "Yet now He has reconciled in the body of His flesh through death, to present you as holy and blameless, and above reproach in His sight— **IF indeed you continue in the faith, grounded and steadfast, and are not moved away from the hope of the gospel which you heard**".

5) Hebrews 12:6, "See that no one is sexually immoral, or is godless like Esau, who for a single meal **sold his inheritance rights** as the oldest son. -So, we're being warned to not be like Esau in giving up our inheritance by living according to our lusts and lack of self-control!

6) 1 John 2:24-25, "As for you, see that what you have heard from the beginning remains in you. **IF it does** (remain in you), **you also will remain in the Son and in the Father** (and His will!). **As this is what he promised us—*eternal life*.**" It's very clear that abiding in the ways of Christ and His kingdom are what defines if we truly believe and submit to Jesus as King. Not genuinely abiding in Christ is stepping out of the will of the Father and away from the inheritance of eternal life. Yes, first we must repent and believe. But if we do that but then remain in the ways of darkness, not really believing in God's power in us to overcome sin, not

really seeking and learning the right, holy kingdom ways of being, not letting His power transform us, not growing in the attributes (fruits) of His Spirit, having no heart for truth, **then that's choosing to be joint heirs with the devil and his pending fate, not Christ's.** *(Now, I'm not referring to people who are struggling with sin who haven't been able to overcome yet. They hate their cycles of sin and repent. I'm referring to willfully continuing in our old ways, serving self and the world without conviction and with no regard for Christ outside of "saying the sinner's prayer" and going through the motions.)*

7) Romans 8:1-2, "**There is therefore now no condemnation** (which is katakrima - <u>damnatory sentence</u>) **to those who are IN Christ Jesus, who do not walk according to the flesh, but according to the Spirit**. For the law of (obedience to) the Spirit of life (abiding) IN Christ Jesus has made me (Paul) free from the law of (obedience to) sin and death (eternal damnation)". -Yes, Paul specifically said HE was the one free from eternal damnation, **not all believers as many Bible translations wrongfully say,** because HE personally walked in obedience to the Spirit and not his flesh. Paul explained in Romans chapter 7 that he recognizes how his spirit wants to do right while his flesh, his members, strive to do contrary. He declares how wretched he is except that God delivered him from his sinful nature through Jesus Christ. This is why he could only speak to his personal freedom from eternal damnation, not everyone's. The emphasis is he personally accomplished this freedom from damnation **via the crucifixion of his flesh / members and living according to the Spirit.** [Several translations leave out half of Romans 8:1 and then say, "has made *you* free" in Romans 8:2 where it's actually "has made *me* free" in the original text. This is dangerously misleading to the body of Christ. The true text clearly establishes that believers have a choice to yield to the sinful nature that still resides in us, or to crucify it and yield to the Spirit of righteousness that resides in us, and that it's only by living in resistance to sin and in submission to the Spirit whereby we have eternal life.]

8) Galatians 5:4, "You who are trying to be justified by the law have been alienated from Christ; **you have fallen away from grace**". This right here clearly states that the heir, by stepping outside of the conditions of the will, has disqualified themselves from receiving the inheritance. Unless they come back into compliance with the will - via genuine repentance and submission to His conditions, they're damned.

9) 2 Peter 3:18, "Therefore, dear friends, since you have been forewarned, **be on your guard lest you also, being led away with the error of the wicked, fall from your own steadfastness. But <u>grow</u> in grace.**"

10) Titus 3:9-11, "In speaking to believers, Paul says, 'Warn a (quarreling) divisive person once, and then warn him a second time. After that, have nothing to do with him. You may be sure that he is warped and sinful; **he is self-condemned**'". Here we see Paul speaking to "believers" who were once condemned (born sinners) but redeemed through Christ, yet are now self-condemned again. Are the "condemned" heirs to the Father's will?

11) 1 Timothy 4:1, " Now the Spirit speaketh expressly, that in the latter times some (Christians) **shall depart from the faith**, giving heed to seducing spirits, and doctrines of devils..." Sadly, these believers think they're still in their adoptive Heavenly Father's will, but they've actually abandoned the conditions of God's last will and testament by chasing after the false, "all goodies" gospel which caters to their flesh. Except that their eyes are opened and they repent, the last will and testament of the Holy Father will be lost to them forever.

12) 1 Timothy 6:10-12, "For the love of money is the root of many evils: which while some coveted after, they **have erred from the faith**, and pierced themselves through with many sorrows. But thou, O man of God, **flee these things; and follow after righteousness, godliness,**

faith, love, patience, meekness. Fight the good fight of faith, laying hold of eternal life, whereunto thou art also called (unlike how those who do not follow after righteousness will not lay hold of eternal life)".

13) In referring to the Church of Sardis (the dead church) Jesus told John to tell them that, "He who overcomes shall be clothed in white garments, and I will not blot out his name from the Book of Life; but I will confess his name before My Father and before His angels". Revelation 3:5. **In other words, if these Christians do not overcome, Jesus WILL blot their names out of the Book of Life!**

14) Matthew 7:19-21, "**Every tree that bringeth not forth good fruit is hewn down, and cast into the fire.** Wherefore by their fruits ye shall know them. Not every one that saith unto me, Lord, Lord, shall enter into the kingdom of heaven; but (only) he that doeth the will of my Father which is in heaven". This shows that not every "believer" truly belongs to God's family and His promised inheritance. Because they live according to their own will, their flesh, not the Father's. These "believers", therefore, have no part in the inheritance.

15) "But now after you have known God, or rather are known by God, how is it that you turn again to the weak and beggarly elements, to which you desire again to be in bondage? You observe days and months and seasons and years. **I am afraid for you, lest I have labored for you in vain.**" Galatians 4:9-11. Many interpret that Paul is saying these Galatians returned to observing Jewish holy days but this is wrong. Galatians never observed Jewish traditions in the past, so how could they return to it? Further, would Paul call God's festivals and holy days weak and beggarly? No! So, what Paul meant was they were going back to observing all their old pagan holidays and rituals. If Paul was fearful for these folks, clearly it had to do with the potential of losing their eternal inheritance - because other than that, what else would there be to be so afraid for them about? And we

need to ask ourselves if that which we observe and hold in such sacred regard (despite pagan roots) is something that would provoke Paul to fear for us as well.

16) Galatians 4:30, "Nevertheless what saith the scripture? **Cast out the bondwoman and her son: for the son of the bondwoman SHALL NOT <u>BE HEIR</u> with the son of the freewoman".** You understand that we are children of the freewoman now because we have been born again, by believing in Jesus. But realize that the children born of the free woman in spirit (as Isaac was born supernaturally in Sarah's barren womb via Abraham's faith in God and the power of the Spirit) are the heirs because we are delivered out of our old identities as children of the slave woman - through Christ. So, technically, we have two distinct identities. And what this passage is commanding is, "Cast out (renounce, crucify) your old identity! Cast out (renounce, crucify) your flesh, sin, and your will. These shall not be heir with your new, spiritually living identity". In other words, if we continue to live out of the aspects of our dead, flesh identity after receiving our new spiritual ID, thinking we can bring it along for the ride, we're wrong. **Prior to receiving new life in Christ, our dead flesh selves had no ability to partake of an eternal inheritance in Glory.** And they still don't. So, if we've received Jesus but have our old ID in our back pocket, unable to completely part with it, then we're in danger. Our old selves have no inheritance with Christ! So, if our old identity still runs our life despite our receiving a new one, how can we inherit eternal life? I mean, think about it. If you're a history professor but get a degree to be a surgeon and get hired by a hospital, if you show up for work teaching history all day, never walking in your new identity as a surgeon, how long will you last? You'll be kicked to the curb because your history professor identity has no place at the hospital!

17) 1 Peter 1:7-9, "That the trial of your faith, being much more precious than gold that perisheth, though it be tried with fire, might be found unto praise and honour and glory at the appearing of Jesus Christ: Whom

(despite) not seeing him, you love him; in whom, though now you still don't see him, you believe, rejoicing with joy unspeakable and full of glory: **Receiving the *end* of your faith, even the salvation of your souls**." What a perfect summation. This passage outlines the reality that the believer's faith must be tried, proven and established by fire, so that it is found blameless at Christ's return (when He comes for His spotless bride). And Peter points out that those whose faith is tried by fire, are those who truly love and believe God, so much so, that they rejoice with unspeakable joy, full of glory, despite it. And finally, note that it is through the trying of the believer's faith whereby we can receive the END of our faith - the salvation of our soul. So we see, then, making a profession of faith in Christ is only the **beginning** of salvation through Christ. It's via the repentant, submitted, selfless, ongoing, whole-hearted pursuit of Christ and His ways, through a great trying of our faith and the application of faith in our lives, whereby we work out our salvation, laying hold of the inheritance of eternal life; the will of the Father. To the contrary, not staying the course, not living according to the law of the Spirit which is outlined throughout the entire last testament, is to our eternal demise.

I'd like to close by touching on a most profound condition of the Father's will that I've never heard anyone acknowledge or discuss. Of course, we know Mark 16:16 says, "Whoever believes and is baptized will be saved". So, whenever someone gives their life to Christ, they go through the ceremonial baptism of proclaiming their death and new life through Christ. But I don't think that's all there was to baptism.

John the Baptist reports, "I baptize you with water. But one who is more powerful than I will come, the straps of whose sandals I am not worthy to untie. **He will baptize you with the Holy Spirit and fire**", Luke 3:16.

First, why "fire"? We know the Bible speaks of the refiner's fire (Zechariah 13:9, 1 Peter 1:6-7, Isaiah 48:10, Psalms 66:10, Proverbs 17:3) whereby He purifies His children via trials as a refiner would purify silver or gold via fire. So then... Luke 3:16 is saying while John, the preparer, the minister, the teacher, baptized with water, Jesus would baptize us with the Holy Spirit and trials, to purify us. Look specifically at 1 Peter 1:6-7: "...You may have had to suffer in all kinds of trials. These have come so that the proven genuineness of your faith—of greater worth than gold, which perishes even though refined by fire—may result in praise, glory and honor when Jesus Christ is revealed."

Now let's look at the definition of baptism:

1. a religious, ceremonial dedication with sprinkling or immersion
2. an initiation into a particular activity or role, typically something perceived as difficult.
3. **to cleanse spiritually**, initiate or **dedicate by purifying**.

As I said, we're all acquainted with the first part of the definition of baptism. But when John the Baptist said Jesus would baptize with the Holy Spirit and fire, it definitely refers to our being tried and proven, spiritually cleansed, and dedicated to God via trials that purify us.

To understand more clearly, remember how Jesus referred to His pending death on the cross as a "baptism" that He must undergo in Luke 12:50? And remember how, after James and John asked to sit at his right and left hand in Heaven, Jesus said, ""You don't know what you are asking. Can you drink the cup I drink or be baptized with the baptism I am baptized with?" Mark 10:38.

Jesus was giving us clues as to what He really meant when He said, "He who believes and is baptized will be saved" in Mark 16:16 - which is that **those who believe on Him who also submit to being purged and purified, potentially even unto persecution and death like Him, will be saved.**

The purpose for the new believer's ceremonial baptism was to serve as a public declaration of our laying down the old and taking up the new, but even more, as the entry into the purification process of the refiner's fire. Together the ceremonial declaration along with the refining of proving of our faith are a complete baptism that, because we believed and were baptized, inherit eternal life.

So, then, yes, it is by grace we are saved through faith (and the process of Christ finishing it in us via our submission and cooperation). And yes, if we repent, and believe (which is demonstrated via our actions according to James 2:14-26)... and if we *are baptized* (cleansed and purified by the Holy Spirit and fire), then yes, we will have met the conditions of the Father's will and shall receive an "inheritance incorruptible and undefiled that does not fade away, reserved in heaven for us." 1 Peter 1:4. Amen.

God's Last Will & Testament

Questionnaire

Please answer the following to ascertain what you took from the teaching:

1. You've probably heard it said, "Once saved, always saved". Though this is true in so much as once you're in Heaven, you're there forever, you should now understand that salvation actually:

   a. Depends on our faith commitment
   b. Is guaranteed to all who say the sinner's prayer
   c. Is worked out with fear and trembling (reverence and honor)
   d. Can be thwarted / lost
   e. All of the above
   f. A, C and D

2. We cannot earn salvation by our works or religious traditions, but our reverent obedience to Christ is a part of how we *work out* our salvation.

a. True
b. False

3. 1 Timothy 6:10-12 tells us to fight the good fight of faith in order to lay hold of eternal life. Record scriptures here that will help you to fight the good fight of faith: _____

_____

_____

_____

_____

4. As per Matthew 7:19-21, every tree that does not bear good fruit must be torn down and thrown into the fire. Please list all the fruits / attributes of God (His Spirit & kingdom) that you currently exhibit while dealing with an unlovely world. Do you respond to adversity with patience, love, self-control, peace, faith, forgiveness, humility, assurance, etc.?

_____

_____

_____

_____

5. Now list the fruits of the Spirit you are weak in. Be sure to repent and ask God if there're any deep-seated reasons you struggle to bear these fruits and what you should do about it.

When troubles arise such as _____

_____

instead of responding in unexplainable peace, forgiveness, mercy, self-control, love (etc.), I tend to (or used to) respond as follows: _____

_____

_____

_____

_____

Dear Lord, from now on _____

_____

_____

6. You're here because you choose God at your core despite surface behaviors. In looking back over the year(s) since you first yielded to Jesus, how much of your old self remains? Is your old flesh, carnal, spiritually

dead (non kingdom of God) ID tucked away for safe-keeping somewhere? Is he/she trying to maintain a place in your Christian life? If yes, you are now reminded that your old, carnal man has NO inheritance in Christ. Please earnestly pray about this, repent, and ask Father why you refuse or struggle to surrender your whole self. Be real with Him so He can show you what's going on. He will help you come out of this and into complete commitment to Him.

Dear Heavenly Father, _____

_____

_____

_____

_____

_____

7. Now that you thoroughly understand that being saved requires believing and being baptized (purified and proved) which is a process that includes trials whereby you establish your faith, will you be more inclined to use the issues, challenges and obstacles of this life to prove your commitment to God by responding in love, peace, patience, joy, kindness, self-control, gentleness, faith (trust and confidence in God) and meekness?

_____

_____

_____

Answers to Questions on page 212: 1) f- A,C,D   2) a- True

Intro to the Two Kingdoms
MY PRAYER FOR YOU

I'm excited to finally spend some time discussing the significance of the supernatural kingdoms. Sure, we know they exist. But we're about as conscientious of them as Jupiter and Mars. We know about them, but really aren't aware of them. Though they're as relevant to all that goes on in our world as the physical realm (if not more so), we hardly acknowledge them!

So, let's get to it. But first...

Heavenly Father, I'm so thrilled that you are STILL on your throne. This is the one sure thing we all can forever count on. You are perfect in all of your ways. You are constant. You are steadfast. You are ALWAYS good, always just, always all knowing. Nothing compares to you, my King. I'm so thankful for all that you are and all that you will forever be.

And thank you, Father, for keeping _____. Thank you that you said Jesus will not lose a single soul that you have given Him. Thank you that _____ is yours!

Father, I don't know what's going on this week, but you know all things. You know what the enemy is up to, and you know what _____ is up to. Father, I pray that wherever _____ 's heart and focus is right now that you help _____ to get centered in the palm of your hand. Lord, I ask you to do whatever it takes to bring _____ to a new, deeper level with you very, very soon. I speak to the powers of darkness that attempt to oppose your work and plans, Father. Satan, get out of the way; I cancel your plan to circumvent and hinder the work of the Spirit of God in _____ right now, in Jesus' Name.

Father, your will be done. Please breathe upon _____ your breath of invigoration. Lord, it's you that makes everything wonderful and possible, even our ability to rise up in truth. So, please make this so. Clear out the cobwebs and all that's NOT of you, Lord. Please illuminate the facts and let the fiction, deceptions and false ideals be dismantled in _____ 's mind, heart and soul. Father, clear the path and have your way in this life that you purchased. I pray that you will make things clear and that _____ steps into, realizes, embraces and receives all that you have provided at this time.

Bless your holy name, Father. Please protect _____ and continue to enlighten, lift, encourage, exhort, and refine your workmanship, Father. And let your love abound. Let your love abound.

In Jesus' Name, Amen.

Notes/Prayers

When it comes to living spiritually solid and prosperous lives, half the reason we don't is because we don't consider the "whole picture". All we concern ourselves with is what's in front of us, in the natural realm, and that's what we go by. We also go by past experiences. We rely on our carnal senses and limited logic. And despite Proverbs 3:5 telling us not to, we *"lean on our own understanding"* in how we approach or respond to the matters of this life.

If I were to paraphrase what I've always understood Proverbs 3:5-6 to mean, it would go like this: *"Lean not on your own perspective of everything, but, in all that you do, acknowledge God and work with Him concerning it, acquiring and gleaning from His* **all-knowing** *perspective, and He will direct you as to how to handle things"*.

Learning to consistently deal with circumstances by truly leaning on God's full knowledge instead of our limited understanding is taking a significant step towards spiritual stability. But again, we'd do all the better if we'd continually consider the "whole picture". Because we'll lean all the more on God's understanding when we appreciate that **what we see via our human eyes is not all that's going on.**

Sure, we know there's more out there than what meets the eye. We know there's a God and His angels. We know there's a devil and his demons. And we know there is a spiritual realm. But, do we respect the reality that these two spiritual realms are not only here among us in the earth implementing the occasional miracle or tragedy, but that **they're both actively**

working, either for or against us, ongoing? I mean, we know this, but, since it's out of sight, it's out of mind. We don't sit around pondering that **there are at least three sets of criteria at work in most all situations.** There's our personal criteria, perhaps another person's as well, the enemy's, and God's.

All three + parties have a vested interest in what goes on in our lives. While we are plugging away at our jobs, watching television, or serving our neighbors, there are other (invisible) parties on the scene, each with their own agenda. (They are often aware of each other's agenda, and fight about it, too!) But these two invisible parties aren't just random entities doing scattered, random acts. No, the two opposing parties are servants of two mighty, organized, methodical, vast kingdoms. Of course, you knew these supernatural kingdoms existed. But do we really comprehend it? Do we consider that angels and demons aren't just aimlessly bouncing around, flying in and out of heaven and hell, looking for random people to do something with?

These two supernatural kingdoms are as interested in the matters of earth as humans are, if not more. Obviously, we know the kingdom of God is interested in rescuing people from the dominion of darkness while the kingdom of darkness is striving to take over the world. But see... Each kingdom can only accomplish their agenda "through" mankind by working with each person intricately and strategically.

Now how well would you do if you wanted to rescue or take over the world by just sending out random angels or demons to accomplish your bidding - without planning, orchestrating, plotting and strategizing? That's no way to run things. We need to comprehend and respect the profound significance these two kingdoms have in our lives, and see them for what they are. We need to stop going about our business looking at this life as though that's all there is for now because eternity comes later. No. The eternal kingdoms are here. And they're working hard to promote their opposing agendas.

We know Satan was cast out of heaven and that 1/3 of the angels followed him. And we know that when Adam and Eve fell in the Garden of Eden that, via Satan's deception, he acquired an authority in the earth. In Ephesians 2:2, Satan is referred to as, "the prince of the power (exousias G1849; authority, jurisdiction) of the air". And though Jesus reports that ALL authority had been given unto Him prior to His ascension to Heaven (Matthew 28), Satan's kingdom continued to maintain dominion within the earth realm. Colossians 1:13 states that God rescued us (believers) from the dominion of darkness and transferred us over to the kingdom of His dear Son. So the issue of dominion and authority in and over the earth goes three ways.

1. Man was given charge over the earth by the Supreme Authority, God Himself.
2. Man gave allegiance to the devil granting him a position of authority/rule/dominion over mankind.
3. Jesus has authority over all.

Each party has their own version and measure of authority, but note that man gave the devil authority over mankind, not over the earth like the corporate body typically says. It's often taught (and I saw it this way myself until recently) that man gave up his dominion over the earth in the Garden. But I realize now that's not correct. Man still has authority over the earth, the fish of the sea, the birds of the air, etc. It's obvious man still exercises authority/dominion over animals and the systems of this life. However, Satan does not have authority over anything in the earth, including mankind, UNLESS it is granted to him via allegiance, agreement, or submission to him BY MANKIND.

Consider the school systems in America, how they were under Christ's authority until 1962 when prayer and the Bible became banned - after which came academic and moral decline, greater behavioral issues, and terror. The point being Satan never had authority over American schools until it was granted to him. The dark kingdom strategically worked towards this, manipulated mankind into rebelling against the holy inclusion of the Creator's Word in the school system, and they bowed. So, I reiterate: Satan's kingdom never has authority over the earth, a person or even a system of the earth UNLESS MAN gives it to him. Why? Because man never lost their charge over the earth. We simply granted the dark kingdom a place, too. But his power could only be exercised by getting permission from God (as was the case with Job) or by getting someone to buy into what he was selling. And this was the case even before Christ died to rescue us from the dark kingdom.

Consider Noah, born into the same fallen, sinful world as every other human. Though not perfect, God said he was the only righteous man on earth, and was protected from the destruction of the world. The prince of the authority of the air, through which the rain so heavily fell for 40 days and nights, had no say in God's judging the earth via the global flood. Satan couldn't prevent a single raindrop from falling, nor could he impede on God's elect, to destroy the Ark and its passengers. This gives us a clear perspective that while Satan does have authority, it's not automatic. It must be acquired just as it was with Eve and the American school system.

We can also look at Abraham and Moses, sinners born into the same earth wherein Satan is "prince of this world" (John 12:31), and how God set them apart and called them into covenant with Him in teaching them that if they abide in Him, they would be protected and blessed. Again, this all being long before Jesus came to rescue mankind from sin, death, and the prince of the air. The point again being, though Satan does have authority, he must acquire it. Man still has to "grant" the devil a platform. Otherwise he has zero rights to exercise it. His power remains "in the empty air" which is ineffective (unless he illegally trespasses, but that's a whole other topic).

But yes, these two kingdoms are as real as (if not more real than) you and me. And they're as driven for a particular outcome as (if not more driven than) you and me. Again, it doesn't matter what you are doing, there's a lot more going on behind the scenes. Angels and demons are assigned to heirs of salvation and they all work avidly to steer believers in the direction that accomplishes their task. It's important that we become and remain mindful of the "whole picture" because it completely changes our outlook. And it may even influence how careful we are to know the policies of God's kingdom so to be sure to adhere to them more faithfully. If anything, it should make us more careful to not be so inclined to grant the kingdom of darkness a platform. (We'll talk more about how this happens in the next module.)

I want to share a story that demonstrates and hopefully drives home just how prominent the two supernatural kingdoms are among us.

Back when my very first book was published I was formatting the layout of the manuscript using online software that went haywire. The program seemed to have a mind of its own. Words would be divided from one line to the next. Lines that were justified would become centered. Paragraphs would separate and move. And attempting to correct the mysterious changes only caused new errors to appear. After a week of working day and night fighting to undo the damage only to see the manuscript more and more botched, the software program would close out with none of my changes saved. I'd have to shut down the computer and reboot... only to find the manuscript in even greater disarray. By the end of the week, after probably 100 back to back hours of striving to fix things, I realized it was a losing battle. I just hung my head in despair welling up with tears when suddenly the Lord spoke clear as day, "Take authority".

My immediate response was, "Take authority? Why? You are here with me, Lord!"

You see, though this terrible and ever increasingly problem had been going on all week, I never once doubted God was with me because I felt His presence through it all. I saw God's hand in all that He'd accomplished in the book and felt His supernatural peace throughout the peculiar chaos. I KNEW He was there. I just had no idea why this software wasn't working or what I was going to do.

The problem was I had assumed that since God was there, since I felt His peace, and since the dark kingdom had no legal right to be on the premises, that this meant the enemy couldn't have been there messing things up. I was wrong. This was the moment I realized the dark kingdom will illegally trespass onto private, God-ordained property to attempt to sabotage things. Hence, the reason we need to take authority over such matters.

So, when God said to take authority, I asked why would I need to if He was there with me and He said, "I *am* there with you. But the demons are trying to prevent your book from being published and my angels have been fighting them on this all week. Now help them out by taking authority over your property in My name."

I finally understood and right away I said something like, "Devil, take your hands off my property! This book is God's and I command you to take your hands off now in Jesus' name!" Afterwards, I rebooted the computer for the last and final time and instead of finding the manuscript even worse, it was suddenly back in order other than some minor discrepancies! I was astounded! So I fixed them and the book was ready for publication in a little more than one hour! No exaggeration! My husband is my witness.

Gosh, I learned a lot that day. But I share this story to show that there were three parties at work all week as I presumably worked alone to format my book. The fact was, I wasn't alone and there was a major, literal battle going on right there in my midst over my book. And I was none the wiser for it.

If I had to wrap up what it takes for every believer to succeed as a Christian who literally has Satan under their feet into one thing, I'd say it's knowing and respecting the reality of these two very powerful, supernatural kingdoms; and cooperating with the holy one. The first most significant necessity being to seek, know and abide in God's kingdom with all our hearts. And the second being to not be ignorant about Satan's agenda and tactics of the dark kingdom, so to not be played for a fool. "My people are destroyed for lack of knowledge." Hosea 4:6.

And do you know something else that would help us appreciate the significance of the two invisible kingdoms here among us is if we grasp that the idea of what makes a kingdom a kingdom didn't start in the earth. In fact, nothing "started" with earth. Everything about the earth mirrors something from eternity. The system of a kingdom didn't originate in the earth because God's kingdom existed long before earth did. And since everything on earth is God's design, I assure you, the idea of a kingdom was an eternal creature first. Therefore, the order for all things including that all kingdoms have kings, servants and armies of varying ranks, orders and assignments, etc., came from above. As such, all kingdoms have statutes, policies, and decrees that must be obeyed. All kingdoms are territorial, typically striving to expand. And all kingdoms share in the similar vision to rule over all, in so much as they succeed. Now of course, God's kingdom is the only kingdom that will succeed at this. It seems senseless that any other kingdom (natural or otherwise) would bother trying. But, such is life.

To add a bit more perspective, just sit and ponder everything that goes into what makes a kingdom and then flip the switch in your mind taking it from the physical realm to the spiritual. See Satan as the father, prince or king over the vast kingdom of darkness. See how he has millions, if not billions, of various ranking officers, high powers, principalities, minions and more. Think of Michael the Archangel, or Gabriel and how they are very high ranking officials in God's kingdom. God gave us this clue for a reason. These two angels have greater abilities than lower ranking angels. This demonstrates that the supernatural kingdoms are very well orchestrated, perhaps even better than earthly kingdoms! All this to help solidify the comprehension of these two vast systems.

And here's food for thought... Remember the tower of Babel from Genesis 11? This was a "one world order" endeavor. Now who do you suppose was behind it? The devil has been striving to rule as god over all the earth for millenia. We can see, he's made great strides. The antichrist is soon to rise.

Also, have you ever wondered where the whole dynamic of a kingdom being majestic and royal came from, where you could be killed on the spot for daring to even approach a king without permission? I don't know how God pulled it off, but he had man implement their kingdoms in this very fashion. God deliberately wanted "kingdoms" to be sovereign, prestigious systems of royalty and honor for a reason - despite the fact that no human could ever truly be sovereign or deserved to be so renowned. I was always stumped by this as a youngster, never appreciating that earth kings had such insane reverence knowing full well they were just as fallible and wretched as anyone. But now I understand God put this system into place because Father God wanted to train the world on what it is to revere a king so that when Jesus brought His kingdom into the earth (2000 years ago), we would have no excuse for failing to revere the Almighty King, bowing to Him in all our ways, honoring and revering Him above all things, thereby granting His (now invisible) kingdom **manifest** presence in the earth.

Thankfully, God's kingdom was brought into the earth through Jesus Christ over 2000 years ago, to call people out from under the rule of the dark kingdom, and into citizenship of His Holy kingdom. But THIS is what we haven't really understood or paid much mind to. Despite the so-called hundreds of millions of Christians there are in the earth, barely 1% comprehend the significance of these two invisible, rival kingdoms. Nor does the world, even the Church, realize how much liberty and power they grant the dark kingdom. The corporate body of Christ continues to deal with this life as if that's all there is, having no idea how much their every decision either works for or against the kingdom of God and its manifest presence in the world. What's worse is our application of the reality of God's kingdom and authority is vaguely present. Though this won't remain the case for long because God's raising up an army of steadfast believers, there's been minimal manifest presence of the kingdom of God despite our numbers for the past 2000 years.

Meanwhile, realize that despite our ignorance, there are billions of strategies plotted out and implemented on a daily basis by both of the invisible kingdoms. God has millions or even billions of angels strategizing and working to call us out of deception, calling intercessors to pray for chains to be broken off the body of Christ, calling teachers to teach real truth and what's really going on, etc.

But keep in mind what was previously discussed, that both kingdoms, regardless which, must accomplish things through mankind, since God set things up that way. The enemy only rules over and through those who submit to him (if even unwittingly), and God's sovereign, incomprehensible power, is typically only implemented or manifested through those who submit to Him and exercise authority in His name. Therefore, the kingdoms must strategize so to get our cooperation, so that we'll operate according to their policies and via their authority. For example, God had His angels fighting off the demon's attempts to keep my book from being published all week non-stop. But I had to be the one to put the power of Christ's name into effect. When I did, boom, my angels defeated the demons and they were put out *instantly*!

In closing, I'd just like to share something my husband told me years ago. We were talking about how after Jesus resurrected He was able to walk through walls. I said something to the effect that He was able to do that perhaps because He was in His glorified spiritual body which must be like a mist, which I was confused about because I had thought our glorified bodies would be solid, like our earth bodies. Right away my husband said no, Jesus wasn't like a mist walking through a concrete wall, rather, He was solid and it was as though the wall was the mist - because the eternal, glorified body is what's more real. This did not compute so he explained how the eternal realm, or Heaven, was "more real" or "more solid" than earth. He said, "We are the spoken imagination of God". So though we are real and solid here, this realm as it is currently is temporary... dust. And though we do not see the more real realm because it is presently invisible to us, that's the realm that is concrete; not us, not here.

I shared all that to help give more perspective and respect for the eternal - simply because some of us are so locked into strictly revolving around the realm we see and understand. This is wrong. God says to, "Fix our eyes *not* on what is seen, but on what is unseen, since what is seen is temporary, but what is unseen is eternal", 2 Corinthians 4:18. Brothers and Sisters, we need to fix our eyes on the eternal and keep them there. If we'll just get to know God's unseen kingdom and operate within God's kingdom parameters, precepts and dynamics, we will rise above all the matters of earth, including over every power of the devil. And we'll begin to live spiritually solid and prosperous lives as a result. Amen.

God's Kingdom is Perfect

As you know, in the kingdom of God, everything is always perfect. But God's kingdom is here, with you... in you. **An entire system / kingdom / world of perfection is in you.** Just because you're still physically here in this fallen, broken, corrupt and sometimes ugly world doesn't mean you yourself are still fallen, broken, corrupt, or even ugly. You've been transferred from that broken kingdom into God's perfect kingdom. Meditate on this. Not comprehending this is to our defeat. But this is who we are.

Now please don't misconstrue what I'm about to say as meaning "don't worry about sinning", that's not what I'm saying. Rather, don't be so disheartened that your carnal self still doesn't know or walk in the ways of the holy kingdom as well as you think you should; **God's grace is sufficient.** Sure, there're areas in you that aren't perfect, but such is the case with all believers to one degree or another! Especially nowadays, because of how meticulously the devil has learned to brainwash the souls that belong to God. **God is fully aware of what's stacked against us and again I say, His grace is sufficient.** I should know. The Lord has put up with SO very much with me. I cannot count how many times He's forgiven me, despite how wretched I've been. And it doesn't matter the sin, big or small. We're all equally wretched.

But to believe in the power of the blood of Christ is to embrace the truth that you have been made righteous by it. This means, spiritually speaking, so long as you are submitted to Christ, you are perfect. Indeed, as you mature in truth, yes, your carnal self and all its wretchedness decreases more and more. You literally begin to look like Jesus. **But even if you**

were born again just yesterday and still have yet to grow up in the sanctification process, you're still perfectly and completely righteous today by the blood of the Lamb!

Look, if your heart has ever been broken over your self-awareness, if you hate sinning (regardless if you're full-blown addicted) and you repent sincerely intent on turning from sin, trust me, God's grace is sufficient. So don't dwell on your weaknesses and failures. That, my friend, is a policy of the dark kingdom. Abiding there, focused on your failures after Christ made you righteous by His blood...is aligned with the dark kingdom and serves to keep you full of weakness and failures. If you've been cleansed by the blood of Jesus, then this trumps your weakness and failures! I know it seems hypocritical to stand boldly wearing the royal robe of righteousness when there's some ugly stuff still lurking in you, but it's not. YOU are RIGHTEOUS because Jesus and His kingdom is in you working to transform you! But if you sit around beating yourself up for the ugliness in you, that's acting like Jesus didn't cleanse you! So stop. You must, instead, **focus on who you spiritually are, and rejoice that your carnal self is, in fact, in a transformation process.** That's what matters.

Because, according to Colossians 1:13, you HAVE been transferred into the kingdom of God's dear Son! You HAVE! Meditate upon this. This is who you are. And stay there. Even if the shards of this broken life pierce your carnal being, rejoice that your eternal being is untouchable, secure, and safe. Rejoice! Delight in God's kingdom so that its supernatural dynamics can manifest, even while the shard is still embedded under your carnal skin. Meditate on this and let your carnal, sinful self be transformed by the renewing of your mind and the liberation of God's Spirit in you. The key is in KNOWING THE TRUTH - as in KNOWING it, not just knowing about it. It has to become a part of you.

Look at it like this: You knew about the last house you moved into the day you moved into it. You knew what it looked like, how many bedrooms it had, how big the kitchen was, etc. But it wasn't until you lived there for a while that you REALLY knew the house. And even if you moved out of that house yesterday, you still "know" it. It's a part of you. This is how well we are to know the reality of God's kingdom and Word. It becomes a part of us. Who we are.

As for the sins that still may rule you, your soul simply hasn't understood that all sins really have been DEFEATED. You have yet to comprehend that the authority of Christ in you can truly dismantle whatever mess is in your soul that has you bowing to these dark ways. Understand the problem is in your soul - not your heart or mind. Something in your SOUL is detached from God, His love, His truth, His reality, and His power. So what you need to do is search God as to what's off in your soul. From my experience, there could be numerous things. For me, I subconsciously felt abandoned by God. Also, I perceived that the reason all the bad things happened in my life as they did was because I was a loser. I felt so ugly, dirty, and unworthy - even though I was cleansed by Jesus. I had severe self-loathing as a result. All these were lies. LIES. Yet they were my truths which gave sin power over me. It all boils down to what your soul really believes. My mind and heart knew they were all lies, but my soul dwelt there. Consequently, though I loved Jesus, I was in alliance with the dark kingdom at soul level. And this was why the power of Jesus was not effective in my life. I had to recognize the false programming in my soul and CUT IT OFF - just as 2 Corinthians 10:5 tells us to do. In so doing, I came out of alignment with the powers of darkness and into alignment with the power of God - which took over. And THEN the authority of Christ in me became effective to putting out the sin.

So find out straight from God - what lies does your soul believe? How does your soul doubt God? And this will empower Christ in you to defeat sin in your life.

Proverbs 3:5-6, "Trust in the Lord with all your heart and lean not on your own understanding (rely not on your own logic concerning a matter). In all your ways acknowledge Him (getting His input and all-knowing perspective) and He shall direct your paths (showing you how to deal with it)."

Repent for all the times throughout your life that you handled things according to your own perspective. Repent for not turning to God for HIS insight and direction. *(Mind you, I said repent - not beat yourself up - which is shunning God's grace).* Meditate upon this passage and be resolved to lean on God's understanding instead of your own from now on. Yes, God did give you a brain. You will always have a perspective and logic concerning things. And you'll often be correct in how you see things. BUT, the point is to not automatically lean on it without double checking with the One who knows far more than you. Besides, it's a way to show your humility and dependence upon God. You can take your perspective to Him but acknowledge Him, that He may have something more to contribute to the matter.

2 Corinthians 4:18, "So we fix our eyes not on what is seen, but on what is unseen, since what is seen is temporary, but what is unseen is eternal."

This one is self-explanatory. But meditate upon this passage as well and become resolved to remain conscious of the "whole picture", not just what's plastered right in front of us. Remember, the dark kingdom is very prominent and active. Therefore, a lot of what we see even in the physical realm is via the influence of darkness. In fact, so much of it is a big song and dance in attempt to manipulate, lure or side-track believers. We all hear the world fussing about "conspiracy theorists" as though they are insane. I won't claim that all are sane, I have no idea. But I will say I know who the prince of the air is. So to believe that the chance of everything being corrupt is minimal, now, that's what's insane.

But anyway, just please make it a point to drive these scriptural truths deep. Make every effort to lean on God's understanding, not your own. And make every effort to remain conscious that our little individual lives aren't the whole picture. What's going on with the government isn't even the whole picture. What's going on globally isn't even the whole picture. The whole picture is that two very vast and proactive, supernatural kingdoms are right here among us working diligently behind the scenes. Respect this...and learn to cooperate with the holy one. And rise.

Heavenly Father, I pray that _____'s ears were able to hear and digest this message. If not, please don't let the matter go. Please continue to bring _____ back to these passages and drive their truths deep into _____'s understanding. Glory to God. You are awesome, Father. We praise you!

Notes/Prayers

We'd like to think the kingdom of God is the glorious place called Paradise where believers in Christ get to spend eternity. While this is true, you hopefully realize by this point in the program, the kingdom of God is actually here, too!

A little recap here: The kingdom of God is a supernatural governing system of the Almighty. Within this spiritual kingdom is a very real King, very real policies, a very real army, very real messengers, and very real divine power. Though it is invisible to us earth-bound beings, this holy kingdom came here 2000 years ago and was made available to us through faith in Jesus Christ.

The kingdom of God is righteousness, peace and joy (Romans 14:17). These aren't just a few nice characteristics of this kingdom, they ARE the Kingdom. Just as Jesus is light, is the way, is truth, is the living Word of God, the kingdom of God "is" the tangible embodiment of absolute righteousness, unexplainable peace and incomprehensible joy. These aren't carnal matter; they're eternal substance. These dynamics are a realm all their own - the realm where Christ Jesus sits at the right hand of His Father. The realm we can barely comprehend except that the Holy Spirit reveals it to us - if we seek to know it.

When Jesus came and provided the way to salvation, He likewise showed us how to align with this divine, holy realm. The top two ways, of course, being through repentance and faith in Him, followed by application and demonstration of it.

"And he said unto him, Why callest thou me good? there is none good but one, that is, God: but if thou wilt enter into life (which is God's kingdom realm), keep the commandments." Matthew 19:17.

"If ye keep my commandments, ye shall abide in my love (which is abiding in the realm of God); **even as I have kept my Father's commandments, and abide in his love.**" John 15:10.

Do we suppose the point of John 15:10 was to emphasize that Jesus merely 'obeyed' the commandments? Well, partially, yes. But the deeper truth conveyed here is that **because Jesus operated in accordance with the policies of the invisible, holy realm, He was, therefore, one with it, and this is what enters us into or aligns us to life, to the very realm of God's kingdom**.

We might assume that Christ being God meant He was automatically aligned and one with His own kingdom the day He was born, but this wasn't so. Jesus was born as a man so that **as a man** he would have to unite with His invisible kingdom the same as any other man - based on which kingdom policies He lived by. You see, Jesus wasn't to be King over a kingdom He personally did not perfectly adhere to. And He would have to demonstrate this submission to His own statutes by living a life in obedience to His Father's commandments.

Consider how Jesus had been on earth 30 years but performed no miracles until after He and John the Baptist first revealed that the Kingdom of God was at hand. Until then, the Master of the entire universe never once took authority over the kingdom of darkness (that we know of). This is because He, too, like us, needed to be spiritually transferred into His divine kingdom.

Though repentance is the first step for mankind to come into Christ's kingdom, Jesus being perfect did not need to repent. But He did need to submit to baptism (to both water baptism and the baptism of His crucifixion). In fact, it wasn't until Jesus humbled Himself to John's baptizing Him that the Holy Spirit and supernatural kingdom power came upon Him. This was undoubtedly the moment Jesus became an official citizen of His own kingdom - whereby He could begin to operate supernaturally from that realm. The limitations He placed upon Himself as man were now broken off. His kingdom was here and via His submission unto baptism and to His Father's will to lay His life down for us, He could now exercise invisible kingdom authority on earth. ~This is why Jesus emphasized the point that even HE had to obey the commandments – showing that this is how to align with His kingdom.

Like the kingdom of God (though inferior), Satan's kingdom is also an invisible government with a prince, an army, messengers, policies and divine power. And while we carnal beings think we are only subject to visible governments and authorities, we're wrong. Yes, earthly kingdoms have policies that determine how things must go in the physical realm. But as we've discussed, the invisible kingdoms are very much involved with what our earth governments are up to. They're behind it all. No exaggeration. Remember, that though man has charge over the earth and its systems, the devil and his kingdom are working avidly to take over the world. I'd be shocked to find one government on earth that the enemy hasn't infiltrated to implement his policies to one degree or another. In fact, every single policy that governments put into place is either a policy of the Kingdom of God or a policy of the kingdom of darkness. Every last one. There's no neutral policies.

And it's the same for mankind. The policies individuals adhere to, promote, abide by, believe, honor, and follow in their personal lives determines which kingdom has authority.

For example, when a person worries about something, cheats, manipulates, intimidates, lies, steals, and so on, they are operating in dark kingdom policies. And like I said, whether they are a follower of Christ Jesus or not, implementing dark kingdom policies grants the enemy a measure of authority.

Again, every action we take is in agreement with and submission to either the kingdom of God or the kingdom of darkness. Fortunately, Jesus provided a "Get out of Satan's kingdom Free" card. And it works via genuine repentance. Unfortunately, we often choose to stay in dark territory – knowingly or not. Or else we don't realize to repent.

Despite being invisible, both of these kingdoms are territorial. Obeying their policies, then, is stepping into their territory. Again, this means whatever policy you adhere to concerning how you do this life, is either in compliance with the dark kingdom or in compliance with the kingdom of God, and subjects you to their rulers and divine authorities. It's the same as how things work in the physical realm. You may be a citizen of Country X but if you visit Country Y, you are subject to the laws in Country Y while you're there. If what you're doing while in Country Y is against that country's law regardless if it's legal in Country X where your citizenship is, you will suffer the consequences in Country Y.

Now let's talk about dark kingdom powers. The kingdom of darkness has specific powers and principalities in charge of seeing to it little minions lure believers into aligning with their kingdom. They very strategically organize and plot how to bring believers into dark territory so that they acquire legal access. Regardless what strategies are implemented or which demons are used, the end goal is to get the Christian to yield to lies and sin.
Now the thing is, the enemy knows he has to entice you to willfully come over into dark kingdom territory of your own accord. They cannot pluck you out of God's territory. They can only rouse you by pushing buttons that are sure to work on you. And believe me, they know which buttons work. They've been around, studying you since your birth. They know your every weakness. Sure, they know you belong to Christ. They always knew you would. But if they can get you to agree with them or yield to something

false, they know they acquire legal access to you and can sabotage the breath of God in you, your destiny, or your purpose. Even if just temporarily. You may be a citizen of heaven but you're touchable while hanging out in dark domain. That's why right after Jesus was spiritually transferred into His own kingdom upon John's baptizing Him, Satan personally followed Him into the wilderness to get Jesus to agree to something, ANYTHING, false that he had to say. Because had Jesus submitted to the devil, this would have given Satan authority over God Himself! *(I'm still astonished that the devil actually thought God might submit to him. I just don't get that.)*

But realize that when you agree with the devil in any way, shape or form... When you bow to any idol or love something more than God... When you believe and practice any type of false doctrine or teaching... When you willfully do or believe anything that is a dark kingdom policy, you are aligning with the dark kingdom. You are stepping in dark kingdom territory where they have authority and you are thereby subject to it. You have stepped out of the realm of God's Kingdom over into the danger zone. Does this mean you belong to the devil now? No. Not unless you choose to stay there. And the longer you do, the greater the devil's authority, and the harder it is to go back to Jesus. It might take something terrible to get you out of the pit and back into Grace.

Now, I want to give an analogy as to what it looks like stepping over into dark kingdom territory if even temporarily. Imagine if an abusive neighbor comes over to your house, enters, puts an evil movie on your television, tells Alexa to play dark, satanic music, puts a case of beer on your counter, dirty magazines on your coffee table, and he begins verbally assaulting you. You know you have every right and the authority to remove everything from the premises and tell him to leave. If he refuses, you can call for higher authorities to assist you to get him and his stuff out. On the contrary, if the same abusive neighbor invites you to come over to his domain to do drink, see his dirty magazines or movies, or listen to his satanic music, if you go and he starts verbally assaulting you, you cannot tell him to leave. YOU have to leave. You can't tell him to stop watching the bad movie. And you cannot throw his trashy magazines into the garbage. Try to call the police to have him or his property put out all you want – it won't work. It's precisely the same with the invisible authorities. If you willfully step onto their domain, they have the authority. Try to cast the demons off you in Jesus' name all you want – it won't work. You're the one that has to leave enemy territory by repenting and stopping whatever it is you're doing or agreeing with.

A concern I have with some deliverance ministries is many of the demons they attempt to cast out are either not going to budge because the believer is the one in their territory, or the demons will leave on command but come right back - if the believer hasn't come out of alignment with the evil policy in their heart and soul. The minister may have the full authority of God but telling demons to leave God's domain won't permanently work if the believer is the one in dark domain. Therefore, the believer is the one that has to do the exiting. Ministers do often discern that the believer may have opened the door via a particular area of sin or unbelief, so they'll work with them to repent and close the door to that spirit. This is right on, but the next question is what if deep down the believer still carries approval for it? Yes, they repented and hated their sin. But what if they don't yet know, understand or own the truth of what God says concerning the matter? This means this area that was cleaned out remains empty and the spirits can and will come back – with seven more! This is why so many report getting prayer and deliverance, feeling better for a time, only to end up worse soon after. It is imperative believers come to understand where their allegiance to darkness is, get to the root, and put an end to it. Then telling the dark powers to leave is as simple as pie. Because the combination of repentance (coming out of submission and alignment with darkness) + using Jesus' name is all that's needed to overcome.

Sounds simple but in order to do this, we must first know where we are in alignment with darkness. I can't tell you all the ways I was in alignment with darkness for twenty years as a genuine, passionate Christian! Though I thought I was living a life of obedience to Christ (except for the seasons where I rebelled and backslid), I wasn't. When I wasn't backslidden, I was on fire for Jesus. I was even having encounters with Him at times. I did all the things Christians do. I passionately worshiped and prayed. I served, love, gave, etc., etc. Yet, the dark kingdom prevailed. I did not experience victory. I was defeated. And now I know it was because of all the ways I was unwittingly aligned with the dark kingdom. If the devil told me I was a loser, for example, I believed him. So there I was, half of me believing I was victorious through Christ with a destiny, and the other half of me believing I was a defeated loser. I had one foot in kingdom of God territory, and one foot in dark kingdom territory.

Now you might not be so gullible to believe such an obvious lie of the devil like that. But I assure you, if you aren't victorious in Christ, there's something in you that's out of alignment with truth somewhere. All you have to do is find out where. And be prepared to receive a lot of correction. Like I said, the number of ways I operated according to dark kingdom policies was countless.

The thing is, earnestly finding out where you are misaligned and believing things wrong is one of the best things you can do on this ODJ. And then buckle down and zero in on Jesus, learn His policies inside and out and live them while also rejecting all the lies. As you do this, the kingdom of darkness powers have no grounds and you can simply use the name of Jesus to put them out when they trespass. Indeed, the more you mature into the full stature of Christ, the more desperate they'll become to ensnare and stifle you. They don't just get up and walk away. They'll look for ways to send troops over into your territory in hopes that they won't be noticed. But they're very nervous about doing so, though, because believers who aren't easily deceived or manipulated by the enemy at this stage of their growth are typically well versed in the Word of God, will discern the evil spirits, and cast them out. Therefore, dark powers will only attempt what they think they're likely to get away with because, sincerely, they're chickens. They're terrified of Christ and His authority. That's why they've worked so hard to come up with new, sneaky tricks to lure us onto their turf and then blinding and deceiving as best they can to hold us down again. -Always remember that no matter how mature you become, they're looking for ways to trip you up. Never be overconfident in your growth. Always be humble so that you won't be set up for a fall.

And finally, please understand that believers who are severely oppressed are subject to a deeper level of authority of the dark kingdom on account of which policies they're adhering to – and these are usually ideals that we don't realize oppose God. The evil empire has done well to bamboozle these believers, so they feel trapped in dark kingdom territory despite having the trump card in their back pockets to walk right out. For example, many people hate themselves and are clueless that this is a dark kingdom behavior. They fail to realize they are insulting God for what He created, and they are in agreement with demons. The Bible says every person is fearfully and wonderfully made. We have no right whatsoever to despise God's handiwork. Doing so is bowing to darkness and LIVING in their domain.

Other examples of being in deep alignment with darkness would be having unresolved bitterness, resentment, or unforgiveness, being insecure, feeling abandoned if even subconsciously, doubting God's love, blaming God for things, etc. Though the pain and reality behind all these syndromes is legitimate, when we're confident in the Word, secure in Christ and aligned with His reality concerning all matters, then the pain is dealable and does not drive us into deep darkness. And in all honesty, we should be able to still rejoice that our King is still wonderful and still on His throne and best yet, that we will be with Him soon despite it all. Because though stuff hurts here, it's really irrelevant to your eternal hope. We can sincerely say,

"Though they slay me, yet will I trust Him," Job 13:15. And in so doing, we are aligning ourselves with God.

It's the same with feeling bitter about a crappy situation, being jealous, worrying about the bills, etc. These may seem to be justifiable responses to authentically bad things going on, but these reactions are alignments with the dark kingdom and give them authority. They aren't holy kingdom policies. God's policies include trusting Him, focusing on the eternal, rejoicing, thanking Him despite the uncertainties of this life, and enduring through the garbage. This is where walking in the fruits of the Spirit comes into play. If when we're troubled we'd learn to cast our cares upon Him for real and let Him help us with the pain, then we'd respond in peace, joy, humility, love, kindness, self-control, etc., even while the wound is still bleeding. We won't respond with jealousy, worry, bitterness, hatred, discord, etc.

We think because we obey the big stuff by not cussing, smoking, drugging, drinking, fornicating, murdering, stealing, etc., that we're in alignment with God's kingdom. But that's not necessarily the case. Anything we do that is contrary to what the Bible says, including worry about a bill, or feel sorry for ourselves over injustice, etc., is operating according to dark kingdom policies.

The exciting news is the Holy Spirit truly does an excellent job showing us which dark kingdom policies we abide by – if we're open to face the truth, that is. But that's the key. We have to be sincerely willing to find out plus diligently work with Him and His Word to gain further understanding as to where we're going wrong. I've discovered too many people, including myself, are afraid to be wrong. We have to get over that!

Few of us, if any, rise to perfection. We all stumble to one degree or another. And yes, if we don't repent, we've granted the enemy access. **So, the key to victory over the wiles of every foul entity roaming**

about the planet, is first and foremost, to repent and secure our faith walk by knowing and owning the truth, living it, and applying it; all the while working with Holy Spirit to come out of agreement with darkness by repenting and closing the doors. On one hand this sounds very simple. On another hand it may sound daunting. I admit, it is a process that requires diligence. But the more we align with God's truth, the more experiential victory over darkness we walk in! I know this is true because it's my testimony! Amen.

Does God Seem Far Away?

I'm going to step out on a limb and say that, despite every challenge, every situation where it has seemed God is more absent than present, that you are still convinced He is God despite it -because you've had profound moments of "connection" with Him through the years. Though I don't know when or how often you have experienced God personally, I believe you had to have at least once in order for you to be here doing this program.

I've shared how we have spent years, even decades, esteeming the charades of the devil as reality. But that God's reality is the REAL reality. I know, that seems to make no sense, but it does. The "reality" of the devil is real, yes. But dark kingdom reality does not have to be "a" reality at all. In the least, not the reality of a believer.

What I'd like to drive home is... the dark kingdom realm or "reality" will only manifest if it is bought into, adhered to, or believed. That's why the devil has to work tirelessly to get the world to agree with, approve of, and yield to his kingdom and principles. Otherwise, the devil's reality WOULD NOT MANIFEST AT ALL! It would be as though it does not even exist!

Likewise, God's reality can only manifest if it is adhered to and believed. Not because God is too weak to manifest otherwise, but because He designed things to work this way. God leaves it up to US to determine which reality we live!

Let me repeat that... That which manifests in our personal worlds is contingent upon which invisible realm's policies, ideals and dynamics we mind and adhere to. You can take this to the bank: The only reason darkness is getting away with perverting so much in this world is because humans have listened, agreed, approved, adhered, and yielded to it (or didn't know to take authority over the devil when he illegally infiltrated something). TRUE, humans have the sin nature. But evil is rampant because we have accepted and adhered to dark kingdom policies. Therefore, evil is no longer just present within human nature, but it is BECOMING MANIFEST PRESENT in all things. This is why the antichrist will soon take a global position over the earth. Because he has finally, after thousands of years of hard work, acquired global submission. Even despite Christ's kingdom coming to earth. The dark kingdom has brilliantly infiltrated the Church in such a way as to hold her back, keeping her powerless for the most part, so that he could acquire a global platform whereby the masses are in agreement with him one way or another, yet completely under his spell. That's why the world will bow to the antichrist!

But realize... the hour has come for God to wake His body up, deliver her from the illusions, and raise her to power to do a mighty work amidst the rise of the antichrist - prior to her departure. To date, however, the devil has been doing well keeping the body of Christ distracted from who she is, thinking on things he wants us thinking on, seeing and handling things of the world through tainted perspectives, busy with self, struggling with problems, chasing this life, and more... all to keep us bewitched and from entering the REAL reality.

I know I'm repeating myself but it all leads to what I hope to get across here, which is that the more we come out of false perspectives and from operating in false ways, the more we align with and experience the reality of God's realm! Sure, in this life we will have trials. But that's because we're in a fallen world that gives allegiance to the dark kingdom. To the contrary, snapping out of the illusion we, the Church, have been in, and coming into alignment with the Father means we'll experience more and more awareness of the good of His realm, and "connection" to God!

I can say this because it's what's been and still is happening to me. The more aligned I have become, where my core, my soul and actions, perspectives, reactions and outlook mirror and agree with God's dynamics, the more God is evident to me. The more noticeable His presence is, and the more His essence becomes my reality! Not only do I feel God's love for me which used to be a foreign concept that did not compute, but I feel the affections and passion He feels specifically for 'me' more, too! And His goodness is manifesting more and more in me and in my circumstances. His handiwork is so evident. I can see all these things He is strategizing and working out on my behalf! Best of all, it no longer feels like He's an absent parent that only loves me from afar any more! I'm telling you - as my perspectives have changed and aligned with the true reality, my life has, too! Once you become secure in God, the reality you've known which was dictated by darkness is nullified and your life takes a new form that's solid, sound, and whole!

Now that's not to say God was absent and doing less for me while I was so dreadfully out of alignment with His reality. No. He was as passionate then as now. He was as intricately involved in every detail of my life then as He is right now. The difference was I COULD NOT DETECT OR EXPERIENCE IT. There was an invisible chasm between me and all that God was to me! Therefore, He felt far away. Though I "knew" He was there, I could not sense Him the way I can now. It's like I was blocked from His presence!

But again, the more I come into alignment and the more deceptions and false perspectives fall off like dead flies, the smaller the chasm becomes, and the more I sense and experience God's manifest reality.

Think of it like this... Say you moved into a room in the spring when the weather was changing. The room has both heat and air conditioning which is set to maintain the room temperature at 72 degrees F, depending on whether it's cold or hot outside on a given day. The blinds are closed on the windows and all the doors are kept closed. If, for whatever reason, you stayed inside this room for months with nobody coming in or out, and no information as to what is going on outside, you would have no "sense" or "awareness" that right outside your room on Monday it was uncomfortably hot and humid while on Saturday the temperatures mysteriously dropped to nearly freezing. You would not have "experienced" either of these realities. Not that this typically happens but stick with me. All you are aware of is the comfortable room you are in. This is your reality. And because you don't seek to know otherwise, you are completely unaware of the REAL reality that's outside of the four walls you are in. This is because your understanding of reality is influenced, skewed, or "controlled" by the implementation of a furnace or air conditioning. And the walls, closed doors and blinds which shield you from the REAL temperature, serve as the chasm between your "controlled" reality, and the actual reality on the other side of the chasm.

Now here's what we need to realize: We've been duped into, lured into, and manipulated into just staying in that room. Though there are doors to exit (Jesus), we don't notice because our focus is strategically thwarted from them. Though we know there are blinds on the windows, it never dawns on us that we can actually open them. We just don't think of it. Why? Because the master over the room is controlling things, enticing us with this, preoccupying us with that, entangling us with this and getting us addicted to that. We listen to the subliminal suggestions of the one in charge of the room. We yield to whatever distractions he provides or charades he puts on to keep us busy focusing on what he wants us focused on. And we're so gullible to all this because we're clueless that someone else is controlling things. We think it's just us. So we remain mindless about the fact that there's a reality beyond the four walls, and that all we'd have to do is ignore the one in charge of the air, wake up, snap out of it, and walk through a door into the REAL reality. But we don't... because we're comfortable where we are. And he entertains us so well.

Just the same with God, He's right there but because we are so accustomed to the controlled environment, because we're so attuned to and acclimated to paying attention to all the noise and charades of the dark kingdom, that that's all we can see and sense. Even though we know about our Lord and learn many things about Him, and despite the fact that He breaks into the room to get through to you from time to time, we continue to live according to the dictates of darkness, the world we'd always known.

What's worse is the enemy works diligently to suggest that the controlled environment of that room is the given, written in stone reality. He does this through suggestions in our thoughts, through assaults, through manipulating our soul wounds, through the lusts of our flesh, through our false perspectives, etc. He uses what we're most vulnerable and accustomed to, things that are sure to capture our focus and allegiance. And we yield to these, which is the same as choosing to remain in that room, paying mind to whatever it is the dark kingdom uses to keep us under foot, so that we'll hopefully never grasp that we can leave it. So we unwittingly choose to adhere to and remain in the fictitious reality. True, it's real in that the air conditioner and furnace do cause the temperature to remain at a comfortable 72 degrees F. But that's not the real, non-manipulated temperature, is it?

So please be encouraged that no matter where you are in the scope of your journey with God, know that the reality you have known where God may have felt like a long distance daddy, or perhaps like He doesn't care, isn't real. It's a controlled reality and one that, the more you come out of alignment with it and into alignment with God's, will be dismantled and replaced by God's reality where you'll experience HIM, His LOVE and His HELP unlike you have ever been able to like when you were stuck in that room. I guarantee you that the more the false things come off and out of you, the more you'll recognize the blinds that can be opened or the doors that you can go through. The more you come into alignment with truth - which is the REAL reality, the more you will experience the manifest presence of God! And the more you sense that connection and His presence, the more secure and resolved you will be, and you will prosper in every possible way! Everything in your life will come to order and you will daily experience the manifest reality of God. Amen

Notes/Prayers

_____

_____

_____

_____

_____

_____

_____

_____

_____

_____

_____

_____

_____

_____

_____

_____

_____

_____

_____

_____

Religion is not Alignment with God

We know being right with God is only possible via repentance and knowing/believing Jesus. And that *staying* right with God requires us to continue in submission to His Lordship, which includes repentance and cleansing as we go. Remember how Jesus washed the disciples' feet before He was crucified? Though afterwards Jesus told them He did it to set an example for them to follow, that's not the only reason He did it. Let's take a close look at what Jesus said to Peter:

> Jesus came to Simon Peter, who said to him, "Lord, are you going to wash my feet?" Jesus replied, "You do not realize now what I am doing, but later you will understand." "No," said Peter, "you shall never wash my feet." But Jesus answered, "Unless I wash you, you have no part with me." Then, Lord," Simon Peter replied, "not just my feet but my hands and my head as well!" Jesus answered, "Those who have had a bath need only to wash their feet; their whole body is clean. And you are clean..." John 13:6-10.

In saying that Peter had a bath, Jesus was saying Peter was right with God (aligned with His kingdom) because Peter had already repented and believed on Him as the Lord Messiah. But interestingly enough, Jesus said Peter did need his feet washed or that Peter could have no part with Him. And He told Peter that he would understand later.

Well, it's later. And the understanding is that even though Peter was clean and right with God as a whole, He would still need to receive regular washing from Jesus (via repentance and the cleansing power of the blood).

All that to say, once born again, we must remain in humble submission to the King, and repent when we step out of line and get our feet dirty. And in so doing (continuing in the way of repentance), as well as believing, **we remain in alignment with God. Mind you, not because we're perfect, but because we repent and believe.**

That said, now let's look at the issue of religious spirits:

As you probably know, religious spirits con believers into taking security in their works and subconsciously equate their works with their alignment with God. But like I once thought, you might presume you do not have any religious spirits. So, we need to hash this out because if we feel more right with God because, for example, we made it to church on Sunday, we read our Bible, we gave tithes or offerings recently, we volunteer, we pray, we worship, etc., then that's a religious spirit. We're subconsciously leaning on our performance to feel good about our walk with God. Consequently, we may feel more qualified to pray and even make requests since we're "doing well" following religious protocol. To the contrary, if we feel distant from God, a little hesitant about going before Him in prayer because we're slacking, it's because we subconsciously believe that our alignment with God is dependent upon our Christian performance. And oh, are these spirits sneaky. There are Christians that know their salvation is not based on their works, yet, indirectly, most still feel like they are in disobedience or sin for not soaring in these religious duties.

For example, there's this religious dogma that if you do not belong to or attend church regularly, you are in violation of scripture! Not true. Though it's best to connect with a sound group of believers, though this is God's desire for us, to be in unity, to worship together, to edify one another, etc., there's no scriptural mandate to do so. None. It is not sin to not be a part of a church. The mandate, as we learned in the "Greatest Commission" module about the imperative to bear fruit, is to BE the Church wherever we are. Because WE are the Church. And where two or more are gathered, WOOHOO, all the better! Indeed, it is unwise for Christians to not congregate, because that's a huge part in how we grow and it's so powerful being able to worship our God together, as one. But there's no "mandate" for this. It is not sin to not be a part of the modern day institutionalized system of organized religion. This is a lie that puts a religious spirit on the Church.

I've heard pastors unwittingly promote this religious spirit by misrepresenting Hebrews 10:25, preaching the false doctrine that "not forsaking the assembly" means to not forsake going to church. Meanwhile, based on the Greek and not the faulty translations, the entire context of the passage from Hebrews 10:23 to 10:27 *actually* says,

> "23 Let us hold fast the confession of our hope (not faith as KJV states) without wavering, for He who promised (to return and gather us) is faithful. 24And let us consider one another in order to stir up love and good works, 25not forsaking (the hope of) the gathering together of ourselves, as is the manner of some, but exhorting / comforting / encouraging one another, and so much the more as you see the Day approaching (what day?). For if we sin willfully (by rejecting the profession of our hope discussed in verse 23) after we have received the knowledge of the truth, there no longer remains a sacrifice for sins, but a certain fearful expectation of judgment, and fiery indignation which will devour the adversaries."

The context of this passage has nothing to do with "going to church" or even Christians getting together. Instead, if you study out the original Greek terms and their usage throughout the New Testament, what you discover is it's all about something that's not commonly taught in the Church - which is the gathering to Christ at His return. Below is a link to a point by point breakdown which clearly lays this passage out, but I'll summarize:

Hebrews 10:23 speaks to "a confession of our hope". We have to ask what that hope is. In short, based on plenty of other scriptural evidence, this hope refers to the gathering of the believers unto Christ at His return. In fact, that's the "Day" verse 25 is referring to; the day of Christ's return. When the book of Hebrews was written, believers were living in anticipation (in hope) of Christ's return and of being gathered to Him out of this world, because that's what Paul taught them. Unfortunately, several years had passed since Paul taught them this, and Jesus hadn't yet come back to gather them, so some abandoned their hope for it. Therefore, Paul warned others to not forsake this hope, but to, instead, encourage or exhort each other to persevere in the hope of Christ's return and His gathering us to Him - and all the more as the Day approaches! Because times will be so difficult for believers the closer the Day gets, that more and more will fall from the faith (the Great Apostasy of 2 Thessalonians 2). Paul then explains that those who know of this truth but give up on it, abandoning the hope, will suffer judgment and fiery indignation (be left behind to endure the tribulations).

Note: 1 Corinthians 5:4 says, "When you are *'gathered'* in the name of our Lord Jesus (as in having church)...". The Greek term for gathered here is sunachthentOn, Strong's G4863. And this Greek term is used quite frequently throughout the New Testament. Whereas, the Greek term used for Hebrews 10:25 re: forsaking the assembling is episunagOgEn, Strong's G1997. Interestingly, episunagOgEn is only used one other time in scripture: 2 Thessalonians 2:1, "Concerning the coming of our Lord Jesus Christ and our being gathered (G1997) to him, we ask you, brothers and sisters, not to become easily unsettled or alarmed by the teaching allegedly from us—whether by a prophecy or by word of mouth or by letter—asserting that the day of the Lord has already come. Don't let anyone deceive you in any way, for that day will not come until the rebellion occurs (the great falling away) and the man of lawlessness (antichrist) is revealed, the man doomed to destruction. He will oppose and will exalt himself over everything that is called God or is worshiped, so that he sets himself up in God's temple, proclaiming himself to be God." Clearly you can see that this gathering has to do with the Lord's return after the antichrist is revealed, just as Hebrews 10:25 also reflects upon "that Day".

So, there's no way to substantiate Hebrews 10:25's "not forsaking the assembly" as having anything to do with going to church. Such a claim is a complete deviation away from what Paul is speaking about. It's a false teaching with one goal - to hook believers up with religious spirits who will take on a subconscious works mentality, feeling distant from God, guilty or defeated if they aren't a part of a church or attending regularly. It's just one clever way to oppress the body of Christ.

This misuse of scripture serves as a perfect example of how sneaky religious spirits can be. I personally never thought I had a religious spirit because I knew my salvation was not works based. Meanwhile, because of the abuse of this passage, there were times I wrestled with great guilt and fear for "forsaking the assembly" when I didn't attend church. I had no idea that I had submitted to the lie and accepted the doctrine of religious spirits. Consequently, my shame served well to make me feel disconnected from God and stunted my comfort in approaching Him. And I venture to say, you might just have the same thing going on or something similar...?

Other sneaky aspects of the religious spirit are, like I said, when we feel guilty or like we're failing as Christians for not praying, worshiping, serving, giving, volunteering, or even doing our ODJ Program as much as we think we should be. True, doing all those things is a part of the fabric of the kingdom of God. These are dynamics of God's realm. So, if we aren't doing them, yes, these are symptoms showing that something in us is wrong. Doing these kingdom acts does not align us with the kingdom of God and keep us "right" with Him; doing them is a RESULT of ALREADY being aligned with God. These practices merely follow suit. If they don't follow, then we need to find out what's going on in us that's not in tune with truth but, instead, is attuned with darkness, and pulling us away from the kingdom of God into bondage. We need to see that our lack of practicing these kingdom protocols as a **warning sign** that something in us is wrong.

Remember, alignment with the kingdom of God is repentance and knowing/believing God's truths. True, you don't know all God's truths the moment you are born into His kingdom, but in so much as you have repented and believed what you do know, you are aligned because God's

GRACE covers what you do not yet know. Meanwhile, you may still be vulnerable to lies that you YIELD to which may keep you going back and forth between the two kingdoms, even unknowingly. One of them being, "I'm not following religious protocol very well, so I'm in trouble. I'm in disobedience. I'm not right with God. I'm terrible. I'll never be right", etc. ---That's all demonic oppression via the spirit of religion and must be put out.

Ahhhh! I've lived that life and I'm angry that this is such a rampant false belief in the body of Christ. I hate it. *The Lord rebuke you, spirits of religion!*

Just please do me a favor and ask God to reveal if there's anything in you that bows to the spirit of religion to any degree. And then kick it out. Lay down the lie. Realize that even if you are in a season struggling with sin or aren't performing very well at religious or kingdom of God protocol, so long as your heart is humble before God, repentant, and seeking Him in the matters of your struggle, YOU ARE ALIGNED with the kingdom concerning those issues. **Your repentance and relying upon God's grace concerning a sin or failure makes you aligned.** Meanwhile, **if you feel guilt and shame** for the struggle, THAT is where you are not aligned with truth. THAT is where you are disconnecting yourself from God's realm. Because you believe a lie and are squandering the grace of God which covers you for the sin that you are struggling with. Feeling guilty is not being secure in what Jesus did for you - which is a dark kingdom policy. (Write that in your notes!

If you'd like to look more closely at the breakdown of what Hebrews 10:23-27 actually means, please visit:

https://www.wordofhisgrace.org/wp/hebrews_1025/

We need to obey the Holy Spirit; not man's or religious protocol.

Sometimes, we want or think we should do something simply because it's "the right thing to do". Indeed, God is the Lord of compassion, kindness, and love. As children of His kingdom, we carry His gracious heart in us, and God calls us to continually operate in these ways. There's plenty of scripture that says so.

But is this *all* the Lord says?

Concerning a man in the church that was in sexual immorality by taking his father's wife, 1 Corinthians 5:5 says, "Hand this man over to Satan for the destruction of the flesh, so that his spirit may be saved on the day of the Lord."

Wow, where's the compassion in that? How is it love to tell a brother in the church "you need to leave"?

When new believers who began their journey down the narrow path realize they can no longer participate in the activities that their broad pathed friends are still on, where is the love and compassion in saying, "I can no longer be your friend"?

Kicking people out of the church or out of our lives seems to be the opposite of love and compassion. Especially for those we were really close to. Though this seems cruel and heartless, the Bible is clear what walking with Him looks like. Truth be told, they'll feel rejected, judged, and abandoned. They will likely accuse us for being hypocrites or holier than thou, saying we are the real sinners for our hatred or self-righteousness. This is understandable, because it does seem to be the opposite of love.

We know the truth though, that it's not rejecting them, but their lifestyle. And in the case of the man in sexual immorality, turning him over to Satan so that his soul can be saved is the compassion of Christ. When you understand that a person's eternal fate is more pressing than their earthly happiness, you care to do whatever is necessary to see them in Heaven with you one day. That's love.

I bring this side of the coin up to not only show that not everything God calls us to do seems loving, but also because sometimes we may not know that God is disciplining or purifying someone, so it might not be best to bestow compassion upon them. Helping or doing "the right thing" might actually work against or delay what God is working on in them. I've seen this several times with different people over the decades where, despite knowing their propensity for the sin, I was compelled to give the benefit of the doubt, and give these different folks a chance or two, opening my doors to them. Unfortunately, I never asked God if it was what He wanted me to do; I just did it because it was the right thing to do. I had this motto that if somebody that crossed my path was in need, God wanted me to help them. I now know that's not necessarily true but back then, that's where I was. Consequently, things not only back-fired on me, causing me distress AND interfering with what I actually was supposed to be doing for the Lord, I also saw how my trying to help them walk the narrow path only delayed the inevitable. Eventually they ended up in the very painful predicaments that I had desperately attempted to help them avoid. All I really taught them was to believe how I once did - that you "always" have to help someone in need so that when they became homeless again for the hundredth time, I was the one in the wrong for no longer taking them in.

The devil knows you have the love and kindness of Christ beaming in you, so he'll try to use it against you. The enemy will play on your big heart, compelling you to do good deeds that he knows will actually cause more problems for someone, including you. And the thing is, as you know, he'll taunt you about it saying things like, "you haven't visited so and so in ages, you are not a good friend" or "you haven't helped so and so" or, "you haven't volunteered, you aren't being a very good Christian", etc. And he does this to tangle you up because you won't feel as close to God if you are tormented over all the goodness you are not bestowing on the world around you. This is just one strategy of darkness to keep you preoccupied and weighed down - which is to your spiritual dysfunction.

Just because something is "the right thing to do" doesn't mean it really is the "right" thing to do. God has literally had to tell me no, do not help a particular person, because it would interfere with what He's doing. It's very difficult, but we must lean on God, not our own understanding. **We cannot operate out of protocol**. We should never do something just because "it is right". We need to listen to God. He knows what is best in every situation. If you are surrendered to God, humble and eager to obey Father God, always asking God to guide you according to His heart and knowledge in every matter, then you will have peace when you are led by God to help someone. Follow the Lord's lead. But, don't be presumptuous. If your heart is so big that you do for others constantly without even thinking, simply double check with the Lord or at least always be on the alert for a red flag. Ask Him daily to give you a check in your spirit if you're about to be gracious in a matter that might interfere with His plans for someone, or that just might not be something you should do for no known reason.

On the contrary, what about those times you get the unction that you should do something, but you do not want to or feel like it? For example, maybe you have the thought that you should take a plate of cookies to your new neighbor. Or perhaps you feel you should go visit someone in a nursing home. It most likely is the leading of God, but... not necessarily. The goal of this module is that ODJ Members will be delivered from false guilt over not doing something just because it's "the right thing to do". And to know to lean on God better concerning what He wants us doing; always checking with Him. And lastly, not letting the devil play the guilt-trip game anymore.

I know someone who, not being in the greatest financial situation, was invited by a relative to come live with him. Her relative had been living with the owner of the home who'd just passed away, and now there was no income to keep the home going. So, being family, the idea was she would leave her home, her town and life to go live there to take over the bills. Though in the long run it would be less expensive for her to live with her relative and she knew it would help him be able to remain in his home which made her feel pressed that she should do it, because it was the right thing to do, she also felt hesitant. But she shared about her struggle with me, so I prayed for the Lord to give her peace if it was truly the right thing to do, or to close the door if it wasn't the right thing to do. Within three days she had her crystal-clear answer that it was not the right thing for her to do. And though she felt bad and this was displeasing to her relative because he didn't know what he would do now, she knew she was not to feel guilty because we checked with God. ~Sometimes it appears we are the source, the answer to a problem, which compels us to think we have to do it. This situation proves that this simply isn't so. God always has a solution if people will just ask and trust Him. (Not trusting Him will interfere with His getting the solution to us.)

As for those times God is the one nudging you to do something good but you avoid doing it, what might that look like? Does He harass you about it?

Over the course of a couple months, I kept getting the idea that I should reach out to a distant friend, offering to help with a particular matter. (I say distant because we were never close, but very basic friends that chatted a bit a few times, and we'd help each other out on occasion.) However, something happened the year before where she was super mad at me out of nowhere and said some things in a way that made it seem she hated me, so I backed off. Honestly, I didn't know what to do. Talking things out just wasn't going to happen. Meanwhile, I didn't hold any angst against her, I actually felt bad for the blow-up. But at the same time, it was very awkward when I ran into her because of the situation. So, I preferred to just steer clear and not face the tension. But after a year had passed, I kept getting the nudge to offer to help with a particular matter, but kept saying, "Okay, I will, soon, Lord. If you provide the opportunity, I'll take it." Well, two months went by and no opportunity arose, so I assumed God wasn't the one prompting the matter. Until one night while not even thinking of that situation I prayed, "Is there anything you want from me, Lord? Anything you would like me to do for you?" And He said, "I've been asking you for two months to... and you still haven't done it."

I reminded God how I'd been asking Him to open the door and He gently scolded me saying that was my way of avoidance. All I needed to do was approach her. So, I repented and obeyed right away. In so doing, the relationship was totally mended and all the tension disappeared. God showed me it displeased Him that two of His children would be at odds like that. And after a year of it, He wanted it put to rest. Honestly, we never discussed what had happened which is unusual for me. I prefer to get to the bottom of things. But the Lord just told me to show my love by offering to help her with something. I finally did, and wow.

Of course, that was an instance where God was directing me to do something and I was resisting Him. But the reason I shared that story was to point out that for the two months that I resisted God, He never laid a guilt trip on me. He did bring it up more than a handful of times, but He did not harass or manipulate me with guilt. Though I was convicted when God pointed out that I was dissing Him, I did not feel small, heavy, or distant from Him. Based on past experience when (unbeknownst to me at the time) the devil hounded me that I should do this or that, I now know it was the devil because I was always so tormented and guilt-ridden if I didn't do it. Or worse, giving in and doing it ended up causing a problem as I shared above. So, I've learned that if I'm compelled to do something that I don't want to do, if I become anxious over not doing it, it's a red flag. So, now I try to take everything up with God to confirm either way.

I also want to point out the very fact that you do not desire to do something may actually be the result of a check in your spirit that God put there. It may very well be the Lord saying, "No, do not take cookies to your new neighbor!"

In the late 90's my brother and I had driven about 1.5 hours away for a special church service. On the drive home we were passing near where our dad lived. We were estranged during our childhood, but had gotten to know him some. So, since we were together and passing by his town and coming to the exit we would need to take to get to his place, I asked my brother, "Should we stop and see dad?" to which he almost violently said, "NO!" I was like... "Uh, okay." He said he had no reason for saying no which may or may not have been true, but that he just wanted to get home. To me, however, it was more than a "I just prefer to get home" kind of no. A few days later I received a call that my dad had been deceased for four days. My brother and I would have been the ones to find him had we stopped a few nights before. Meanwhile, I'd felt bad for not stopping when we had the rare chance - because it was the right thing to do. But I now know and believe with all my heart, God put that peculiar, strong resistance in my brother, to protect us.

For all you know, if you get a nudge to take cookies to the neighbor but you keep putting it off for reasons you don't know, it very well could be that God is protecting you. Or He just does not want you associating with this person because no good can come of it. So, the resistance you feel may very well be God stepping in to stop you. The Holy Spirit or your angels may be steering you away from the idea.

At the end of the day, though, how do we know if our inclination to do something good, especially because it's "the right thing to do", is actually something we should or should not do? The short of it is that we simply need to check with God. We must run it by Him. If it's not a problem, we'll have peace. And if we are avoiding something, we can ask Him about that as well - if we're disobeying His lead, or if it's a bad idea for some reason.

Trust me, I don't have to tell you that there are a million ways we can be compassionate every day, and that the first instinct is to always take the opportunity to do what we can for others. It's actually great if that's our first inclination. But there are particulars and variables we do not know. On top of that, there are other things God would prefer that we do instead that we'll miss by doing the "wrong" right thing. Including doing nothing at all but resting, which is sometimes crucial to our health and well-being. Not to mention, the devil will also play on our Christendom to keep us so busy with good deeds that we aren't able to rest in God properly - wherein we'd see what God really has for us. There's all sorts of reasons that we should just check with God.

I repeat: Just because something seems like the right thing to do does not mean that it is. Again, the enemy can use our big hearts to trip us up or even lay guilt trips on us to keep us off track or tangled up. We must always ask God to guide us to do what *He wants* and to give us a check in our spirits loud and clear if we're about to do something 'wonderful' that might not be a good thing after all.

And again: **Keep in mind that our duty is to obey the Lord; not protocol**. The reason I wrote this module is because I've been more conscious lately of God's pain over His children living their Christian lives full of guilt and being run-down over the false teachings in the Church (such as the false representation of Hebrews 10:25 supposedly meaning it's sin to not be a regular member of a church), and our vulnerability to feel guilty for not following protocol. **The guilt plague is literally a rampant virus in the body of Christ.**

As I've been sharing, and as you probably already knew for yourself, God is raising up His army. But an army cannot fall for the lies of the enemy, or they're defeated. One of the enemy's lies is that we need to feel guilty if we are not comfortable with doing something that we think "we should" just because it's the right thing to do or protocol. That's wrong. To super simplify things, I'll just put it like this: If there's something God sincerely wants someone to do, He'll speak to them about it and make Himself known. But He won't harass them even if they avoid His unction. He won't strike them with lightning. He won't torment them. And He won't manipulate them into it using people to play on their emotions or push their buttons. That's how the devil does things.

> *Dear Heavenly Father, I pray for all ODJ Members that if they have the propensity to feel bad for not doing good things that you never said for them to do, or if they have a history of being tangled up or tormented over what to do when they're just not sure, or being lured into doing good things for the sake of wrong reasons, to set them off course, or cause them problems, I pray they have clarity of mind and heart from now on to know when you are the one leading them as opposed to the devil. And I pray they will always check with you, and that you will give them profound peace if it's right to something, but give them a huge red flag or a check in their spirit if the right thing is actually not good. I ask you to give them clarity and wisdom in all they do. And I ask that if there's something in their soul or belief system that's made them vulnerable to the devil's guilt trips or persuasion, that you illuminate it. I speak to spirits of pride and insecurity, that you be dismantled from the ODJ Members so that they will no longer be vulnerable to yield to you. Whatever the case, Father*

God, please get to the root and cut out the problem, so that they will no longer be tripped up by the devil under the guise of "doing the right thing". Thank you for helping and delivering them from all this, Lord. Thank you for reminding them to check with you from now on. And lastly, thank you that they will no longer be weighed down by such issues any more.

In Jesus' Name, Amen.

Notes/Prayers

This is a personal story about an experience I had as a babe in Christ in 1992. I was a single mother of a five year old little girl, and a two year old little boy.

Depression had always been a part of the fabric of my life but there were times that I had bouts so severe I could barely move. Getting my two year old a drink of water was overwhelming, like climbing a mountain with one leg and one arm. I can still remember his little voice begging me to get him a 'dwink' and feeling like 5,000 pounds of sludge, coming to tears for his having to beg for some water.

Though it's clinically proven that there is a myriad of chemicals out of balance in someone with depression, I found out one night that the kingdom of darkness definitely has its hand in depression, too.

My children and I hadn't left the house for three weeks. This was highly unusual since we were very active in our church, and I had a few different Christian friends with children in the neighborhood that we regularly hung out with. I was just so depleted. I'd just lie in bed or on the couch as much as my children would allow it. My house was a wreck. The dishes and laundry were both piled a mile high. I just kept saying, "Lord, please send someone to help me." I was too weak and embarrassed to call anyone. I just kept hoping one of my friends would call or show up. And what's strange was nobody ever did which was so unusual. To this day, I believe there was spiritual influence behind that, perhaps even the Lord's, because I was about to experience an awakening that I wouldn't have, had someone showed up or called.

After the kids were in bed one night, I was lying on the couch listening to some Holy Spirit teaching tapes, I believe on the subject of God's authority. The message wasn't helping (or so I thought) so I just shut it off and began crying out to God over my situation. I needed help. I began pleading with God to help me, to have someone show up or call the next day. I asked Him why He wouldn't answer my prayer and just send someone to the door. What I expected they'd do, I don't know. But that's what I was crying out for very specifically when suddenly, I heard the Lord say, "You do not need someone to come to your door, the Helper (or Authority) is in you!"

I can't remember exactly how He said it but upon telling me the Helper was in me, I knew instantly it was the Holy Spirit who was the Helper and Authority, that His authority in me was my source of help. My help was the authority of God. It's difficult to explain, it all happened in an instant. One minute I was lying there begging for help, the next minute I was charged, battery full, and knew with all manner of knowing that the authority of the glorious, all powerful Helper was in me.

Suddenly this surge of energy and joy overtook me. It was purely supernatural. I jumped up off the couch (at like 1:00 a.m.) with such strength, passion and vigor I could have climbed a mountain. And I instantaneously found myself praising the Lord with tremendous zeal, saying, "This is Holy Ground! These are Holy hands! The Lord is HERE, RIGHT HERE IN ME, and He is Holy!" I felt the power of God fill me from head to foot. I felt on fire. I felt electrified. I knew "The Authority" was in me. I didn't just know *about* the Authority, I was *experiencing* Him. His manifest reality was suddenly very plain and apparent to me! What that actually meant beyond the fire surging in me, I didn't know. All I knew is, it was.

After several minutes of passionately praising the Lord, dancing around the living room fully alive and almost screaming for the glory of it all, the Lord told me to go upstairs and pray for my little girl. She, too, had been struggling with peculiar fears and issues. So I obeyed and tiptoed into her bedroom, standing over her. I began taking authority over her regarding the issues, declaring the truth for her (whispering so low, there was no way to hear me - yet nearly screaming in the spirit).

I was still completely caught up in the awe and wonder of God in me, and a couple minutes later I found myself praying in an unknown language! I had been asking for the gift of tongues and here it was! Of course, I was whispering super quietly, but this stuff was coming out of my mouth that I knew was from God. Then after just a minute of this, I found myself praying in English, praising the Lord again, declaring "this is Holy ground", screaming inside of myself that the Holy God was in me. That's how violently passionate and super-charged it was. It was so profound. I honestly cannot convey it well enough. But anyway, then I would go back to praying in tongues, then back to English. It went back and forth like this a few times when suddenly, without thinking, my right hand flew upwards towards Heaven and out of my mouth (quietly) came, "Father, Pour out your power like a lightning bolt!"

Immediately after saying that (again, in a whisper) my two year old baby boy two doors down shouted, "NO!" in his sleep. I NEVER heard him talk in his sleep before. And it stunned me. I just stood there frozen for maybe twenty seconds when the Lord said, "Keep praising Me". So, I resumed doing exactly as I had been, speaking in tongues, then praising God in English, back and forth for a few minutes, until again, without thinking, my hand flew up to Heaven and out of my mouth came, "Father, Pour out your power like a lightning bolt!"

Immediately upon my saying that the second time, my son two doors down cried out violently in his sleep, "I DON'T WANT TO!" I was stunned once more. Something was going on, but I had no idea what. I just stood there frozen. And after twenty seconds or so, God said, "Keep praising Me". So, I resumed doing the same thing, going back and forth between praying in tongues, and then praising God in English. But this time I heard, "Peace. Go to bed". So, I did.

In the morning, I woke to the sun shining through the windows and for the first time in a long time, I felt alive and got busy taking care of some much needed housework. A few hours later, low and behold, the phone rings. Finally, a friend called. One of my best friends, actually.

As I cleaned that morning, I felt this sense of a "holy hush" because I was still so stunned and in awe. I felt such reverence for God. What exactly happened? Whatever it was, it felt so holy that I dared not even ask God. It was as though God's handprint was so heavy on the matter that all I could do now was bow before Him. So, this was where my spirit was, humbled and prostrated before His Majesty. That's how intense the awe was. You know how when you are a child and you know not to overstep and presume the right to something from an adult, out of respect and reverence? That's kind of how it felt; only with awe. So, I resolved to not even ask the Father, "What was that?".

When my best friend called and she asked about what had been going on, I had trouble bringing myself to speak of the holy matter, but ultimately told her everything that had happened. And despite sounding nutty, I even shared how each time I cried, "Father, pour out your power like a lightning bolt", my son shouted "no!" the one time, and "I don't want to!" the other. To my surprise I heard her sobbing and asked what was wrong. She replied, "Paula, when you said 'Father pour out your power like a lightning bolt', God said to the enemy, "GET OUT!" and the enemy said no. And then when you said it again, God said to the enemy, "I SAID TO GET OUT!" and the enemy said, "I don't want to!". Once more, I was stunned.

Now, how the enemy could tell God no, I do not know. Perhaps it was that my angels were there fighting the demons, commanding them to leave, but they were obviously resisting. But that's why God spoke to me twice, "Keep praising Me", because this was what empowered my angels to win the battle. And perhaps, by then, God showed up personally to route them! Psalm 68:1 says, "Let God arise and His enemies be scattered...". As I praised God, His authority rose up in me, His manifest presence took over - and scattered the evil that had been dominating me so severely those three weeks!

But that's not the end of the story. A month or two had passed and I had come upon the following passage which reads:

"The cords of death entangled me;
the torrents of destruction overwhelmed me.
The cords of the grave coiled around me;
the snares of death confronted me.
(That's how I felt)
In my distress I called to the Lord;
I cried to my God for <u>help</u>.
From his temple he heard my voice;
my cry came before him, into his ears.
The earth trembled and quaked,
and the foundations of the mountains shook;
they trembled because he was angry.
Smoke rose from his nostrils;
consuming fire came from his mouth,
burning coals blazed out of it.
He parted the heavens and came down;
dark clouds were under his feet.
He mounted the cherubim and flew;
he soared on the wings of the wind.
He made darkness his covering, his canopy around him—
the dark rain clouds of the sky.
Out of the brightness of his presence clouds advanced,

with hailstones and **bolts of lightning**.
The Lord thundered from heaven;
the voice of the Most High resounded.
He shot his arrows and scattered the enemy,
with great **bolts of lightning** he routed them."
Psalm 18:4-14

Once more... I was stunned. That passage disclosed exactly what I had just personally experienced. At first, I assumed the Lord led me to it to confirm that what happened really was of Him. But no, that wasn't it because I was already certain of this. No, the reason He led me to it was to show me His heart for me. To show me His passion for ME! Suddenly it hit me that God did not just help me because He is a good God that is well able. No, He did it because He was FURIOUS with what the enemy was doing to His daughter!

"The earth trembled and quaked,
and the foundations of the mountains shook;
they trembled because he was angry."
Psalm 18:7

Was God kicked back in Heaven with His feet up getting a manicure or chilling over a cup of tea? No, He wanted me to see that because I cried out to Him for help, He flew down in fury and poured out His power like a LIGHTNING BOLT!

"He shot his arrows and scattered the enemy,
with great bolts of lightning he routed them."
Psalm 18:14

Wow. God loves us! He doesn't just help to be nice. God passionately wants to route the enemy on our behalf. But if that's the case, why didn't He just do it on day one, when the severe depression came over me? Well, He probably would have had I sincerely cried out to Him for help. But I didn't. I whimsically, in between sighs from a distance, not even looking His way, talked "at" Him, requesting that He please send someone to help me. True, that was still asking, but, I wasn't addressing God directly, so there's a lesson in this. Have you ever had someone throw comments or requests at you as they walked by, never even looking at you? Like they knew you were there but didn't have the courtesy of acknowledging you? That's what we do to God sometimes. We need to not be so rude and humble ourselves before His throne to petition Him directly, not just talk at Him from afar. Because it wasn't until I actually went into a deliberate conversation with Him, directly, to cry out to Him over the matter that He responded.

Please don't take this that I'm saying God won't answer us if we just off the cuff cry help. No, there are certainly desperate moments where we cry out to God and He'll answer on the spot. Let's not turn this into a legalistic doctrine where you must follow a specific protocol before being heard by God. The key is to not talk at God, but to Him from the belly, from the core, directly. The night God rose up in me, I had finally addressed Him for real. And it was only for a few moments, too. There was nothing religious or profound in my approach. I simply engaged Him from my heart, this time.

So many lessons in this:

1. Engage God for real, from the heart. Cry out to Him with earnest intent for Him to hear you.
2. Praising God truly makes Him manifest present. Keep praising Him until the job is done.
3. When you pray in tongues, you don't even have to think about it; it just happens.

4. God isn't just casually on our side. He's the most passionate Father you could ever imagine, full of zeal and desire to do powerful things for us. And He's especially infuriated over what the enemy does to His children.

After this happened, depression never had quite the same hold on me. It was a battle for several more years due to the PTSD and all the other false programming in my soul that had yet to be undone, along with the chemistry / hormone side of things. But even though I'd go through several bouts thereafter, I wasn't as spiritually debilitated. But honestly, I wasn't always spiritually conscious of the authority of God in me all the time, either. I was not always mindful of what I had learned that night. My transformation was still a major work in progress, with so very much wrong in my soul and belief system. But as the years passed and God re-programmed me according to truth more and more, all the truths began to come together and become my constant. Though not 100% constant, far more constant. Consequently, depression remains a propensity but hasn't had the upper hand in several years now. Even despite PTSD and chemical imbalance!

But what about you? Do you have a history of depression? If so, I speak to the Authority in you to rise up. I speak to your soul to be reworked according to all truth - and all false belief systems and dark kingdom programming to be undone. And I ask you, are you ready to let all things false go?

I didn't have teachings or mentors to turn to concerning my situation. I had to learn every microscopic detail from the Holy Spirit. I'm not complaining. The point is that's why it took me decades to put it all together. But you have this information at your disposal to refresh yourself when in the face of issues. Down the road, after you've studied this entire book, you can go back to any module at any time as encouragement that will help you recenter. At least, I hope you would. I believe that's what God intended.

I say all that to encourage you that if depression is a serious battle, you can use this as a resource to remind you that the Helper is IN YOU. The Authority is in you. Cry out to the Authority. Ask Him to rise. Then stand up and praise Him with vigor. Get excited over God being in you. And praise Him. And praise Him more. And keep praising Him. Let God manifest His power! Let Him shoot bolts of lightning at the enemy and route evil!

If you do have depression in your history even if you do not have it right now, please make a special note of this module and ask God to remind you to reflect upon it if you find yourself severely tormented by depression.

Amen.

Discouragement is Displacement

Though I didn't realize it, I lived in a state of discouragement for decades. It was my normal (and to my defeat). But now I recognize it and discern this same heaviness is upon my brothers and sisters. And I'm here to say... it is NOT normal. In fact, it's a place. Moreover, it is being 'displaced' from God's kingdom!

If you are discouraged, I'm not going to tell you the issues of life that have you feeling this way aren't real, but I will tell you that your hope is not in what goes on here. I'm not preaching something I don't practice. Trust me, I still have plenty of aspects of my life that displease me. Things I deeply dislike and wish would change - and even things I want to up and walk away from. I wait on the edge of my seat sometimes for things to finally break forth only to discover it's not going to happen and that I'm still in the same boat, with no end or answer in sight.

It's old, already. And often very painful - especially concerning matters with family members. Things you can't escape, necessarily.

But let me tell you, even in disappointment or pain, I no longer live in discouragement. Because beneath my aspirations for things here in this life, my deepest hope and joy is in my forever tomorrows in Paradise. I have such internal satisfaction in this which outweighs all of my greatest desires for or distresses of this life! Sincerely! And I want to pray that you would decide to dwell in this place, in this kingdom of God place, too.

Heavenly Father, The last thing I wish to do is undermine the pains of this life because they are very real, but I now know that we do not need to be perplexed or forlorn by the temporal things of this life, and I'm asking you to impart this knowing to every member of this program as well. Father, it's in knowing the truth whereby we are free, according to your Word (John 8:32). So, please, impart this truth deeply into this member's soul right now. Without this truth taking hold, we remain devastated at the let-downs of life. Please deliver ODJ Members from the propensity of the heaviness and discouragements of life.

Father, please help every ODJ Member to come into an eternal mindset and to stay there, even as the disappointments of life occur.

But Lord, I also know that sometimes our discouragements are because we get hung up on what we want or need. We want or need something so desperately that life is unbearable if we don't acquire it, and it's all we can think about. Sometimes all we crave is relief from struggle and injustice which is certainly understandable. But we're so desperate for relief or fulfillment that we become devastated and over-run with despair for lack of it. If this is the case, to any degree, even subconsciously, for any ODJ Members, oh God, please help them see that it is idolatry to chase anything - including justice or relief, because it's loving (wanting) something more than you and our eternal hope.

I know it's so easy to idolize and idealize the things of this life. Especially when we have a history of let-downs and hurt. This compels us to chase satiation all the more. But Father, I know now that we must put everything into your hands, rest in you, and trust you with it. Even if it means continuing on the path we dislike, or going without. Especially since you often use these circumstances to refine us as gold. But meanwhile, Father, I ask you to deliver them from the pain and dysfunction of the soul which makes one vulnerable to desperation and idolatry. Show them how to truly rest in you concerning everything. And restore them to a healthful perspective where there's no more need to compensate or fill voids.

Meanwhile, if there are things going on in their lives that you have not authorized or approved, Father, I speak to these matters right now. Father, YOUR will be done for every ODJ Member. Please correct every situation. Please uproot the wrong and make things right. Please send forth the resources and provisions where they have been thwarted, stolen or veiled. Father, whatever you intend, make it so. Deliver your children from evil, I pray.

Thank you so much for being there for us, Father. You are such an amazing God. Now I ask you to fill everyone with this truth and lock it down. Help all ODJ Members come out of the propensity for discouragement but to instead, live in the joy of your kingdom - regardless of the disappointments of this life. In Jesus' Name, Amen.

Now, whatever it is that may be going on, whatever the mess your life may even be in at the moment, the best way to see things come to order and the best way to experience the all that God appoints unto you is to fix your eyes on your eternal hope and rejoice. Even and especially if things are lousy right now. So, please... give the mess to God as well as all that you are longing for right now. Put it into His care... be still... and delight in your future with Him.

"I Know What I Need To Do, But I Can't Seem To Do It!"

Below is an email correspondence with a woman we'll call Vanessa. It's likely you have experienced something very similar, **where you just can't seem to get your game on and do what you know you should**. There's reasons for this. Primarily, it's because something in your soul is still not syncing with truth. This leaves us vulnerable. Please check out how our conversation went:

"Dear Paula,

Thank you so much for the message (Discouragement = Displacement) and prayer. It truly spoke to my heart about my situation. I don't know who else it was for but it was surely for me. I am often disappointed and discouraged and overwhelmed by depression. Your program helped me pinpoint my problem and although I have moments that seem to move me forward I find that they don't last long before I'm struggling again. My home is a wreck and my office is too. I know what I need to do and can't seem to do it. In my despair I often drink alcohol. I stop and then start again. Not moving forward in ministry is a part of my woundedness. It's just so much. Nothing coming to pass. I believe and then I don't really know if I do or not. Lord help my unbelief.

Thank you for being obedient to the Holy Spirit.
Vanessa

Hi Vanessa,

I'm all too familiar with what you shared.

This is a side note to the main point I'd like to convey, but a very prominent one nonetheless. Due to what I've seen in my own history, my children's, other relatives, research and knowing the toxic inundation in our world, I know for a fact that many people are vulnerable and struggling as you have described, some even more severely with major mental health issues and/or disease. The majority of the vulnerable people just aren't feeling well, can't think straight or stay on top of their responsibilities or missions as well as they want to. And many need to self-medicate (alcohol, cigarettes, drugs, etc.).

However... Your struggle with depression, alcohol and functioning will heal as your soul prospers in truth - just as mine did. It's all a part of the same kingdom of God package where, the more you come into His kingdom truths, the more you reap and experience God's manifest reality. Everything about you and your life prospers. And that's where you're heading even as we speak.

For this moment, the reason you're going back and forth with the alcohol is (in addition to toxic inundation impacting your body's chemistry and balance) **your soul is not fully connected with the Father or His love; or there's something out of sync with Him and His truth.** *So you're still desperate to rely on carnal remedies and substitutes such as alcohol.*

What you need to do is find out what's causing the wall in your soul that is between you and God. *This disconnect leaves you feeling desperate for satiation through other things. I assure you, however, that once the issue(s) of your soul are rectified and the wall(s) are torn down, and the connection to Father God and His love and goodness is fully made, alcohol will not have the upper hand. Even if you have a chemical or hormonal imbalance from toxic inundation or some other reason which compels you to self-medicate, this will be healed as your soul prospers. Just as my health improved as my soul prospered! Your body will be* *forced to submit to the well-being of the kingdom of God and not remain vulnerable to the toxicity of the world. Consequently, you'll no longer be desperately compelled for alcohol or anything else - but God. Because you'll be whole and prospering in every way.*

*In the meantime, **don't sweat the failures**. Do your best but don't take on dread over the mistakes and beat yourself up over them, because that feeds defeat. Focus on the wonder of Christ, your future with Him even if and **especially** if you mess up. Be free to rejoice in the One Who Is Perfect despite your troubles and failures. Don't be so disheartened for having not moved forward previously, because that's what's holding you back, too. What's done is done. Just be thankful for God's grace and forgiveness and rest in His love. I'm not saying to take His forgiveness for granted and be careless about sin. Just be sure to always rejoice over God's love for you even when you sin! Doing this is life changing! Trust me, I know!*

Sure, you have moments of pain that you have to process where you won't be doing cartwheels for Jesus, but otherwise, spend your time making every effort to give thanks, resist heaviness, negativity, etc., even if you mess up! These are what's holding you down. These are dark kingdom living. Leave the dark kingdom, Vanessa, by embracing your freedom in Christ. Rejoice no matter what.

*And finally, **you said one minute you believe and the next you aren't really sure that you do**. This confirms that this is an issue of the soul. Ask God to rectify this - to show you why you go back and forth between belief and doubt. Ask Him to **expose what's hidden** deep inside so that you can get rid of all doubts once and for all. This instability is interfering with the manifest power and presence of God in your life and must be addressed.*

Blessings,
Paula Cross

Anger: Purging Toxic Emotions

Anger is a normal part of life, but it seems Christians often feel it's an abomination to feel it. All the more if we find ourselves spewing rage from a seemingly endless pit. Such was the case with a woman we'll call Sue. Please read our correspondence discussing her struggle with anger and rage:

"Paula,

I continue to struggle with rage and anger... I've been crying all day.... I had a hallucination of a massive venting pipe in my bedroom. It was huge!!! So I do what I always do, searched the word "vent" in the bible and it led me to Job 10.... It is exactly how I feel... except Job wasn't as sinful as me .. I even thought yesterday if I could have sewn up the womb of my mother to prevent me from being birthed I would have. As I am saying this I recall a coworker speaking to me these words "if I had your life I think I would crawl back into my mother's womb" and I just laughed and agreed with him in my spirit..... it's funny that that comes to my mind. I was in my 30s then... Job 10 is how I feel. Not sure what I'm supposed to do with this emotion.

~Sue"

"Dear Sue,

There's so much going on in you right now. Your soul is clearly loaded (overloaded) with toxic emotions and since you're connecting / aligning with God's reality more and more, **these toxins are stirred up and being addressed by the Spirit of Christ in you.** They are reacting to the increased presence of truth and glory that's begun taking over your soul. As the good of Christ in you prospers, the toxic emotions/memories are being forced out. They cannot remain.

What you are going through now is a process (obviously). All the anger and rage, hurt and violations that have been buried are being excommunicated from your soul. Again, as Christ increases in your soul, your anti-christ programming of self-loathing and all else is being purged so the correct programming can take its place.

(This is overstating the obvious, but) let it out and let it go. Cry and scream for the pain that it all was, telling the violations and assaults that the redemptive power of Christ has rescued you, thanking God for His love that you are finally coming to relate to in a real way, praising God that though this life hurts, greater is HE that is in you than all the hurts in the world combined, and praise Him that someday we'll all be with Him in paradise where there will no longer be hurts.

ALSO REPENT for questioning and loathing God's sovereignty over your life. Tell Him to do whatever it takes to change your perspective about how you have been seeing things, including despising the day you were born. I know Job was venting and this is what you are doing, which God understands, but it also is a matter of rebellion to loathe your birth, as this is challenging the Author of life and all things.

Look how despite God saying Job's three accusers were the ones he was displeased with, God seriously rebukes Job for questioning His sovereignty (Job 38-41). So, though God certainly understands all your venting and the course of defeat your soul took, as well as your hatred for it, it is time to repent and humble yourself to the sovereignty of God over your life.

Doing all this will let the LIGHT take over your soul once and for all. And the day will come where this rage won't exist in you. Of course, it won't all come out at once. Remember, as more of God and truth goes in, it uncovers and stirs the toxic emotions/memories. Right now, it may be a HUGE chunk that's being vented out / forced out of your soul by God's reality taking over. But it's not all of it. So, down the road you'll have other venting sessions. But they'll decrease in intensity, you'll be quicker to release and process them out, and you certainly will be far less disturbed with what's coming out now that you realize what's going on.

Does this make sense?

~Paula"

"Paula,

YES it makes so much sense to me... Thank you for responding to me, I so needed to hear these words of life and truth. I feel that the Lord is wanting me to let go of a lot that is inside. <u>That I have never allowed myself to be angry</u>. I also feel that although I can be angry and let it out, I feel that the Holy Spirit is saying to choose to Love and to choose to let TRUTH in my life. <u>It's been a lifetime of believing lies and not allowed to feel or voice anger towards all the injustice</u>. I keep asking the Lord about Justice. What is it, what does it look like? And I was pondering this today. Am I angry that there was no Justice? No one paid for what was done and is still being done. And I thought to myself would I want my enemies to go through what they put me through? And I decided I would not want to hurt anyone that way. I feel I'm so immature in seeing the real enemy!!! That Satan is behind this attack on my life..."

~Sue

"Sue,

Wow, you really are making progress! Identifying that you have never allowed yourself to be angry is a HUGE step in the prosperity of your soul!"

Okay, let's look closer at what's going on:

1.   Sue was perplexed because of all the anger and rage surfacing. Experiencing the purging of toxic emotions can make you feel like something's wrong with you. But this is normal. It's no different than when someone gets food poisoning and they vomit it out. Better out than in, but not so pleasant a process, unfortunately. So, the first thing Sue hopefully realized was she didn't need to fear that she was regressing or off on an emotional sin tangent.

2. The second thing Sue hopefully realized was the reason she was in that state of temporary emotional chaos. Though this isn't always the case, I knew that Sue had been working diligently with the Lord, seeking Him and meditating for two months on the truths taught in this program. Having experienced this myself and with the help of the Holy Spirit, I instantly recognized this was a purging of toxic emotions. So, if you have a history of repressed hurt and anger, despite being emotionally sound on the norm, don't be surprised that the more you press in to truth, the more it will take over your soul and force the toxins out.

3. We see that Sue realizes her propensity to not allow herself to feel angry. This is a classic strategy of the dark kingdom. Genuine Christians are often extremely sensitive about doing wrong, especially concerning areas of the heart. So, being angry seems like a sin when you're in the heat of it. It feels like you're the one doing something wrong. How we handle our anger is often sinful, so it's easy to mix everything up and feel guilty for simply being angry. The dark kingdom knows this all too well and plays on it, taunting sensitive believers, driving them into guilt for having legitimate angst

283

concerning something. It's an easy way to tangle a believer up, which hinders their confidence in Christ. But the truth is Ephesians 4:26 says, "Be ye angry, and sin not: let not the sun go down upon your wrath". Anger is allowed. So, it's important to not allow the enemy to make us feel guilty for being angry anymore.

4. We see Sue questioning if part of the reason for her anger is injustice. Clearly, this is always a part of things. She goes on to question if, in her anger for the lack of justice, if she would do likewise to her offenders, to which she said no. So, this shows that Sue is not harboring unforgiveness or resentment. It shows she is simply and rightfully angry over the wrong being done. She is angry just as Ephesians 4:26 permits, but not unforgiving, bitter, or full of vengeance. It's possible she has had moments of feeling these, but ultimately, Sue chooses the way of the kingdom of God. Therefore, she will surely see justice. Not because she is chasing it; but because it's God's way. Let me share that there have been three different people on three very different occasions who wickedly lied about me to the judge/magistrate presiding over court cases I was involved in. Two of them ended up dying very tragic, horrific deaths that I would not wish on my worst enemy. I'd even prayed God would forgive them for what they'd done years before either of them faced death. I'm not saying God did it. I honestly don't know what to make of it. I'm just sharing what happened. Wicked people that do not get off their wicked paths will sadly see horror - if not in this life, the next.

5. We see that God revealed how, despite the legitimacy of Sue's anger, her turning it against herself and loathing the very ordination of her life is a form of rebellion. It's a lack of submission to the sovereignty of God. If we presume to curse anything God does, this is inadvertently coming against Him and is wrong. Though it is understandable to feel the pain over what's happening, it is still wrong to rise up in contempt against anything God does, including placing you in this world.

If you have repressed anger, it will eventually need to come out. In fact, like I told Sue, the deeper into truth you go, the more truth you digest, the more the buried anger will be forced out. So, here's a breakdown (mentioned above) of what you can do to overcome and be sure to move forward in your journey in Christ:

- Let it out and let it go
- Cry and scream for the pain that it all was
- Tell the violations and assaults that the redemptive power of Christ has rescued you
- Thank God for His love that you are beginning to relate to in a real way
- Praise God that though this life hurts, greater is HE that is in you than all the hurts in the world combined
- Praise God that someday we'll all be with Him in paradise where there will no longer be any hurts
- Repent for challenging or daring to curse God's sovereign will for you to be born (if applicable)

Amen.

Anger & Rage: Vomiting Toxic Emotions Part II

Below are the final portions of the discussion I had with Sue concerning her struggle with anger and rage. Please note that my replies are in *italics*:

Dear Paula,

Thank you. I have been a very passive person... all my life I was never allowed to speak about what was physically and mentally done to me as a child and I continued this 'silence lie' all my life into my senior years. *This is why the purging is so intense. It's decades of repressed toxins.*

In the midst of my 2nd breakdown, it was so bad I was in a fetal position on my bed having flashbacks of me sucking my thumb. I was in such a bad way, I cried out to God and said "what do you want me to do?" I heard the Holy Spirit say almost in a command "I want you to get up and DANCE!!!!".... so I took my half dead soul and danced with the Lord in a very slow dance. The very next morning, my doorbell rang . It was a co-worker / friend of mine. She said to me I don't know why I bought you this but here. She handed me a book with a CD in it. It was the song "I hope you dance. I'd like to say I was cured after. *You weren't cured, you have been going through a process.* **But I am in my 3rd mental breakdown.** *This is not a mental breakdown, <u>it's a purging</u>. When you are vomiting, the body is eliminating bad stuff at which time you may have a fever, be weak, feel awful, but the vomiting and fever are indicators of the healing process going on. Yet, despite the healing that is going on, you may feel like you're dying. That's what's going on with you. First, your chemistry is undergoing a major overhaul. That alone can make you feel like you are dying or want to be dead. But as you know, you* *are going through a major emotional, mental and spiritual overhaul, too. You have been gobbling up mega spiritual truths, taking holy medicine for months if not years now, so all the emotional, mental and spiritual toxins are flying all over the place being purged. You're essentially buckled over the toilet right now, spewing it all out. That's not a mental breakdown, it's a healing process. As the vomit comes out, it feels like a position of weakness, defeat and vulnerability, but it's a part of the healing.*

It is the worst darkness ever. *It's the worst darkness because you've taken tons of medicine. You've taken in so much TRUTH that all the FALSE LIES are spastic in you. Everything is crazy in you at the moment. And all your old belief systems, all the pain, all the feelings you experienced ten, twenty, thirty, forty and fifty years ago and everything in between are all coming up and out. The thing is as you feel these old feelings, they feel real right now, even though you know the truth concerning them. Even if you have forgiven, etc. Because you repressed the feelings and never processed them, they are all coming up demanding to be PROCESSED at once. This includes all the anger. I mean, we're talking decades of experiences that made you legitimately angry - which you shoved down. It all needs to be processed. That's why I said to:*

- *Let it out and let it go*
- *Cry and scream for the pain that it all was*
- *Tell the violations and assaults that the redemptive power of Christ has rescued you*
- *Thank God for His love that you are beginning to relate to in a real way*
- *Praise God that though this life hurts, greater is HE that is in you than all the hurts in the world combined*
- *Praise God that someday we'll all be with Him in paradise where there will no longer be any hurts*
- *Repent for challenging or daring to curse God's sovereign will for you to be born (if applicable)*

Doing this is processing it out and getting past it. There may be a bit more to it than that, God may address specific things more intricately. But this is the overall way to process out the toxins. But remember, you have tons of it coming up just like if you were over the toilet vomiting. You throw up some, then later more, then later more, etc. That's what's happening with you - mentally, emotionally, spiritually and chemically. It's a lot. It's not a mental breakdown. It's a purging.

This is where the passivity comes in , I forget who I am in Christ. I forget that I have authority in Jesus' name. I have come to know that there is a time where passivity must die and we are to rise up in what Jesus blood did for us. He has made us all Commanders of His Word... we must take an active stance...Paula I know this truth but to get there is as far as A is from Z.... *When you are vomiting, you're in a healing process. There's a time for everything. Yes, the authority is in you, <u>but right now the authority is cleaning you out.</u> So you aren't going to be focused on commanding this or that, you are too busy having stuff purged out. Don't be disturbed with where you are in the process. I know you think you "should" be at Z right now, but you must go through the process to get there - without berating yourself for where you are. It's okay. I used to be where you are, feeling I would never get to Z. Well, I may not be at Z yet; perhaps V, perhaps S, perhaps Y. All I know is I did move drastically forward and you are too. It just doesn't feel like it while your head is stuck over the toilet.*

I spiritually feel I'm in a body cast.. unable to move or speak! Have you ever seen someone dance in a body cast??? *I hear you, I know what you are saying. But part of the "power" of the body cast is due to the wrong belief systems still in the soul. What will happen is as the truth solidifies, the power of God will lift you out of the body cast. Indeed, sometimes it is a matter of getting up "in" the body cast to dance, as you* *once did. See, there's a lot going on, many variables to the process. Rising up in your lack of strength is sometimes one of those variables, one part, one key to overcoming. Tapping in to His authority and commanding is another. There is a different time for that. But the greatest key or variable... is KNOWING THE TRUTH. This is what makes us free. Sometimes, though, while we are in the process of healing and transformation, when the truth is trying to take root and is pushing out the toxins, we have to make the effort to rise up and dance and praise the Lord to let God manifest.*

But I just might go ahead and do it. ...I'll call it the "you can't hold me down" dance... as I move like Frankenstein throughout my house. Lol... for some reason I just saw in a vision of Lazareth coming out of the tomb. And the Lord saying loose him from his grave clothes... What amazing truth. ~Sue.

To my replies in italics, Sue responded:

Wow your words 'it's not a mental breakdown but a healing process' was like a truth awakening. I never thought of it as such. And your repetitive use of the word "vomit" instantly brought back a vision I had at 23 years ago of being chased by Satan down this hallway with all these doors. In the vision I was running and then stopped abruptly and my mouth opened really wide and I started throwing up petrified vomit that had been there for years.... I was pulling it out helping it out with my hands, it had to have been a few feet wide and solid.... is that not just the wildest of things to remember so very long ago? ~Sue.

OMG, do you see it? God has been walking you out of the dominion of darkness for DECADES. He showed you 23 years ago the process you'd be undergoing. You are living what you saw 23 years ago. Now pull it out - all of it - all of the petrified vomit. Pull it out!

Wow, eh, now that's a process!!!!! That is 35 years of process!

YES! See it for what it is - which is part of the END of the process!

If you were here I would give you a big hug... lol... this is huge for me, really huge... great revelations!!!! Thank you!!! ~Sue.

This correspondence with Sue concerning the purging of her toxic emotions may be an extreme situation, but the Lord has impressed upon my heart that it's quite common in the body of Christ. To one degree or another, God's people have repressed emotions and when they come up, they think they're failing or, as in Sue's case, having a mental breakdown - or a minor version of one. But, as we saw with Sue, the more we chase God's truths and embrace them, the more the pain, anger and lies in our souls must be purged. This may occur subtly, or, like Sue, violently. For most, somewhere in between. And though it feels like a defeat or breakdown in severe cases, it's not. It really is just part of the transformation of the soul. It's a purging of what does not belong in there. And it's ugly. But not to our defeat.

The point in sharing this is to ask you to please be aware that as you align more deeply with truth, do expect garbage to come out of you and don't be alarmed at your ugliness. Sue was quite disturbed at her anger. She felt terrible for this and thought something was wrong with her. But that's not the case. It was all old stuff coming up and out.

The other thing to remember is anger is normal. Sue needed to learn it's okay to be angry. Of course, when there's so much that you're enraged and you're acting like a monster because it's spewing up and out, you feel like a mega sin ball. But that's simply not the case unless you allow the anger to drive you to pride, vengeance and unforgiveness.

Have you ever heard about the detoxification process? How, for example, if you had a history of bronchitis or sore throats, during a detox regimen (pending how deeply you go into it), you might get bronchitis or a sore throat. But, you aren't actually "getting" these illnesses. It's old remnants of previous infections being pulled from the molecular level, up and out. During the process of it coming out, your body acts and feels exactly as if you developed a whole new infection. And it's the same with whatever is deep in your molecular system. All the old garbage will come up and out and you'll experience it as though it's a fresh illness. But it isn't.

This is what was going on with Sue. Though her detox was initiated via the impartation of truth into the soul, it caused a detox just the same. So all the repressed anger, pain, lies and so forth are being kicked out. She, therefore, went through the emotions and distress of the "sickness" as though these were brand new hurts coming on her all at one time. That's why it was so severe of a purging.

What I've seen more commonly, though, is the process is less severe. In her vision, Sue was pulling out tons of petrified toxic emotions all at once. That's a mega purging. But more often than not, it's a situation of "bouts of anger" that can't be explained. Sudden sadness or remembrance of something that happened forty years ago, etc. The point is, there's all sorts of things deep down in the soul that are contrary to truth, contrary to security in God, contrary to God's love. And they have to come out somehow. And aligning with truth forces them out.

On another note (this does not pertain to toxic emotions, rather sin) but sometimes you'll dream of being sinful in ways you would never act out in real life. This happened to me a lot during my soul transformation. I'd have dreams where I woke up shocked at what I did, saying, "God, why did I dream I did that! I'd never do that in real life!" And He said, *"Yes you do, only to a much, much smaller degree. I'm showing you the sin in your soul, the pride, the lies you appeal to by letting you see yourself act them*

291

out in extreme ways." I was stunned. I understood what He was saying right away. I did do those things in far more subtle ways. FAR more subtle. So subtly that I didn't even realize the sin. Seeing the exaggeration made me see it. And I've heard others share, "I asked the Lord to show me what I need to work on and I had this dream where I did such and such, it was HORRIBLE. I would NEVER do that! Why did I dream such a thing?" And I explained that it's an exaggeration of what they actually do.

The point of my sharing is that because we were pursuing God and truth more deeply, God revealed the toxicity of particular sins we had in our soul via our dreams because it was time for those toxins to be purged. Though different from toxic emotions, a purging is just the same. Consequently, I venture to say that a person with a history of habitual sin will feel like they are being tempted afresh in that area during a purging of their soul. What I mean is as you align more with truth, the sin that you've overcome might have remnants deep in the molecular level of your soul (so to speak) and during your soul's transformation, these remnants may surface and cause you to feel the temptation as though it were a new, fresh temptation so we feel like we've regressed. After all the time that has passed where this sin was "gone", now that it suddenly appears out of nowhere again, tormenting you, beckoning you to go back to it, you may feel it's hopeless or that you didn't truly overcome it. But in the case of soul transformation, I venture to say it's just a purging and don't be distressed. Just treat it the same as a fresh temptation. Resist it, tell it no, and kick it out.

All this to say... just please be aware that the closer you get to God means the sin, lies, anger and pain in you will indeed come up and out. And it won't be pretty. If you keep this in mind, you can make reference to the bullet points above and follow them in order to process the garbage out properly and completely. And you won't have to be so disturbed because now you understand... it's just the process of the purging. Amen.

Guilt Over the Lack of Discipline

The following is my reply to an ODJ member (I'll call her Kelly) who was concerned she had blasphemed the Holy Spirit. There have actually been others in the past that reached out to me who thought they, too, had blasphemed the Holy Spirit. The devil seems to do well binding believers up by convincing them they committed the unpardonable sin.

Dear Kelly,

I asked the Lord to give me wisdom and insight, and then re-read your summation. The most prominent impression I have from God is He is saying the disgust you have with yourself for not being disciplined concerning reading the Bible and praying is an agreement with a lie, not truth. The dark systems that are in place in your life are good at laying guilt trips on you, making you feel guilty where you don't need to - where it's actually wrong to do so.

God has been speaking to my heart for quite some time that He is grieved how His children spend so much time being bogged down feeling horrible because of how little they read the Word or pray, etc. Yet, there is no prescribed mandate as to how much we are to read the Bible. True, we cannot become familiar with God's truth without consuming it's truth one way or another. And true, a genuine disciple (Christian) is a student of the Word. But this doesn't mean following a schedule or that reading the Bible everyday is a requirement. Every person is different. We all have our own way of being with God.

Jesus said our work is to "believe", John 6:29. Believing is faith - and faith comes by hearing the Word. So, listening to people teach the Word is "hearing the Word". And yes, reading the Word is another way of hearing it. But the point is there's all kinds of ways to get to know the truth. And yes, when we are free in Christ, we will want to consume His Word out of hunger. But the thing is God NEVER placed this yoke upon His people. Not in the way we wear it, at least. No, it's a spirit of religion that's been put around people's necks and it's adding to the defeat, not the deliverance.

Am I saying to not read the Bible? No. I'm saying get rid of the false yoke. Get rid of the spirit of religion. Stop allowing the traditions of man to tell you how to be one with God. Be free. Know that God will inspire you to read what He wants you to read when He wants you to read it. Or He'll send you to a teaching video or a sermon or a blog or an article or whatever - to speak His Word to you. Right now I'm speaking the "Word" to you, as you know. Somebody in passing might just say or do something that conveys a truth from the Word that God wants you to hear. There's all sorts of ways God reveals His Word. Why do we have this protocol that leaves us feeling guilty if we aren't disciplined Bible readers? It's wrong. It's of the dark kingdom!

Think about it...When Jesus went to the synagogue to read the Word, it was a few lines and that was it! In fact, if you research it, you'll discover it took THREE YEARS to get through all of the scrolls (Torah/Old Testament) by how they divided up the weekly readings! And back then, you know they didn't have their own copies at home that they were required to read all week. So if Jesus didn't "read the Word" at home, why is it an unspoken requirement?

As for praying, the Bible tells us to pray without ceasing (1 Thessalonians 5:17). In other words, we are to live in a state of prayer. Always mindful of God and deferring to Him. Always bringing Him into the matter. Always praising Him. Lifting people up to Him as we go along and He places them on our hearts.

Surely, God didn't mean we would or even could pray in the sense of literally speaking to God 24/7, such as in the middle of a presentation at work on scuba diving, or something. It's rather difficult to carry on two conversations at once. So, what does it mean to be praying without ceasing even while doing a presentation on scuba diving? To me it means to be in a place - a state of condition in my innermost being. Though my carnal, earth person is discussing scuba diving, my spirit is prostrate before God at His throne. No, I'm not thinking about it. But it's a state of condition.

For example, I just now ran upstairs to take my probiotics. As I jumped up from my seat, without thinking, I found myself praising God, loving Him, just reacting to how great He is. As I went up the steps, I had a very quick impression that my spirit was at His feet in paradise. And that's when it hit me that this must be connected to the whole praying without ceasing. Because the moment my mind stopped working on this writing, and even though it was on getting the probiotics, my spirit was subconsciously, actively communing with God. This is what I experience on a regular basis now that I've overcome darkness. As soon as my cognitive assertions stop, I'm in this place of communion with the Lord. It's not a cognitive assertion, rather, it's a river flowing up and out as soon as my carnal mind is out of the way. It happens in my sleep, when I'm waking, when I get up to go to the restroom, when I'm leaving a store, etc. Whenever my mind is not focused on something, I'm in this place. At which time, I don't just praise God, I'll pray, too. But since this comes out of me without cognitively going there, this means my spirit is already doing it.

So, that's what I personally believe praying without ceasing means. It's our spirit being in constant communion (prayer) with God. If when your mind stops focusing on a matter at hand, what comes up out of you? Or, where do you go? What place are you in? This reveals if you are praying without ceasing. ~ By the way, I used to be in a very empty, distant place because, though I was a very active Christian and loved God, I was disconnected from Him at my core (for numerous reasons) which means despite praying a lot through the day and night, I really wasn't praying without ceasing. I would pray, then cease to wander the desert, then pray, then wander, then pray, etc. It's no wonder I was so defeated.

Anyway, think about how the Bible points out that Jesus would go off to pray. Note that it never said He had a system, a scheduled time, that He always prayed early in the morning or anything like that. No, the emphasis was He went off at different times. The point being He got alone with the Father when there was something He wanted to pray about. It wasn't a routine. It was out of the compelling of His heart.

Kelly, you are disturbed with yourself because you aren't "disciplined" with these Christian practices. But did Jesus go off to pray out of discipline? Not at all! He went off out of desire or necessity.

I hope you see more now that these perceptions the Church has taken on are not from God. They are just a way for the enemy to make us feel defeated. So what you need to do, Kelly, is to shed this false yoke.

Our embracing this religious yoke is submitting to a dark kingdom policy. It's the dark kingdom that says we need to discipline ourselves to reading and praying in a "disciplined" fashion. When we agree to this notion, then that spirit makes us feel heavy and defeated...and disgusted with ourselves. I'm not going to say discipline is a bad thing. But the idea of reading the Bible or praying "as a discipline" is - at least for the most part. Because it's a program, ritual, and quite possibly legalistic if it does not also include compelling desire. If someone is systematic in these practices, this is wonderful so long as it's from the belly. Don't get me wrong. Sometimes we read the Word or pray when we don't feel like it because we are sowing to the Spirit and not the flesh. But don't confuse this with discipline.

For those who just don't operate in such a disciplined, routine fashion who are heavily ladened over it, the Lord is grieved that we have fallen for this invasive ideal. He's heartbroken seeing us this way, God never put this mandate upon us! It hurts Him especially when we just want to give up because we concede that we will simply never get it right and "be disciplined" - such as what happened when you thought you blasphemed the Holy Spirit by telling Him to not speak to you about praying and reading the Word anymore.

Now about that and how you heard "cut off, no remedy" after you told the Holy Spirit to not bother you about these anymore. It wasn't God saying that! It was a demon. See, because you had already agreed with and submitted (as so many of us have) to the false teaching that you should be reading and praying in a disciplined fashion, the spirits were able to make you feel heavier and heavier, and more and more disgusted with yourself to which you finally SUPER yielded to their suggestion to just give up and told Holy Spirit to leave you alone about it. When you went that far into their territory, you could hear them more vividly in their saying, "cut off, no remedy", pretending to be the Lord. (Do you see... the more attuned and in agreement you are with either the kingdom of God or the dark kingdom, the more clearly you hear that particular kingdom in the moment?)

Grrrrrr! The enemy and his systems are quite clever and they got you good, there. I'm telling you, that wasn't God. The proof is that hearing that did not help you or God's kingdom. When God scolds or disciplines us, it doesn't feel dark. One time God scolded me and then I went through a season of discipline which was extremely difficult. But it did not feel dark. It felt tough, but not dark. There's a difference.

Kelly, you need to reject and renounce this spirit of religion. I'm telling you the truth - there's no mandate to be a disciplined prayer or reader of the Word. Get rid of this spirit, don't believe this lie any longer. Be free.

And you'll find in your freedom that you'll gravitate naturally to the place where you'll read and pray far more. Not as a routine, unless that happens naturally or via the unction of the Holy Spirit for you.

The thing is - when you're free and you naturally start your day in a right spirit of freedom, joy, security, and submission to the Lord, with your spirit in the right place in constant communion with Him, you'll BE LED! You know the Bible says God guides our steps - but we must be "in" Him. Right now, He can't guide your steps very well when you're so focused on what the devil is telling you. See how that works?

And realize... God'll lead you to read the Bible one time, but you'll come upon an article another, or a teaching, or a sermon, a song, etc. GOD will often put the manna right in front of you because you're in that "place" where He can reach you! YOUR job is to believe and be submitted. When He leads you, for the most part you're going to follow His lead with zeal, because God is cool like that. He woos us. He draws us. Simultaneously, you'll get the desire to study something in the Bible or whatever the case may be. You may even find yourself getting up every night a 2:00 a.m. with this notion to read the Bible and pray for a week or two. But does this mean "Oh, God must want me to do this permanently!" No! He was just working with you on the points He wanted to get to you and happened to choose 2:00 a.m. to do it for a while. After two weeks of that, He may lead you to a specific teacher or something to listen to. You might spend ten hours a day listening to teachers for the week after that. Then after that maybe you'll catch wind of a Christian blogger that you read a bit every day because God wants you to know what He's speaking through them. And so on. Why do we have to be so gullible to the liar and let him lock us up in chains of religion? Why can't we just be okay with resting in God, trusting Him, and letting Him lead the way?

So do you see it clearly? That this religious spirit is a huge problem in the Church? Get rid of it. Be free to love God and let Him lead you as He so desires. And when you do, you might just see your joy return. I'm not sure what other unresolved issues may be in your soul. You shared about your family history so there's plenty that still needs sorted out. But getting rid of this religious spirit is top priority for the moment. The Lord is done seeing you bogged down in this defeat and it putting such a huge wedge between you and Him. Get rid of it.

Hope this helped!

Blessings,
Paula Cross

Broken Wires Disconnect Us From God

Someone named "Dorian" recently reached out to me concerning deliverance, wondering why it never works for her. The short answer is you can have demons cast out of you all day but if your soul has a short (is disconnected from God through lack of confidence, security or trust in Him), then the demons can stay or come right back.

But that's not all I have to say concerning deliverance. I've discovered I'm rather isolated in my perspective concerning what true deliverance really is...

Dear Paula,

Does deliverance work? I've gotten several of them but they don't seem to work. Can you help me?

~Dorian

Dear Dorian,

In my opinion, "deliverance" is a man made doctrine that, though based on truth, isn't directly in the Bible. Jesus is our deliverance. Rather, faith in Jesus is our deliverance. The need for elders to pray for the sick (James 5:14) is because sometimes people young in the faith need the mature in faith to help them. We also know the Bible tells us that Jesus "cast out demons". So these are where the idea of deliverance comes. Obviously, the foundation of the deliverance doctrine is scriptural. But this doctrine has taken on a life of its own, having somewhat of a greater emphasis than faith in Jesus alone.

Think about all the times Jesus said to people, "Oh wow, I haven't seen so much faith as this! Your faith has healed you!" Therein is the purest deliverance. These people just believed. They knew connecting with Jesus was the answer. Period. No need for elders. No need for Jesus to go to their house to cast out a demon. All they wanted was His Word and they knew it was done. Not out of a religious perspective, but out of their bellies. They knew His Word was good enough.

Well, we have that Word. It is done for us. Everything we need - is done. But our faith isn't solid. (For many reasons.) So... we seek help via the deliverance doctrine - for others to pray for us, cast demons out, etc. Which yes, is a legitimate recourse since the Lord knew we would struggle with our faith. And yes, it does work, but only by faith, too. AND when there aren't holes in the soul where the enemy still has control, whereby he sabotages the person's faith and reception of the truth.

I hope this helps,
~Paula Cross

Dear Paula,

What are the holes? Are they doors? Something followed me at the hospital to nursing from my home.

~Dorian

Dear Dorian,

By "holes" I mean issues in your soul. For example, if a person is mistreated/abused or perhaps has "bad luck" throughout their life, they learn to not trust anyone, including God. Yet, when they come to Jesus, as much as they want to or think they trust the Mighty King, deep, deep down in their soul, they don't. Maybe they believe and trust Him at the surface when nothing is going wrong. But not when the going gets tough. So, this is a problem (a hole or broken wire) in their soul which disconnects them from God's goodness, power, authority, and provisions. He has the answer, healing, deliverance or provision right there for them, but they cannot lay hold of it because of this hole or broken wire in their soul, where they deep down do not trust God.

It's no different from an electric toaster that you plug in to an outlet, if the cord has a short in it or broken wire, the toaster will not work. You are the toaster. Your soul is the cord. The outlet power source is God. You are plugged into God because you received Him as Lord and Savior, but you have a short or broken wire in your soul / cord because you don't trust God - because of all the abuse or let-downs you endured. So, to get the toaster to receive the power to function, it has to be fixed and get rid of the short in the cord / soul.

Not truly trusting God is just one example of what could be wrong in your soul. You need to ask God where or what the broken wire or "hole" is in your soul that's keeping you from connecting to the goodness He has for you that's literally right there at your finger tips. He has already provided your answer, provision, help, healing and power over the devil. You just need to connect to it. But you have to ask Him what is wrong in your soul, which wire is broken, that is preventing you from connecting to and experiencing Him fully.

Blessings,
~Paula Cross

Dear Paula,

How do they enter me, how they can manipulate my muscle, mouth and nose head etc. How do I stop them from doing this every single night, tormenting me internally and externally?

~Dorian

Dear Dorian,

Do you believe Father God loves you? Do you believe Jesus adores you? Do you see Him smiling at you because you are so precious? Does your heart melt with thinking about how tender and beautiful our Lord is?

If not, these are holes in your soul. If you are a toaster, your cord is not working even though you are plugged into God. This is why the demons can torment you.

Find out what is causing the disconnect from God's power. And when the enemy tries to torment you, praise God, focus on Jesus smiling at you, etc. Fix the cord (your connection to God) and the demons won't get away with it any more.

~Paula Cross

(Meanwhile, I had been praying for Dorian, too.)

Dear Paula,

Yes to your question. I learned He smiles at me now. You are so sweet, thank you! I will ponder it and receive it in my heart. Bless you, be blessed, thank you sister.

~Dorian

So we can see that Dorian simply hadn't yet recognized the power of God to halt the torment for whatever reason - be it an issue and disconnect in her soul, a lack of knowing or confidence in God's power, etc. Hopefully now she has moved forward in the truth and has dealt with the nightly torment successfully.

Meanwhile, I want to add that I'm not opposed to the deliverance doctrine because that was Christ's primary goal - to rescue us. But I have learned first-hand that the REAL, COMPLETE deliverance is fully knowing, connecting and aligning with truth. Whenever we are unaware of truth, we are vulnerable to the lies and power of the enemy. Not because it is as great as God's, but because our ignorance makes us easy to deceive.

So please understand... Deliverance is knowing truth. The enemy has no power over those who are rooted and grounded and established in the faith (Colossians 2:7) who KNOW TRUTH. None. Jesus said, "If you continue in my Word, then you are my disciples. And you shall know the truth and the truth shall set you free." He didn't say partially free so that you'll need a deliverance minister or demons cast out. No. Totally free. We have the ability to be completely free in and of ourselves just by learning the truth.

Unfortunately, the truth has been so diluted, mis-represented, and misconstrued (via the infiltration of darkness), that the body of Christ has minimal understanding of it. I cannot even count how many things I learned through corporate Church beliefs where God said, "I never said that" or "That's not what I meant". The enemy has infiltrated God's truth and twisted it all up all sorts of ways across the board. So that's why the body of Christ is discombobulated and powerless for the most part. But not for long.

Because of this, yes, there are times we all must reach out for help. In fact, that's what God made elders, teachers, and prophets for. To edify the body of Christ - teaching and helping them in the truth. Consequently, demons need to be cast out. Many prophets, teachers and ministers have been hi-jacked as well, unfortunately. But God's on the move, straightening things out aggressively. Those who do not heed Him will be in serious trouble. Meanwhile, yes, the mess we are in has forced people to desperately seek deliverance. Which is fine. But always remember that the greatest full-spectrum deliverance which cannot ever be undone - *is knowing the truth*.

If you're still struggling with things (sin, oppression, not seeing God prevail in your life, not experiencing His promises) then ask God where the disconnect is between you and Him. Ask Him to reveal if you have unbelief, doubt, lack of trust, feel distant from His love, etc. He'll show you exactly what's going. And ask Him to teach you more of His Word. Ask Him for this daily. This doesn't mean you have to fight to read the Bible on some strict schedule, mind you. He'll lead you and He'll provide the lessons He has for you because you SOUGHT Him for it. Amen.

Repentance is Realignment to God's Kingdom
And All His Plans for Us!
~God's Grace Truly Is Sufficient

God recently reinforced a truth to me that repentance is all that's required to re-align with Him, all His goodness, all His benefits, all His power, and even all the amazing plans He has for us!

Let's face it, we all mess up.

Some time ago, I had purposed in my heart to give a donation to the orphanage we support as we're able. But something came up and I decided to put the funds towards that instead. Within a week, I knew I'd sinned by backing out on what I had purposed in my heart when I found out that other sponsors of the orphanage hadn't donated either, and that all the children and widows had to eat all week was maize.

Now, because I had sinned, I began to go into a type of spiritual defeat thinking my sin messed everything up, namely, the business I started by using the funds that were supposed to go to the orphans. This situation exposed an area in my soul that was not yet aligned with truth.

In previous decades, my soul perceived that how things go was indicative of my actions, that I'd get what I deserved if I sinned. Despite being born again in 1988 whereby God's grace changes all that, my soul wasn't affiliated with that reality. This false outlook was a disconnect with God and His kingdom which, therefore, gave the devil a platform.

At the time of this mess-up, God had already been in the process of teaching me that His wonderful will, plans and blessings for us aren't based on whether we're worthy or deserve them, but because of who He is and because He loves us so very, very much! It's true that obedience to God connects us to all that He is and Has for us. Just read the book of Deuteronomy. Meanwhile, abandoning God through blatant disobedience is stepping out of the kingdom of God reality and all its benefits. (Again, read Deuteronomy.) This was what I had done - or so I had thought.

The truth was I did disobey the system of God's kingdom - to "give what you purpose in your heart", (2 Corinthians 9:7). Therefore, that was stepping out of God's kingdom. But repentance is a gift the Lord gave us so that we wouldn't STAY outside in the dark. Repentance is the doorway back into the kingdom of God. Yet, despite this being the reality that applied to me, I began to posture myself for punishment. I began to presume the business was no longer meant to be, or that it would not be blessed because of my sin.

But God had been impressing upon my heart that His blessing IS upon everything I put my hand to, because, though I mess up, I "live" (dwell / abide) in His kingdom. When I step outside of His kingdom, He convicts me and I return by repenting and re-submitting to His ways. Therefore, He has charge over me and since His desire is to bless me so that I can be a blessing, that's the way things will pan out because I believe it.

Let me reiterate that in the past I had this false belief hidden deep down in my subconscious that when I went off course that the consequence is God's blessing is no longer upon what I'm doing (such as the business venture I used the orphans' money to start). But, wow, this false perspective is such an insult to the heart of our Father. How terribly I perceived my Lord! And this gave the enemy the upper hand in my life!

So, there I was - about to operate in that false perspective. Fortunately, I heard the correction of the Lord in my spirit saying, "What have I taught you?"

God also said that so many of His children operate out of this same false perspective of Him, that we just don't see Him for the gracious, lavishing, and forgiving Father that He really is because the enemy has skewed it. That we think He would cancel or take away the special plan He has for us just because we mess up. Indeed, there is a time for discipline, trust me, I know. But that doesn't mean everytime we step out of line God's going to remove His blessing upon us or curse the work of our hands. Why would He send His Son to die to provide grace for us, only to deny us that very grace when we falter?

It saddens me now to realize this is how harshly I perceived Father God. He is the most loving, compassionate, bountiful, merciful, generous and understanding being in all of existence. Though He is just and holy, and will absolutely discipline us when necessary, He is profoundly zealous to perform great wonders in our lives - if only we'd believe Him for it!

I cannot emphasize enough that the Lord made it so clear to my spirit how it pains Him that we just don't get how the desires of our hearts are MORE SO HIS desires for us. That He wants to bless us beyond our imaginations! God has such goodness planned for us but we just don't believe it - and, therefore, let so much of what He intended pass us by.

It's time for us to shed these false perspectives and doubts and walk in the truth, knowing deep in our subconscious, God is amazingly good to us and that His plans for us are YES AND AMEN - not taken away just because we mess up somewhere in the course of things. He doesn't say, "That's it, you blew this one, Paula". No, He says, "You're off course, get back on track, daughter. This is going to be wonderful! This is my desire for you! But get back on course so you don't miss it!". All we have to do is repent and obey - and the plans He has for us resume.

Beyond all that, I got to thinking how sad it was that I had no idea how much God wanted me to start that small business even more than I did!

And how terrible that I almost decided the business plan was botched because I sinned in using money appointed to orphans to start it. Wow, if anything deserves a consequence, it would be that! I honestly felt disgusting for having taken money from the orphanage, and felt the business didn't deserve to exist let alone be blessed by God! And who realizes that what we believe or expect is what we get!? I was about to sabotage God's plan for me!

But God's grace... oh the wonder of it. The Lord still very much wanted me to start the business after all. Father God still wanted to bless it. Despite my stealing from the orphans, repentance aligned me back with what God purposed in His heart for me. Because of His grace.

The bottom line is our shame is not the end of our story and it doesn't change God's mind about us. Nor does it change His mind about His plans to bless us. So long as we operate according to His kingdom - by repenting when we err - then the reality of God's kingdom is ours.

Finally, the Holy Spirit showed me that the only way I will miss my destiny is if I continue on in tainted, false perspectives of God, doubting the profound goodness He has for me despite my failures; doubting in the wonder of His grace.

REPENTANCE IS REALIGNMENT!

In the very nano second we repent we're no longer subject to dark kingdom authorities, rather, God's.

Please search yourself:

- Are you confident that God has wonderful plans for your life?
- Do you remain confident that His plans are yes and amen despite your failures?

- Are you inclined to feel so wretched when you fail that you think God lifted His blessing?
- Do you repent, receive the cleansing, get back on course and quickly move on, confident once again that God's goodness is still for you to behold? Or do you beat yourself up, give up, and throw in the towel because you feel you don't deserve it?

You know what the answers should be, so if you aren't operating in the truth, understand that this is yielding to the dark kingdom and giving them the upper hand. I know you don't want to continue doing this, so it's time to stop and, instead, believe God.

Let's pray...

Thank you, Heavenly Father, that your mercies are new every morning. Thank you for showing me the error of my ways and teaching me this important lesson. I pray I've learned what you intended in full, and that I've done well to convey what you want us to know.

And Lord, I pray that You'll help ODJ members to come into the full assurance that your plans are solid regardless of sin and error. That misalignment with your kingdom doesn't mean "it's over - you lose" rather, it means, "repent and get back on course". Help us all to comprehend that though this life has trials, and though many of the blessings you've had for us have been thwarted by our alignment with the enemy, you still have countless more - because that's who you are and who we are to you. Help us to comprehend that in our depths and step out of this false perspective of you. Help us to see that believing otherwise is TO OUR DEFEAT. To believe, instead, the truth that you really do desire to prosper us even as our souls prosper.

Father, if any of us have gotten off track with anything you planned or if we're not operating according to your policies concerning things, please reveal it. And please help us to not perceive resistance and challenges in our endeavors as indicators that your blessing is not upon something. It's crazy that we have fallen so terribly for this! The Lord rebuke the devil for these lies.

Father, you are CONSTANTLY releasing goodness and blessing. Do you stop the rain from falling on us when we mess up? No. Otherwise, it would never rain - EVER! Your goodness remains. All we have to do is get back on track, back in line. So, please help us get back on track by revealing what needs made right, if anything. Please help us to operate out of your policies in all matters and absolutely not give up or feel like you're "just not in it".

Father, if the enemy has sabotaged anything in our lives, please have mercy on the situation and rectify the matter. Lord, we mess up. That's what we do. But your Word says the blood of Jesus makes us right again. I plead the blood of Jesus over every ODJ Member now and ask you to make whatever is wrong right. Help us to see any error in our thinking, believing, and perceiving. Reveal the truth. Set things straight. And show us where there's misalignment. Get us back on the horse and prosperous in all you have.

Praise you Father, you are truly wonderful even when we fail. We do not deserve such unending grace. I feel horrible for what I put the orphans through, yet you were eager to forgive me upon my repentance. Likewise, please help every ODJ Member to walk in this grace, too, knowing that all we have to do is repent and get back on the horse, regardless of how much we don't deserve it. Because that's not why you bless us. You just do. Our wonderful Father. You just do. Praise you, your Majesty. We love you.

We pray all this in Jesus' Name, Amen.

Notes/Prayers

"Seek Ye First The Kingdom of God & His Righteousness"
Section Two 7

A condensed version of the passage from Matthew 6:24-33 reads: "No one can serve two masters. Either you will hate the one and love the other, or you will be devoted to the one and despise the other. You cannot serve both God and mammon (obsession or even desperation for wealth or financial well-being). Therefore, I tell you, don't worry about food, drink or clothing... Look at the birds of the air; they do not sow or reap or store away in barns, and yet your heavenly Father feeds them... So do not worry, saying, 'What shall we eat?' or 'What shall we drink?' or 'What shall we wear?' ...Your heavenly Father knows that you need these things. But seek first his kingdom and his righteousness, and all these things will be given to you".

For as plain as this is, we, the Church, are missing something. We understand, yet, *we don't understand.*

Thayer's Greek Lexicon at the blueletterbible.org defines kingdom as:

1. royal power, kingship, dominion and rule
2. a territory subject to the rule of a king
3. used in the N.T. to refer to the reign of the Messiah

So Matthew 6:33 would more definitively read:

"Seek ye first the **royal power, kingship, dominion and rule of Messiah** and His righteousness."

313

But what exactly does this entail? How does one actually seek a kingdom and its rule? If God told you to seek the dominion of the United Kingdom, what would that look like outside of literally **going there, becoming acclimated to the unique aspects of its culture, and then abiding within the ordinances of that system**?

Though it's supernatural and invisible, God's kingdom is a culture all its own with a very real government, statutes, rules and precepts whereby the only way to abide there is if we make it our number one priority to **replace the old fabric of our being (which was woven by the dark kingdom) with the liberating fabric of the glorious kingdom of God** by getting to know the new kingdom, earnestly seeking to understand its culture, and disengaging with the old one.

We know that because we received atonement from Christ, we're to be submitted and committed to His governmental reign over us. But not just by turning from sin. And not just by becoming an "active member of the church". *Rather by seeking to familiarize ourselves with everything there is to know about Christ's realm.* The more we understand His kingdom, the more we'll operate according to its parameters, the more the fabric of our being will reflect truth, and the more completely we'll abide there. It's like, we aren't just supposed to receive Christ and purchase a lot in His kingdom that we plan to build a home to retire in someday, rather, we have to physically move onto that holy kingdom lot now, and get familiar with the neighborhood, city, even the whole nation of that kingdom - along with all its profound supernatural dynamics - so to begin wearing, reflecting and closely adhering to the system of this glorious kingdom.

But realize that if knowing and abiding in Christ's kingdom is not top priority, then we aren't really His royal subjects. Instead, because we're still operating in the mindsets we'd always had, because we remain caught up with the system and culture we'd always been acclimated to - where fear or things like animosity or rebellion are common policy, and because we're holding on to the coping mechanisms and false perspectives we acquired via Satan's reign over us, since that's what makes the most sense to us, we, therefore, continue wearing our old, dark kingdom garments and remain as loyal subjects to the dark kingdom - even if we aren't in blatant sin. And remember that the kingdom that we are most familiar with and operate out of is the kingdom we are abiding in, which is the kingdom we grant authority over us. ---Just "deciding" that you want Queen Elizabeth to be your sovereign authority when you live in the United States (hypothetically) doesn't work. The realm (or country) you **abide in, know, and adhere to** is the one you grant authority over you. Think about how, if people want to escape the rule of a terrible king, the only way they can is to leave the territory. So it is with choosing God's kingdom over Satan's. We must leave the entire dark kingdom (not just sin). **But leaving a spiritual kingdom is only possible by disengaging from its system, no longer yielding to its ideals, no longer buying into its lies, no longer adhering to its system - no longer abiding there.** (For example, worrying when you are told you're getting laid off from your job is operating in a dark kingdom system. To the contrary, remaining in confidence and peace that God has your back is operating according to God's system.)

So why do we continue to abide in the dark kingdom after being transferred from the kingdom of darkness into the kingdom of God's dear Son (Colossians 1:13)?

It's because it's the kingdom we know and relate to, and we don't understand Matthew 6:33 that we need to avidly **seek** to become familiar with the mysterious ins and outs of the kingdom of God. Though God sent His kingdom to us in the earth, with all its supernatural benefits, He's been watching for two millennia as the majority of us remain as subjects to the very kingdom He rescued us from!

For the years and even decades prior to meeting Jesus, the dark kingdom was able to present a distorted reality of life and even of God, making it appear that He was amiss. So much of what we saw and experienced were the charades of the devil. Because the enemy had dominion, he could dictate situations as well as twist, stunt, and conceal the presence of God. Moreover, he could train us to operate in dark kingdom policies such as fear, worry, insecurity, self-pity, selfishness, greed, idolatry, and more. All he had to do was train us to operate in and be confident in the power and workings of his system. We are taught at church that the devil tempts us to sin, yet don't fully realize that even things like worrying, feeling inferior or unworthy (for example), are his programming and kingdom policies, too. So when the day came that we found God, though we chose Jesus, our souls continued to go by what they knew. That's why the Bible says we must be transformed by the renewing of our minds (Romans 12:2) - even the mind of our soul and all its false programming.

God desires that we would prosper even as our souls prosper (3 John 1:2). I believe our souls prosper throughout the course of the transformation we undergo - via the renewing of our minds through the Word of God. In other words, though we come to Christ and receive redemption and the forgiveness for our sins, our souls must be reprogrammed by truth. Jesus said we would know the truth and the truth would set us free. But the truth MUST take form in our souls in order for the transformation to transpire, otherwise we'll continue to go by what we've always known. When we first receive Christ as Lord and Savior, the seed of truth is injected into our souls, yes, but must be watered and nurtured by chasing more of it in order for it to take root and prosper. This is the process of the transformation and renewing of the mind. And this process is one of going from abiding in the dark kingdom to abiding in the kingdom of God.

That's why Matthew 6:33 emphasizes that we must seek God's kingdom first - that it must be top priority above all else. We must recognize that so much of how we operate even subconsciously is according to the programming we acquired while living under the dominion of darkness, and that we must be reprogrammed by God's truths. But the only way this will happen is by, first and foremost, **WANTING to know the truth**. Wanting to be tweaked, corrected, and refined, wanting to be transformed from the inside out. Because when we sincerely WANT it, we seek it. Even to the point of crying out to God in utter desperation, "SHOW ME YOUR TRUTH!"

Understand that all there is to "seeking the kingdom first" is "seeking TRUTH first". Seeking truth is seeking God. Seeking truth is seeking God's government. Seeking truth is seeking God's dynamics, system, heart, and kingdom. This is why I came into manifest freedom. This is why God's reality is manifesting in my life now instead of the devil's. Because I have voraciously sought truth. And the more I do it (because there's so much more to know), the more God's realm is my manifest reality!

Not knowing the truth from our belly is to our destruction. This includes all the aspects of God's kingdom's reality and dynamics. Such as how, in His kingdom, there is zero worry. None. Never. One who abides in Christ's kingdom never worries because there is nothing to worry about. This is why Jesus said not to worry about food, drink or even clothing (Matthew 6:31). Because He knows what we need and that, with bringing his kingdom to earth to us, if we abide or "live" in this knowing, then we won't worry. As we rest in such truths, the endless resources of God's realm reaches us and become our manifest reality. To the contrary, if we are insecure about these truths and the absolute certainty of them, this is trusting what the devil says, that you will run out of food, you won't have enough money for clothing, etc. And trusting the devil allows him to hinder the resources God absolutely has for us - from reaching us.

Unfortunately, the majority of us fail to become intimately familiar with the whole, liberating truth of God's kingdom and its potential to be our manifest reality. After 20 years of sitting under teachers, thinking I had a relatively solid understanding of God's truths, I began to discover how so much of the truth is not taught in mainstream Christianity. Religious, man made traditions and doctrine have become the cornerstone of Christianity; not Christ. Jesus came to preach the good news to the poor; to bind up the broken-hearted, to proclaim freedom to the captives and release from darkness for the prisoners. I was captive. I was in a prison of defeat and pain for more than twenty years after I found Christ. Because the message of the Church has veered away from why Christ came - to set us free in the here and now. The message has become that Jesus loves us and made a way for us to go to Heaven - and that "we need to do this and that" to be cookie-cutter Christians.

Where was the message of freedom? Where was deliverance? I was bound up in heavy chains. Where was the message of my release? Where was the teaching of the kingdom? The gospel of the kingdom of God has been thwarted by the enemy to keep the body of Christ at bay. But now... the Lord has begun emphasizing the message of the kingdom. Did you ever notice what Matthew 24:14 says where Jesus is discussing the last days before He returns? Does He say, "And this gospel will reach all nations?" No, He emphasizes "This gospel OF THE KINGDOM will reach all nations". Amen! I saw this years ago - after He corrected me that it's not a gospel of salvation - rather - it's the gospel of the kingdom of God. And if we think about it, hasn't the message of salvation reached all the ends of the earth by now? Well, we can't know for sure but I don't see why not. Meanwhile, it's not the message of salvation that must reach the ends of the earth, but the message of His kingdom! Amen.

So for twenty years as a Christian, I didn't know the truth other than what's taught which only served to keep me going in circles getting nowhere. Not understanding about the truth of God's kingdom and what it really means to seek it as well as what its being here means for me, kept me vulnerable to the wiles of the evil one. It kept a barrier between me and God. My soul remained in the custody of darkness and therefore, did not prosper which held me back in every facet of my life. But when I began to desperately seek to know *the whole truth* (which was seeking the kingdom of God), the truths of His kingdom were unveiled and MY LIFE BEGAN TO CHANGE. I began to be an overcomer. I stopped going in circles. I became affluent to God's manifest reality. And the enemy lost his power over me!

This is why we must come to our end with this world and the false programming of our souls, and desperately seek truth like never before. And let me tell you - I believe the fact that you are reading this is a result of your seeking the whole truth - which is seeking first the kingdom of God. So keep it up. Do it more! Become even more desperate for truth! Don't become comfortable with what you know, feeling it is enough. It's not. There's so much truth we all have yet to know. Let your primary mission for this life be to passionately chase truth without compromise - which is seeking God's kingdom first. And as you come into it, you begin to experience the manifest reality of God's kingdom more and more. You begin to walk in the reality of God's kingdom instead of the reality of the dark kingdom - which is victory!

And let's remember that seeking God's kingdom also includes seeking Christ's "kingship". We know Jesus is our King, but what does that amount to? The problem is we (in the USA at least) have no comprehension of what it's like to have a king. Kings of old were profoundly revered, unlike the chiefs over nations today. We know back then how they could put people to death for not obeying their statutes - which they did! Kings maintained a sovereign, noble stature and often controlled all the land that their subjects lived on. Citizens were required to remain humble and could not dishonor their king without repercussions, unlike today where people pridefully and maliciously assault their 'kings'. We simply have no concept of what it means to wholly submit to a king or anyone for that matter. If the people of today would be picked up and dropped back in time into a royal kingdom, the whole lot of us would probably be beheaded for lack of reverence and submission.

So, we need to ask the Lord:

1. How well we do or do not honor His Highness.
2. If we have truly submitted ourselves to His charge over us
3. If we have a proper fear and reverence of His Majesty

I believe if we'll come into genuine, holy fear, submission and honor of our king we will naturally long to know His truths which will cause His kingdom to become our manifest reality.

Now, I feel it's also necessary to zero in on the term "seek" from the Matthew 6 passage. The Greek term for seek, zēteō G2212, as outlined in the Greek Lexicon at blueletterbible.org says:

I. to seek in order to find
- to seek a thing
- to seek [in order to find out] by thinking, meditating, reasoning, to enquire into
- to seek after, seek for, aim at, **strive after**
II. to seek i.e. require, **demand**
- to **crave, demand** something

What we see here is that seeking can mean something far more than casually searching. If you've misplaced a random pen that you were using, you might look for it briefly but surrender and just grab a different pen. But if the pen had great value, you'd obviously search relentlessly until it was found. I believe the latter part of the above definition of seek describes this earnest form of seeking. And I am convinced this was the type of seeking the Lord had in mind in telling us to seek His kingdom and His righteousness. Let me explain...

Early in the passage Jesus says we cannot serve two masters. That we cannot serve both God and mammon. He said we'll hate the one and *"love"* the other, or that we'll be devoted to the one and despise the other. Well it goes without saying that we tend to strive after something we love and are devoted to. So, this portion of the passage was laying the groundwork for the Lord's final point on the matter. After telling us we cannot serve God and mammon, he then instructs us to not worry about the things we need, such as food and clothing. And finally, after laying out that we should not love or be devoted to wealth, possessions or even our daily needs - which is indirectly saying to love, serve and be devoted to Him instead, He says to *casually* look for His kingdom and righteousness above all? No, that wouldn't make sense. After laying it all out as He did, it's clear Jesus was saying to love, be devoted to, serve and *strive* after the kingdom of God and His righteousness.

Now, if you're like me, you're probably thinking we just can't flip a switch to feel passion for something in order to strive after it, if we don't already. When we all come to Jesus, let's face it - we're often in love with and driven for our lives, our dreams and ambitions. Therefore, most of us aren't going to instantly love God more. This is all normal and God knows it. But He does want us to understand His intent so that we'll do something about it. Once we grasp that this is our Lord's desire, that we would passionately pursue the kingdom of God (His truth and kingship) and His righteousness, then we can honestly tell Him if we don't, and ask Him to change this in us; and He will! If we ask such things, He will surely do it! If we really want it.

If you're stifled in your Christian journey, find out if mammon is your master and determine to lay it down. Do this so that your heart will finally swell with hunger for the whole truth and becoming familiar with the kingdom of God.

If it is not your master, and you could easily lay down mammon, then it's time to seek away - with all your heart - to know the ins and outs of the glorious kingdom of God. Chase down the truth and begin seeing the kingdom of God manifest in your life right before your eyes! Amen.

Notes/Prayers

_____

_____

_____

_____

_____

_____

_____

_____

_____

_____

_____

_____

_____

_____

_____

_____

_____

What Believing The Message of the Kingdom Looks Like
Section Two 8

By now we understand that, beyond the physical realm which we can see, are two spiritual kingdoms that we typically cannot see. But these two kingdoms (one being holy, the other being evil) are ever present and acquire authority in the earth when humans live by and in submission to their principles. And whether they know it or not, every human is either cooperating with the concepts of the dark kingdom, or the concepts of the kingdom of God, in every given moment.

Even those who don't believe in the supernatural or that there's a God or a devil cannot escape the reality that all their beliefs, perspectives, and actions are an affiliation or alignment with one kingdom or the other. In fact, believing that there is no God or devil is a doctrine of darkness that they bought into. Hence, they've granted the devil authority over their lives which enables Satan to blind them even further. Paul said, "But if our gospel is veiled, it is veiled to those who are perishing, whose minds the god of this age has blinded, who do not believe, lest the light of the gospel of the glory of Christ, who is the image of God, should shine on them.", 2 Corinthians 4:3-4.

So regardless what anyone thinks, the fact remains. These two kingdoms, each with their opposing standards and policies, manifest and take charge where charge is given them.

This is why Jesus beckons us to seek His kingdom above all else, and transfer our trust to it. The Lord wants us to separate ourselves from what we've always known, understood, and done by seeking to know and become confident in HIS system and all its goodness. By stepping out in faith and saying, "Okay, you say your kingdom is at hand, Lord? I want to see it. Let me understand the ways of your kingdom. Let me come out of the programming of the only kingdom and system I've ever known, and live whole-heartedly according to the ways of YOUR kingdom, instead."

That should have been the direction we took after being born again. As we discussed in Section One, the message preached to us at the beginning of our Christian journey most likely was, "Jesus loves you and died for your sins. Repent and believe on Him and you will be saved", which totally bypassed the heart of the Lord's three-year ministry. If we were to summarize His mission prior to paying for our sins on the cross, we'd say it primarily consisted of exercising the power of His kingdom against the rulers of darkness (delivering people from sickness, disease, sin, and demonic oppression) and teaching the statutes of His government as well as the truth that, by abiding in His kingdom and its statutes, one would be protected and experience the manifest reality of His kingdom and all its benefits.

Before coming to Christ and even after, we had no concept that the two supernatural kingdoms were intricately involved with each and every one of our lives. We knew we humans have this whole "good vs evil" problem but continued to leave the matter of the invisible "good and evil realms" on the book-shelves with the sci-fi books for the most part. But God continued to try to unveil the importance of understanding the significance of these kingdoms so that we would finally realize the necessity of coming out of the evil kingdom and into the holy one in every way. That's it's not just a matter of saying yes to Jesus and turning from sin. It's a matter of saying yes to His very literal kingdom. Meanwhile, the dark kingdom continued working tirelessly to keep us apathetic about the two kingdoms so that we'd never learn to come out from his control or influence. Therefore, we continued revolving around and operating according to what we see with our physical eyes, disregarding the reality of the two supernatural kingdoms, and failing to come into the fullness of God. Consequently, we go in circles chasing religion and salvation, never knowing the totality of the freedom, authority, power and benefits that God's kingdom provides.

Imagine living 2000 years ago and Jesus showing up in your community to tell you the kingdom of God was at hand. What would that amount to for you? Well, if you were oppressed, it would be liberating. Not because suddenly your governors or king became just, or because wickedness ceased, but because you could have the peace (and so much more) of God's kingdom within you despite it all. You could have joy for knowing the truth that this life is only temporary, and that you could connect with the wonders of God despite all the darkness surrounding you. Jesus taught His followers to put their eyes on the eternal and to not be caught up in the issues or even the splendors of this life – to not esteem them so highly. Jesus taught us what really matters and that we were to live life on earth working for an eternal reward, not a temporary earthly one. Jesus stressed that though the world is dark and that we would have troubles, darkness no longer has the final say over us.

The emphasis behind all Jesus taught was that His kingdom and way was liberating and amazing in contrast to all the brokenness and corruption of the world – and that if we sought His kingdom out and esteemed it above what we'd previously respected as reality, then God's will would be our manifest experience in every situation.

Jesus also demonstrated what living in His kingdom looked like. As we well know, there is no fear, sickness or lack in Heaven. Everyone in Heaven KNOWS they are safe with the Father and that the devil has no authority there whatsoever. Jesus showed us that Psalm 91 was a literal promise – that even while we were still on earth, we could be covered by the shadow of the Almighty. That regardless of the arrow that flies by day or the terrors of the night, God is FAITHFUL to protect us. All by virtue of ABIDING in God's kingdom. And the way we abide... is by believing.

But as I've mentioned before, God told me that we believe... but we don't believe. I speak about this all throughout this program so I won't elaborate on it here. However, I want to discuss what believing looks like.

Believing in Jesus is comprehending and being confident that God:

- Passionately loves you
- Adores you, gets a kick out of you, feels such delight over you
- Literally smiles at your sight
- Has been by your side all your life
- Actually cares deeply about everything you've ever gone through
- Has shed tears over your pain, longing to help you
- Intercedes for you
- Tells intercessors to pray for you
- Instructs your angels to protect you from total destruction when the devil has legal dominion
- Sends His Holy Spirit to woo you unto Him, to draw you into truth, and teach you
- Has great plans and purpose for you
- Wants to give you the desires of your heart
- Is always on your side in the face of adversity
- Really wants you to come out on top
- Sincerely wants to bless you so that you can be a blessing
- Really has washed you clean and doesn't look poorly upon you for your sins
- Is not shocked by your failures and wishes you'd understand this about Him
- Loves you even when you are at your worst
- Has literally rescued you from the dominion of darkness

Believing in Jesus is also believing in the message of His kingdom whereby you comprehend and know with utmost confidence that:

- Again, you have been transferred from the rule of darkness into the rule of Christ which means the life you lived prior to Christ is of a completely different culture which you are no longer a citizen of.
- God's supernatural peace is real and truly transcends all understanding – whereby, in the face of dark adversity or distress, though it hurts or is upsetting, there's still this unexplainable peace within you.
- No matter what happens, God has you. Even if you are thrown overboard and viciously tossed to and fro, beneath all your surface fright, deep down, you know God has you. Therefore, there's no terror in your soul. You are at peace despite all surface emotions.
- Because you seek first His kingdom, He'll take care of all your needs and you, therefore, genuinely carry zero anxiety when or if financial challenges arise. You may not know how God will come through for you, but you just know He will without a doubt. Because you are secure. You believe Him. You trust Him. You KNOW He has your back.
- If sickness or disease comes upon you, you know you do not have to have it. As a citizen of His supernatural kingdom where there is NO sickness or disease, you know you, therefore, do not have to accept or receive what the dark kingdom is dishing out.
- If injustice transpires, God will avenge you. Be it now or in eternity, He will make things right. You, therefore, take great solace in this and trust God throughout the unjust events. You keep on keeping on through the fire knowing one day all will be resolved. And though it hurts to endure, you remain humble and submitted to whatever God tells you to do in the matter; how to handle it. Sometimes, it's merely to go through it. And you obey because you trust the Sovereign Almighty God.

- The joy of the Lord is your strength. Even if the whole world comes against you, your joy for your future with Jesus is bigger than your pain over the ugliness of this life. Your joy for how good God's love feels is bigger than your sadness over the lack of love in this world. Though your heart may ache, you also have such unexplainable joy for knowing God and your hope of a future with Him. He is your assurance. He is steadfast and forever wonderful. You take such refuge in this and carry great satisfaction over your future.

And finally, believing Jesus is demonstrated in your actions by how you:

- Love others unconditionally. Especially the unlovable. (Note: this isn't to suggest tolerating abuse in order to show love. There is such a thing as tough love whereby we refuse to be an enabler, and must release and allow people we care about who are in the darkness to experience consequences.)
- Remain in peace and joy despite the chaos and pain.
- Sow to God's Spirit in patience, kindness, self-control, etc. Because you believe Jesus, you are compelled to honor His system and walk in the ways of His Spirit. Not just when it's easy, but when it's difficult and most challenging to do so.
- Approach all aspects of this life with confidence that, no matter what, your God is above all of it, totally capable, and totally willing to bless you with purpose, insight, revelation, wisdom, resources, authority and the power of His Spirit. Meanwhile, He is also faithful to rectify all unjust matters either now or later, and He is also very eager to reward you for selflessness, service unto Him, and whatever sacrifices you may make for Him.

To the contrary, what believing Jesus does NOT look like is:

- Seeing that the glass is half empty as opposed to half full, feeling defeated, like a loser, hating ourselves, expecting the worst, to be disappointed or let down, or feeling sorry for ourselves over injustice, struggle, or lack. Having such a negative outlook demonstrates the soul only knows Satan's reality and is more confident in it than God's.

- Defending ourselves. These souls don't comprehend God's love, aren't secure in Him, and therefore feel desperate to prove themselves and be heard. This is a dark kingdom behavior. To the contrary, knowing God's kingdom and who we are in and to Him gives us such security that we don't need to prove anything to anyone. Plus, we know that Jesus did not defend Himself. He was humble even unto death. Indeed, there were times He boldly presented truth in the face of lies. But this was in defense of truth, not out of motivation for Himself or needing to be understood.

- Worrying or being anxious over lack. This is a policy of the dark kingdom. It's how darkness runs things. The more one worries, the greater the enemy institutes lack. Being easily driven to worry shows a detachment from God's reality.

- Having hatred, bitterness, or unforgiveness towards evil-doers. However, please note that this doesn't mean loving on them, instead. Jesus didn't kiss butt and sweetly correct the Pharisees, rather, He boldly conveyed corrective truth, even telling them they were of their father, the devil. That wasn't a very lovely thing to say. Yet, He never carried hatred or bitterness towards them.

- Being prideful, self-serving, covetous, greedy, insolent, or jealous. These remain as subtle behaviors among the souls that still believe in and chase the fulfillment of this life. They don't yet know or believe that our fulfillment is in knowing Christ intimately.

- Being religious for religion's sake.

All that being said, which kingdom would you say you live in? Judging by your outlook on and approach to this life, which kingdom do you believe in more - in literal terms? I know you believe in the kingdom of Christ or you would not be here. But do you also wear the fabric, perspectives and manifest reality of His kingdom? I know you believe in holy kingdom truths out of your mind. But I'm asking if your soul gets it, too. Since you were born again, has your soul detached from your confidence in lack, sickness, disease, and all else? Has it since put on the fabric of God's kingdom and become acclimated to its goodness, stability, rest and benefits - exercising His authority and connecting to His perfect will? Or, is your soul still seeing things the way the dark kingdom taught it to?

The kingdom concepts you are confident in and operate out of demonstrate which kingdom you presently abide in. If you want to move forward in who you are, you must first recognize and come to terms with where you abide. You may actually abide in both, as the Lord showed me I was doing. He said I had one foot in the kingdom of God and one foot in the kingdom of darkness. Because I believed Him, but I also continued to believe the concepts and suggestions of the devil.

It's time to put both feet into the kingdom of God. And how we do this is:

1. Recognize the truth of where we are.
2. Repent for unknowingly continuing in our confidence of what the devil says.
3. Renounce all false perspectives and beliefs embedded deep in our souls, even the ones we don't realize we have, asking God to expose them.
4. Voraciously seek to understand God's kingdom, system and reality, chasing it with all we are.
5. Be ever mindful to trust that the liberating concepts are yes and amen, not too good to be true.
6. Continue to repent and detach from false programming and outlooks as God reveals them.
7. Walk securely and confidently in the manifest reality of God's kingdom.

Amen.

Notes/Prayers

As you color... Remember, this is a rendition of God's LOVE for you. Even if you already comprehend it, fill this page with a symphony of colors as you bask in His wonder. **Jesus is all that matters**. Everything else is nothing. God is the only thing that is certain, right, and true. God is our only absolute. He is the only thing perfect and reliable. ***Think ONLY on Him, your future with Him. Peer through the veil and see His face, His Light, His Glory... His Love***. ~Love Him as you color.

Section Two

Though this is the checkpoint for Section Two, I'd like to bring things together by providing a summary of everything that has been discussed. The fact is it is very important to have a solid grip on the overall picture.

Let's look at the primary key points to the bottom line:

- The body of Christ at large has been infiltrated and is oppressed by the kingdom of darkness. She doesn't really know or exhibit God's kingdom power in proclaiming freedom to the captives and release from darkness for the prisoners. And worse, many members of the body are severely oppressed, debilitated and defeated themselves because they are threats to the dark kingdom. They are targeted early on in life and brainwashed at soul level to doubt God so that they won't fully connect with Him and His power whereby they'll do great damage to the dark kingdom. As such, they grow up accustomed to a "false reality", comprehending only that which the kingdom of darkness institutes (which skews God's reality) and they continue in confidence in the only reality they've ever known, even after giving their lives to Christ.

- For centuries, the Christian Church's primary 'gospel' message to the world has been that Jesus loves us and died for our sins to save us. Yet, the gospel is primarily that the kingdom of God is at hand and that those who believe it are rescued from the dominion of darkness (Colossians 1:13) whereby, those who believe and abide in God's kingdom, are set free from bondage, sickness, and disease and are able to cast such out of others, too. They are able to impart the reality of God's kingdom into the darkened earth. They are empowered by the Holy Spirit with supernatural wisdom, knowledge, gifts of healing and so much more, in order to rescue others from darkness. And finally, yes, they are also redeemed of their sins and inherit eternal salvation.

- The corporate Church system believes and preaches the false doctrines that a) everyone is commanded by scripture to preach the gospel, and b) that believers must follow religious practices in a disciplined fashion such as reading the Bible, praying, and attending church. Consequently, many believers carry heavy shame or guilt for their inability to adhere to these man-made religious traditions which further stunts their freedom in Christ. There are far more guilt-ridden Christians than kingdom-powered Christians. It's time to shake off these false ideals that have been weighing the body of Christ down!

- Our greatest mandate is to believe in and grow up in the ways (fruit) of God's kingdom - in supernatural love, peace, joy, self-control, patience, faith, kindness, humility, mercy, forgiveness, righteousness, etc. In so doing, the kingdom of God increases in us and SPREADS throughout the world. And the way this happens is simple: by seeking God's kingdom with all our hearts.

- The true definition of a disciple is one who is a devout follower and student of Christ which means they are sincerely dedicated to their teacher and do their best to represent Him.

- Not everyone (including leadership) at church is truly submitted to and authentically seeking Christ and His kingdom - even if they sincerely believe they are. They live for self and the world and have a form of godliness. I call them the "wicked good" and the Bible warns us to not mesh with them.

- Another false teaching in the corporate body of Christ is the "once saved, always saved" doctrine. As in once you say the sinner's prayer, that's it. This is not true. Indeed, becoming a member of the royal priesthood by repenting and believing the gospel of the kingdom is the way to salvation. But saying the "sinner's prayer" is not the end of it. It's about abiding in God's kingdom and wearing its reality. The New Testament is loaded with descriptions as to what living in God's kingdom on earth looks like. And it also demonstrates what abandoning it looks like as well - which is no longer "working out your salvation with fear and trembling". God's "Last Will And Testament" is that we all are born of spirit by repenting and believing the WHOLE gospel AND by ABIDING in His kingdom which is working out our salvation.

- And finally, everyone operates according to the policies of the holy kingdom of God or the   evil kingdom of darkness - whether they believe in them or not. These two invisible, spiritual kingdoms, are very real and active governments, with profound systems of organized personnel (angels and demons of all ranks). They are more strategic and diligent to perform their duties than any earth system that ever existed. They are very interested in every human being. Representatives of each kingdom are assigned to people to accomplish their goals through them. The dark kingdom's primary mission is to stunt the kingdom of God in the earth - to keep its citizens disconnected from the power and authority of God - so to help Satan become god over all the earth via the antichrist. This is what they have been strategically working towards for thousands of years. Meanwhile, many passionate followers of Christ are still partially under the dominion of darkness because they remain somewhat blind to God's love and truths and, therefore, unwittingly continue to fear the devil more than God, agree with and operate in dark kingdom policies, as well as doubt God's love, truths, grace, and the power of the kingdom they were born into.

To break it all down into simplest terms, abiding in the kingdom of God is being secure and confident in God and His love, where there is no striving, fear, or worry concerning the darkness of this world. Abiding in God's kingdom is putting on holy garments of peace and assurance, remaining wise to the strategic dark forces that strive to hinder us, yet confident in the Holy Spirit and His angels to assist and protect us. It is also rejecting the false reality we were once bewitched by. And it is confidently embracing our real identities and positions in Christ.

Abiding in the kingdom of God is not, however, being religious. It's not about church attendance or reading the Bible out of discipline. It's about seeking God first with all our hearts which is a heart condition - not a practice, ritual, or application of any sort. It's a place. It's being in a constant prostrate position in spirit before God, hungering for Him, regardless what your physical body is doing, regardless what is going on around you. And then as a result, we become one with God's truths. He leads us to His Word, not via religious discipline, but by guiding our steps, bringing things to our attention, drawing us into specific topical truths, giving us dreams and visions, speaking to us in our innermost being, leading us to teachers, songs, sermons, or anything that's speaking the specific message He has for us in a particular moment. Even putting people or situations in our paths which enlighten us somehow.

There are countless ways God reveals Himself, truth, His Word, and the reality of His kingdom to us. Our job is to simply seek, seek, seek truth - which, again, is being in the spiritual condition of want for it. It is merely a matter of asking God to reveal it - constantly. The result is you discover the false things in your soul that you finally, gladly do away with as truths take over. You see yourself transforming, becoming more affiliated with God's reality. And then, as your soul prospers in the kingdom of God reality, God's manifest presence and all that His kingdom is becomes your manifest experience!

Once you do wrap your mind around all that, you'll be on the upwards swing. And see, it won't be because you've become perfect, rather, it will be because your soul is coming out of agreement with and confidence in the dark kingdom. Believe me when I tell you that to date, you have not fully connected with the Lord. Again, you can believe with all your mind and heart that God loves you and has set you free, but if your soul doesn't also believe it, then this is a major disconnection which gives a measure of authority to the dark kingdom over you. The kingdom you fear and operate in is the kingdom you empower.

What I'd like you to do below is answer the following questions and submit them so I can get a feel for where you are. The questions do not cover everything, obviously. However, they will help you determine which kingdom you adhere to the most.

If after you submit the answers below you determine that you're still in the same place you were before beginning the ODJ Program, then please be sure to go back through the previous sections, this time confidently asking God to unveil what you need to see. I assure you, if you really want to know the truth, He will reveal it to you.

BUT, confidence is the key! KNOW that God does speak to you, that He IS right there with you. Stop feeling otherwise, if that's the case. In fact, don't go a step further until you come to terms with the real reality - that God is there with you, smiling upon you, loving you, speaking many things to you. Doubting this puts a veil between you and the Lord, preventing you from hearing and discerning His presence.

Notes/Prayers

_____

_____

_____

_____

_____

_____

_____

_____

_____

_____

_____

_____

_____

_____

_____

_____

_____

_____

_____

_____

Questionnaire:

Please answer the following questions:

- What is the Gospel?

_____

_____

- Do you still feel guilty for not reading the Bible 'enough'? Why not?

_____

_____

- Do you still feel guilty for not verbalizing the gospel to others?

_____

_____

- What is the greatest commission?

_____

_____

- Name the agreements with the dark kingdom that you lay down right now.

_____

_____

_____

_____

- Close your eyes. Look upon Jesus with the eyes of your spirit. Do you see Jesus is smiling upon you right now? Describe it.

_____

_____

_____

_____

- What is/are the biggest lie(s) you ever believed?

_____

_____

_____

- Which lies do you think have had the greatest impact against you - keeping you from experiencing God's manifest presence and reality for your life?

_____

_____

- List the ways you have doubted God.

_____

_____

- List the ways you no longer doubt God.

_____

_____

- Do you strive, long for, feel desperate for anything in this life still? If yes, what? And what are you doing about it?

_____

_____

- Do you pester God for revelation knowledge of His truth?

- What things or aspects of God, His Truth, His reality, His promises, etc., do you long to understand and know deeply?

- Are you completely dead to self? Which parts of you still strive to live / have its way?

- Are you a carrier of the kingdom of God, whereby (despite injustice, turmoil, strife, distress) you remain in and spread unexplainable peace, joy, righteousness, self-control, love, kindness and faith?

S2 Prayer Devotional:

Dear ODJ Member,

I'd like to emphasize that though you've likely come to know deeper truths as to what it is to be a Christian and abide in the kingdom of God, how these truths must take over the soul and BE our truth. The transformation and prospering of your soul takes place when you become one with the truths, not just know about them. And the only way to become one with them is to meditate upon them and preach them to your soul until you wear kingdom of God truth as your reality.

Imagine if you were born into a household of royalty but were kidnapped by poor thieves who tried to ransom you but failed because your parents - the king and queen - were temporarily displaced, perhaps taken captive by another kingdom for fifteen years. So you are raised by the thieves, never told the truth, because they're waiting for the day the king and queen are set free and somehow able to resume their royal throne, to cash in on you. Which they do, sixteen years later. Suddenly, you're rescued by your parents. But despite being royalty, you do not act like it. You only understand the life you lived. And for years, though you are informed of your real identity, you continue perceiving things otherwise. You just don't comprehend the love of your father. You continue anticipating defeat, lack, and suffering - because it's what you know. It takes years of dwelling with your real parents face to face for you to begin wearing the reality of who you are.

It's the same with coming into Christ's kingdom. We only understand things as we've seen through the eyes of one dominated by the prince of the air. We know our real identity, yet, we don't. It takes awhile to shed the old, defeated garments and begin boldly wearing the new ones. Unfortunately, in Christ's kingdom, we are not physically face to face with Him yet. So we must preach the real truth to ourselves in order to take it on.

The following Devotional will help you do just that.

"Dear Heavenly Father, Thank you for your Word and Truth.

Thank you for rescuing me from the dominion of darkness.
I repeat:
Thank you for rescuing me from the dominion of darkness.
And again:
Thank you for rescuing me from the dominion of darkness.

And thank you for helping me to take on my holy kingdom identity!

Father, I've discovered my soul is not quite right with you. I haven't fully understood the reality of your kingdom. And I see now that there are areas deep inside of me that haven't truly trusted you, understood your love, or _____

_____

I see now that I've doubted that:

_____

_____

I understand this means I've been unknowingly in alliance with the kingdom of darkness. Father, though in my mind and heart I know this is wrong, my soul still goes by the only reality it ever knew which was defeat / lack / that I'm alone / abandoned / unloved / unlovable / a failure / inadequate / hopeless / disgusting / _____ / _____ / _____ .

But I see that it's all LIES. So, please forgive me, Father, for believing these lies. And help me to shed them. They are so deeply embedded in me, Lord. Help me to tear them down by the power of your Spirit!

I know in my mind and heart that you are for me, that you love me, that you have always been with me even though the devil was able to cloak your presence and put a veil between us, because I believed the liar over you. But I repent! And I command my soul to embrace the truth!

You were always with me! You have been smiling upon me since the moment you breathed me into existence! You have sent angels to protect and assist me – and they have done so much that I have no idea about, because it was hidden from me!

You have rescued me from the only reality I've ever known and transferred me into your PERFECT kingdom where there is NO LACK, NO DEFEAT, NO SICKNESS, NO SIN, NO DISEASE, and NOTHING TO FEAR. Though this world has troubles, I have PEACE in you! I have JOY in you! I am SAFE in you!

Though they slay me, yet will I praise you! I have the Light of the world in me! I have no shame! Though I'm not yet perfect, I am perfectly righteous in YOU, because of the blood of Jesus Christ! And you are changing me as we speak!

Father, I am so thankful to comprehend more than ever that you LOVE me so deeply. You adore me! You delight in me! You care about every detail of my life! And you are working to pull me out of the pit and into full, vibrant life!

More than that, you understand why I was defeated and you are NOT disappointed in me. You are not disturbed with me.

You are not shaking your head in shame over me. You are not shaking your fist at me.

I command my soul to trust you now, Father. To trust in how wonderful you are. And even to trust in how much you want to lavish me! I get it now that you have not been ABLE to lavish me because I've had such a wrong perspective of you! I've had such doubts concerning your passion and zeal for me. I haven't understood or believed that you really feel that way about me! I just didn't get it but now I do, Lord!

Also, Lord, I know it's wrong to strive after this life / to continue longing for man's approval / to continue worrying about troubles or lack / to continue believing I'm alone / to continue wanting recognition or understanding / to continue chasing mammon / to continue hating myself / to continue fearing what might go wrong next / to continue dwelling on all the garbage the dark kingdom has going on around me / to continue being defeated over how others treat me / to continue feeling sorry for myself for all the misfortune I've faced / to continue _____ _____ . So, I lay it all down now. Again, I repent and declare my soul chooses TRUTH on this very day, _____, 20___. I am yours and you are mine. You are what is perfect, stable, and constant. And I am in you. Though still in this broken world, my real home is in your invisible kingdom of FREEDOM right here among the darkness!

Praise you, Father, for rescuing me and helping me to walk in the reality of YOUR KINGDOM!

You're A Good, Good Father!

In Jesus' Name, Amen."

I'm Stuck! Nothing I Read is Sinking In!"

"Leslie" (an ODJ member) expressed the profound struggle she was going through and gave me permission to share our conversation:

Hi Paula,

Firstly, thank you for your faithfulness and generosity in sharing this program. For the past 6 weeks or more it appears like my brain has shut down and I simply can't think properly. I read the modules but it's like NOTHING is sinking in.

In my daily life I am confused, exhausted and emotionally numb. I struggle to even pray and worship at the moment. Sorrow is my constant companion. My Pastor just keeps "encouraging" me by pointing out the things I should be doing and my lack of commitment - this just leaves me feeling worse and like even more of a failure.

I am just numb- seems the only emotions I have at the moment are anger at the injustices that just keep coming or grief.

How do I get unstuck ?

I have spent so much time face down on the carpet weeping........I just want my joy back.....

Kind regards
~Leslie

Hello Leslie,

I've been praying, asking the Lord how He would address your situation because my first thought was it could be any number of things going on that is hindering you. Indeed, everything that's wrong in our lives is somehow connected to the dark kingdom. Something in us is not fully connected to God's reality.

Again, it could be any number of reasons for your disconnect. The whole point of the ODJ Program is to come into and connect with truth in order for truth to manifest in our lives, defeating the manifest power of darkness. Our belief system, fears, insecurities, ignorance, idolatry, pride, etc., are all what disconnects us from His Majesty and all that He is and has for us. It's all right there. It's simply of a different dimension (the spirit realm) and the only way to connect with God's spiritual kingdom is by faith in Christ. And believing Him (our faith) is more than just knowing Jesus died to save us. It's trusting His will for us. It's resting in Him, knowing He really is for us. It's not striving, fearing, or chasing answers in our own power, etc. I'm thinking with all you have been through, you haven't been resting in Him.

You said your only emotion is anger or grief over all the injustice. And I recall now what you shared with me months ago - you have been through HELL with the terror of your husband dying in your arms and so much more. Your life was ripped out from beneath your feet in numerous ways. No wonder you are in so much pain. I personally have not experienced this type of torture so I cannot speak to the processing of this profound grief. My instinct is the grieving you're going through, even the anger, is normal. You have to go through it. I can only hope this is you finally processing what's happened for the sum total of the past decade and a half and not you remaining stuck in a cycle of pain. As a teacher, I do have to point you back to what scriptures tell us. As I'm sure you know, the truth is that God is for you and loves you. So, if all the hell you've been through has served to stifle your soul by putting a wall between you and God to keep you from connecting with His love, healing power, joy, and peace, then this very well may be the primary reason you are so shut down.

I would encourage you to ask Father God if that is what the problem is, or where you might be giving the enemy a platform by operating in or believing his lies. Or perhaps where your chemistry might be compromised (low hormone levels, toxicity, acidity levels, emf's, etc). Ask God to reveal the issue(s). He surely will. Meanwhile, pay attention to your thought life, making sure you are not entertaining lies from the enemy.

As for what you "should be doing", I would sum it all up as "you need to come into God's rest". You've been through so much. It's time to snuggle up in the palm of Father God's hand, let everything go, and be secure in Him.

Let me know if this helps,
Paula Cross

"Why Is God So Silent?"

Another inquiry I have permission to share. My reply is in bold italics:

"Dear Paula,

I am not sure if l am right, but since I have made up my mind to seek God more, l seem to be under attack at work, home and with family members. ***You definitely are. The enemy cannot afford to let you cruise into the manifest power and authority of God easily. The devil has systems in place working avidly to stir up dust and keep you where you are. There's no doubt about it.*** It appears to be intensifying to a point where l have been shocked by the unexpected outbursts and intense reactions l seem to be getting. ***Yes, exactly! I have been astounded with how vulnerable people are to be used in such insane ways. I'm shocked that people listen to such ridiculous lies of the devil. Not that I'm judging because I have listened to plenty of ridiculous lies myself. But when you're looking at things from the other side, it's shocking that this is how gullible we humans are to the works of the devil. And even though we know his agents are behind the outbursts or reactions and all else, it still hurts. I'm to the point where I'll say, "Wow, devil, you got a nice right hook in there. Clever. But I still know it's you and I choose to trust God and not cave to the pain you're using this person to inflict upon me. God's will be done."***

I have even been questioning myself what l have done wrong to experience such outbursts. ***That's just it - it's not about doing anything wrong - rather, because you are seeking God. Will the devil give you such a hard time if you weren't a threat? If you were busy doing things wrong? No, he'd leave you alone so you'll keep doing***

349

things wrong so that you won't ever manifest in the authority and power of God.

I also **become afraid** because I struggle to hear God"s voice in my situations, even though I have been a Christian for many years. I still don't hear his voice and l still don' t know how to, even though I have read the module and have been praying about this. I even asked God why l cannot hear his voice if l am one of his sheep. This is something that **really worries me** because l hear other Christians talk about how God speaks to them. Yet, l cannot confidently say the same of me. Not hearing his voice has **made me question if l am truly saved**. I have prayed the sinner"s prayer many times. I still don't know his Holy Spirit or know God or his presence like l should. I therefore am **never really sure** if he is guiding me in life, even though I know his word says he does. I read the word whenever l can, but it is still just head knowledge. I have been praying and asking God to let his word become alive in my life. He seems so silent in my life. *I'm not there with you to observe if there's more to it, but what you wrote here is definitely a huge part of the issue. Everything you said that's underlined shows that <u>your soul is divided between faith and doubt.</u> This was my problem - most everyone's problem. We know and believe in our minds what the Word of God says, but our souls don't believe it. Your soul goes by what it has experienced - which was God's silence.*

Here's the rest of my reply in regular italics:

See, Shelly, all the years you grew up in a household under the dominion of darkness, God was still very present. Your angels were there helping you in ways you cannot imagine because the dark minions, which had legal rights, were striving to do so much more harm and false programming than they got away with. But somebody somewhere was praying for you and your angels were allowed to step in to help to whatever degree. But the thing is, <u>God wasn't silent, rather, He was</u>

silenced. _Your ears were kept from being able to hear Him. God is always loving us, adoring us, saying sweet things to us, instructing us, guiding us. But the devil legally has systems in place to drown Him out!_

This is the Lord answering you, Shelly, because I had NO idea what to say at the beginning of this email! None. I thought, "I can't possibly know why she isn't hearing your voice. Help me Lord." And boom, He opened my eyes to what you said.

All your life while the dark kingdom had legal rights, they made it look like the Lord wasn't there, that He didn't care, that He was silent. You have to come to terms with this. Your soul took on a false perspective that God wasn't there. Or that you couldn't hear him. This is what the enemy told you when you started pursuing the Lord. Because you were so insecure, they were able to continue fostering your false perspective even after you were born again. You remained vulnerable to the lie. You continued to listen, and by listening to the liar, you continued to give him a platform or rights to your life. Think about it, if you allow your neighbor that does drugs to come into your living room to snort drugs, then you've given him a place in your life. So, whatever he does while in your living room is on you. And that's what you've been doing with the dark system that's been set up and working in your life for years. You're still listening and entertaining their bull crap.

Everything that you said which I emboldened and underlined shows you are still listening to the liar. You "become afraid" and "really worry". You question your salvation. You "know" the Word says God guides you in your life (in your mind), but you "aren't sure". ---These statements are all insecurity and doubt in your soul. I can say this because it was my case and now it isn't while I'm free. And it's a freedom that will never cease because I know what I know and can't unknow it. Once your soul KNOWS, there's no going back. So, we have to get your soul on board with the truth.

The first thing you have to do is realize your soul is under a false perspective based on all you experienced while the devil had legal dominion over your life. You have to reject the lies you took on that God was silent. He was NEVER silent. He was there, wooing you from day one. See the bag the devil put over your head and put the blame where it belongs. God was never silent. You CAN hear His voice. The only reason you haven't yet is because you continued to listen to the liar. You believe what the devil says. This allows them to muffle your ears. But I command the muffling to cease right now in the Name of Jesus Christ. I command the blockage in your ears to come out now, in Jesus' Name. I command your ears to be opened.

Shelly, now it's up to you to see the false programming that you were under for what it was - a lie. An illusion. And next, know that worrying or questioning your salvation are all lies, too. This is what they tell you to keep you where you are! Tell them to shut up. I mean it. Do not be afraid. Jesus Himself commanded demons to be quiet. So when you get what you think are just thoughts, "Oh, maybe I'm not really saved! Or, "Oh, it doesn't seem like God is really guiding my life. I know the Bible says He does, but I'm just not sure..." Tell the minions to SHUT UP IN JESUS NAME. Stop listening to their lies. The Word says God guides you and HE DOES. But if you prefer to listen to a demon luring you to question this, then you won't be able to PERCEIVE God's guidance.

The bottom line, Shelly, is you have to be confident in the truth. I guarantee you God is absolutely guiding you and speaking to you. But your doubt has forbidden you from perceiving Him. Repent of your doubt and do as I said - telling the demons to be quiet. And I assure you, you will perceive your Heavenly Father's voice.

And let me tell you this... I hear God saying, "Yes she has heard me, she just didn't know it was me."

Just as you think the worrisome thoughts are yours while they are often from the devil, there are many thoughts you have, even dreams, that were God speaking to you. Have you ever been led to help someone, give them something, do something for them? Who do you suppose gave you that thought? Now foster this, give thanks for all the times He has spoken to you - even though you didn't know it. Increase your hearing by believing Him like never before and thanking Him for being there for you all those years in ways you never knew when the enemy had dominion.

This is your turning point Shelly.

God bless you on your journey,
Paula

So, to summarize... We all just need to recognize that the way we think, the way we perceive what's going on is quite possibly of demonic influence and false programming in our souls.

Let's always be in the habit of assessing our thought life and perspectives, asking if they line up with God's Word or not. We're constantly listening to every suggestion of the enemy and need to stop. Such as it was with Shelly - listening to the notion that maybe she isn't really saved. Or, that God's silent or wondering if He actually is guiding her life.

Those are all doubt and insecurity and this ALLOWS THE DARK SYSTEMS TO MAINTAIN JURISDICTION.

Please watch your thoughts and ask God to show you where you are yielding to lies.

Putting a stop to this will be ripping the carpet out from beneath the enemy in your life. It will be a turning point for you as well. Amen.

Notes/Prayers

Notes/Prayers

Why Smokers Love Cigarettes
~ Soul Detachment

An ODJ member (we'll call her Marsha) recently expressed her frustration with not being able to give her all to Jesus. Like many of us, she uses carnal remedies to satisfy her soul (in her case, cigarettes) because her soul is still somewhat detached from the Father. Marsha permits me to share our conversation wherein Holy Spirit sheds light on why so many of us are struggling in this way:

Dear Paula Cross,

"Back to the Father" touched me. As I read it out loud, tears came down. That is what I really want - to be with the Father, even here on Earth... But I need to shift my focus and give my ALL. I'm tired of this reality taking 1st place, but I let it. I must repent and look at the BIG picture! I'm sick of living in sin (smoking cigarettes is the biggest thing now, getting in the way of totally giving my All to God). Thank You for this ODJ program!   With Christian Love, Marsha

----

Dear Marsha,

I hear you - and thank you for letting me know. So if I hear you correctly, you're expressing that the world (or aspects of it) have a hold on you which you put before God? Yes, that's our biggest challenge - loving God first. Mine too. I love Him so much but if I'm not careful, other things can carry me away. But what I learned is He is faithful to pull me back, reminding me that He is what I want above all.

However, the reason I'm so much more easily pulled back now compared to the past is because I'm far more secure in His love. "Knowing" His love (not just about it) - really feeling His love - is what has made the difference. Because I no longer subconsciously feel abandoned by God, but that He really is there for me unlike the past, this is finally what truly makes me whole. I'm no longer desperate for substitutes or idols. So, though I can still be enticed by other things, being whole in Christ helps keep me from loving other things more than Him as easily. When I do get lured away now, my consciousness of God's love and the weight it carries helps bring me back faster.

Your addiction to the cigarettes is because something in your soul is still detached from God. Perhaps you aren't secure in His love or you feel subconsciously abandoned by Him as I once did. Something in you is not fully connected to Him, or cigarettes would not take over. You may always have an appeal for them, but they wouldn't win if your soul was fully connected to God and His love. Your love and dependence on other things would shrink and become a cheap knock-off, because your soul would recognize the truth that they aren't genuinely making you whole the way they pretend to do at present. Regardless of what the idol or addiction is, it's easy to have them when there's a wall between us and God's amazing love for us. And that wall gets built through the years of experiencing what the devil does to us through others - with abandonment, rejection, conditional love, and other violations. These train us to not trust that anyone, including God, can truly love us. I don't know if this is your situation, but I would bet it is simply because of your dependence upon the cigarettes.

So, what you need to do is search God concerning this wall between you two, and get it torn down so that you can fully connect with and "know" His love. This will destroy your love affair with substitute gods.

Blessings,
Paula Cross

ODJ Program Member Meets Jesus Face to Face

My Visit To Heaven
By: Michael Cox

"This is my story about the day I died and my experience of Heaven.

Heaven - Paradise. It is a very real place. Jesus is the Son of God. The only true way to Heaven is by faith in Him and acceptance of His sacrifice on the cross. I know. I've embraced Him.

"For God so loved the world that He gave His only begotten Son, that whoever believes in Him will never die but have eternal LIFE." John 3:16.

I'd had a busy day doing maintenance at our remote beach property. It was around 4 pm when my wife asked me if I wanted a cup of coffee, I said that I had finished preparing the roof for painting and would be right down. As I started to climb down the ladder I felt it move. I grabbed the gutter to slow my fall and ended up swinging into the open window and impaling my lower leg on the open aluminium window frame. I fell about 2 meters to the deck below with the window and frame still embedded in my leg. Without thinking I pulled the frame from my leg immediately, severing the major femoral artery. Instantly, the blood started squirting from my body and straight up into the air.

My dear wife saw the whole thing happening and rushed to my aid. I went into shock and fainted. She apparently placed my hands around the gaping wound and told me to press hard while she sped off inside to find something to use as a tourniquet. I have no memory of her returning but she applied a belt around the lower half of my leg just above the knee and pulled tightly, at the same time she called for help. My elderly mother-in-law who was staying with us was then asked to call the emergency services.

A nearby neighbor heard my wife crying for help and rushed over to assist. While she was running up the property my wife sensed somebody on the deck and looked up to see a man standing beside her. He said his name was Peter and that he had come to tell her everything would be okay. My wife turned as our neighbor arrived but when she turned back to Peter, he had simply disappeared. Our neighbor insisted she hadn't seen anybody on the deck at all. We believe he was an angel sent from heaven to reassure us.

Finally the emergency services arrived and when they saw the blood and the severity of the wound, immediately called for the air ambulance to take me to the nearest hospital which was over an hour's drive away.

The emergency paramedic took my heartbeat and it was down to 17 beats per minute- definitely not enough to sustain life. My veins were collapsing and my body was shutting down. By this stage I was finding it very difficult to breathe. I felt myself slipping away and my sight was the first thing to shutdown. I was aware of people around me, I could hear them but not see them. Everything in my body was closing down from severe blood loss. They eventually found a vein and proceeded to put saline fluid into my body, but as fast as it went in it came out the gaping wound.

By the time I was loaded onto the helicopter I had had 8 liters of fluid infused into me. I sensed my wife beside me and the paramedics trying to help, but it was as if I was drifting away from them. I tried to see my wife but instead just sensed her beside me. Apparently I was lying with my head in her lap. I remember telling her I loved her and she tells me she heard me struggling to breathe and then I was still and she knew my spirit had left me. I also cried out the name of Jesus very quietly just before I was still.

The next thing I recall is seeing all these people dancing, singing and rejoicing. I thought this was strange as I was unaware I had died and thought it was the people who had arrived to help me. I remember calling out to them, "Hey guys help me I'm dying!". But, of course, I had already begun my journey to Heaven. I felt an incredible peace. My body was light and I felt absolutely no pain, unlike when the accident happened. I remember travelling up through the middle of this crowd of people, who seemed familiar but I don't recall any of their faces. I now believe it to be the crowd of witnesses who were there to welcome me to Heaven.

I was drawn to this incredibly bright light that, as I moved upwards, it became increasingly brighter and brighter. In the distance I could make out a figure and as I moved closer towards it, it became apparent to me it was Jesus. He was wearing robes of the most vibrant white that seemed to just glow. He carried such authority but radiated love and peace. His whole body just glowed with light. This light emanating from Him was so intense I could not make out his full face, but I was aware of Him smiling at me and it melted my heart. There are no words to explain how I felt or the peace that engulfed me. Jesus held out His arms and I fell into His embrace and at that moment I knew that I was home, that I belonged here and always had, and that I was never meant to be separated from God.

After some time, He released me and He gently raised his left hand and spoke my name. "Michael, you must go back, it's not yet your time." I didn't want to leave. This place was beyond description and to this day I can not find the words to adequately describe the perfection and sheer beauty of Heaven. The colors were way beyond what we are aware of here on earth. Everything and everyone was perfect and there was no way I wanted to return to earth.

The next thing I was aware of was excruciating pain and being able to see the paramedics getting me ready for the air ambulance. I was still drifting in and out of consciousness but they had managed to stem the bleeding and get fluid into my body and stabilize me enough for the flight to hospital.

While all this was happening at our beach house, a good friend of ours had been out near where we were enjoying a day trip to the beach. On her journey home she felt God urging her strongly to detour down a road and follow it until He told her to stop. She ended up at Aotea Beach (where I was dying) and under God's Holy Spirit prompting, drove until He told her to stop outside a house where there was an ambulance and Fire Engine. She didn't know it but she was right outside our property praying. God is so good and cares so much that he directed her to pray for me at the time I need it most.

Finally I was loaded onto the helicopter for a ten minute flight where I again died from blood loss and in desperation to save my life they performed a transfusion directly into my jugular vein. I remember being above my body looking down on them as they did this. I could make out clearly the doctors and nurses, hear what they were saying, and see my lifeless body on the bed. I saw an angel beside me. Once again he told me it was going to be okay and I would live, that it wasn't yet time for me to come home. They then rushed me into surgery and after an 8 hour operation they reconstructed my leg and miraculously avoided amputation.

During my time in the hospital I again was given glimpses into the spirit realm and saw angels surrounding my bed. Nurses would come into my room and not want to leave because of the peace they felt and the beautiful sweet aroma that was there day and night. When I died and journeyed to heaven I had a large skin cancer on my nose which had been removed twice previously but kept recurring. I noticed three days after the accident that it had completely disappeared and to this day has never returned. There isn't even a scar on my nose. This experience has completely changed my life.

Heaven is our eternal home and is very real. Jesus is our Savior and has reconciled us to Father God through His sacrifice on the cross. We were never meant to be apart from Him. I will spend the rest of my life telling people about this amazing God who is real, who loves each and everyone of us with an intense deep love, who does miracles and heals us and has prepared for us the most beautiful home."

We Cannot Be Blessed - Unless We Rest

I don't know about you, but when I was a baby Christian and found out how Deuteronomy said that those who follow and obey God are super blessed (see all the scripture references below), I believed it. So, I expected that since I followed and obeyed God the best I knew how (and repented when I failed), then everything I put my hands to should be fruitful. And that I should be the head and not the tail. I was a daughter of the Sovereign King, after all.

Obviously to live and breathe and have our being is the most basic form of being blessed. The rains falling to the earth are a blessing. The sun's rays hitting earth are a blessing. So, there are trillions of ways each and every human being on earth is blessed. (See Psalm 145:9, Matthew 5:45 and Acts 14:17.) But I believed that because I belonged to the Mighty One, He would bless me beyond the basics so that I could be a blessing in the earth and also be an example of the profound greatness of God (Psalm 67:1-2). Not that I wouldn't face trials, but that I would be notably blessed despite them.

As you may know by now, this was not the case for me. Despite being a Christian, everything I put my hands to was dead. Everything I tried went nowhere. You could put me into a room full of people with the same level of aptitude, ambition, intelligence, and talents and watch as their efforts blossomed, taking them beyond the four walls of that room, but see me still standing there at the end of the day. Despite being a daughter of the King, there was blockage and interference with whatever I did. How could this be?

We'll talk about that but first let me reveal that this is no longer the case. It took decades, but bit by bit, God walked me out of the defeat. (Now I'm teaching you to do the same and it won't take decades to learn.) I learned the reason why, despite being His daughter, the dark kingdom was able to barricade me. However, now when I put my hands to something, it's fruitful. And I'm seeing that I'm becoming the head and not the tail. The lender and not the borrower. The tide has turned! Why? What's different between the decades of being defeated as a daughter of the Most High, and now?

There were many things I had to learn but the culmination of it all is that **I'm now at rest in God**. Oh, if only I could convey the full meaning behind that statement. I'm blessed... The works of my hands are blessed... I'm becoming the head and not the tail... because I am at rest in God.

Being at Rest in God looks like this:

- Not striving after justice
- Not striving after freedom
- Not striving after deliverance
- Not striving after a healing
- Not striving after acceptance
- Not striving after being heard or understood
- Not striving after well-being, sustenance, or needs
- Not striving after rewards or blessings
- Not striving after ambitions or desires
- Not striving after vanity, appearance, or looks
- Not striving after your own way or being right
- Not striving after riches
- Not striving after success
- Not striving after status
- Not striving after promotion
- Not striving after love, relationships, spouse
- Not striving after a better or healed marriage

- Not striving after (as in begging for) answers from God that He already answered
- Not striving after direction, purpose or destiny from a place of insecurity, fear, or doubt that God's got it

Being at rest is living in a state of true peace and security in the Lord; it is trusting God from your belly. It is knowing He's got it, and all you have to do is ask in confidence. Asking in anxiety is not being secure in God - which is not resting in Him.

The Lord has revealed that the strategies of the dark kingdom have programmed people's souls to not trust Him. To doubt that He truly cares and is there for us. To doubt that His love is unconditional. To doubt that He hears us. To doubt that He protects us. God's passion and involvement in most Christian's lives is a foreign concept.

My husband always used to say, "I know God can. But will He?"

In one sense, it's a fair question because sometimes we ask things that God can choose to say no to for our own well-being. But in another sense, the bigger reason my husband used to ask this is because he hadn't yet perceived God's passion and interest in his life - which includes lavishing him. This very real reality was lost to him just as it was with me and most all Christians. And this is one form of not trusting or resting in God.

Now the way the dark kingdom programs people to not trust God is by making it **appear** that God is not around. Or worse, by instituting patterns of let-downs and defeat in people's lives. Satan can implement these strategies easily when he has dominion and legal rights. Most people grow up under the dominion of darkness. And the children who are born with ministering spirits (Hebrews 1:14) assigned to them because they are heirs to salvation are then targeted by the minions assigned to the household. In fact, new demons will be sent onto the task force of that household and personally assigned to the heir of salvation to learn the vulnerabilities of that child and strategize to program their soul to doubt God via a series of events throughout their childhood. This way when they find Jesus, their soul will be a mess and struggling to fully perceive and connect to the Lord via faith.

A soul that is programmed to anticipate let-downs, injustice, rejection, defeat (you name it) does not trust God. Even souls that don't have histories of trauma or other major issues still experience things in this life that suggest God doesn't always show up or hear them. So, all these souls become confident, instead, in what they have always experienced. God's supposed "absence" as well as any injustice or rejection (for example) is what they understand to be reality. And seeing God not show up to spare them from injustice is what they know to be truth. They don't realize it wasn't that God failed them, or that He wasn't there. It was that He had no legal jurisdiction because of the overseers in that child's life who gave the kingdom of darkness the platform. It wasn't that God didn't show up to protect them. Rather, He was all too painfully aware of the injustice and strategies of darkness at work against them. And even more painfully aware that the household allowed the enemy to have charge - keeping the child from His love, helps, protection, goodness and blessings.

Could you imagine being the Creator of all things, supreme master of the universe, but seeing your heir dominated by darkness and having no legal jurisdiction to step in yet (unless someone prays for them which He's always trying to quicken people to do) because the household rejects God? Indeed, God is the one that set things up this way, so He brought this agony upon Himself - which He knows, obviously. But He had to set it up this way - in order to gain a true family. Had God made it that He would step in to protect everyone from the strategies of darkness, there would have been no need for a devil in the first place. God is the one, after all, that sent Lucifer to the earth. God is responsible, then, for evil. God knew full well what Lucifer would do when He cast him out of heaven down to earth. But what we fail to consider is that God Himself is the one that suffers the most for it. Yet, He chose for evil to be a part of how things go here in order to give humans a choice. God is not a dictator. Some might think it is cruel to create a world and put evil in it. But they do not revere God's sovereignty. First, He can do as He pleases. He made everything. We're all the subjects of His creation. Who are we to presume to have an opinion as to how He did things? Second, you can't have truth without there also being a lie. God always was and will always be. And He is truth. But what of it if there's no contrast? If everyone is born into a world of truth with no contrast, how can they have free will? Perhaps if you were the creator, you might prefer to not give anyone a choice or free will and you'd make everything to always be perfect. Let everyone be born with no potential to sin or oppose truth. Then everyone would go to Heaven and be with you (God) forever. -But then what's the point of earth at all if God made us robots? And who wants paradise to be full of robots? Yet, instead, there will be so much more to Heaven because of how God set things up.

But back to the point, because we do have free will, if a household does not put God in charge, He legally cannot step in when the dark kingdom implements strategies against the heirs of Christ. So they grow up adopting a belief system that God doesn't show up. Once they are born again, their soul continues to operate out of the faulty belief system - which doesn't trust God.

Consequently, they strive after everything but God, because of the void and disconnect in their souls. This was my case. Decades ago when I learned via the book of Deuteronomy that the work of my hands should be fruitful and it wasn't, it was because I was not at rest (confidence/security/trust) in God. I strived after well-being, freedom from poverty, financial stability, success, being loved, being understood, being believed, being believed in, justice, being accepted, being affirmed, looks, marriage, and more. Indeed, I had been born again which required sincere faith. But my faith in Christ wasn't complete. I believed He died for my sins, yes. I knew Jesus was God in the flesh, yes. But my soul didn't believe He was personally there for me (among many other points of unbelief). God told me years ago... "You believe, but you don't believe, Paula". And the part of me that didn't believe strived after everything because I didn't believe God would work on my behalf. I didn't understand everything I chased He already provided for me - and all I had to do was believe... Rest. I wasn't secure in God. Therefore, the kingdom of darkness had rights. And I was defeated.

But today, I'm at rest. Because God revealed the unbelief and all the various false programming in my soul, and because He taught me where I wasn't operating according to truth, my soul is now SECURE in God. No matter what goes on, I trust Him in ways I never did during those decades of defeat. Consequently, I do not strive after anything any more (aside from momentary slippage - just being honest) and I'm connecting to all the blessings, plans and destiny God has and always did have for me! I'm prospering in every way now even as my soul has prospered - just like the Bible says in 3 John 1:2.

But as I said, I have had momentary slips in striving. In fact, there have been a couple instances this past year where I was working on projects (one being ODJ Program) and in the course of things, I got carried away resorting back to doing things in my own strength and understanding, and began getting frustrated when I couldn't get something right or figure it out. And I'd be praying, "God, what's the answer??? This isn't right! Show me, please!" To which He said, **"Paula, the answer has already been given. You asked, I answered. The answer (resource, insight, wisdom, details, etc.) is right there at your disposal. You don't need to keep asking Me. The first time you asked, I responded to you! You're just not seeing (or hearing) it because you're not resting in Me. You are striving again... regressing back to thinking you have to figure this out for yourself and relying on me like some Genie in a bottle at your disposal. You've regresssed back to doubting that I am here for you. Don't forget,**

I really am on your side. I'm sincerely there for you 100%. I desire to help and bless you more than you desire to be blessed! Be secure in Me, Daughter, be confident that I've got your back, and you will see (or hear) your answer as soon as you ask of Me."
--- The last time this happened, I immediately repented for doubting God, resolved in my heart that He was there for me and would show me the way, set the project down to prove my trust, went to sleep, and woke up with a visual picture in my mind of the answer! This has actually happened several times! It's been so exciting learning to trust and rest in God! He's so amazing!

Please believe me that what I'm teaching you is true. I have been experiencing this left and right. All we have to do is rest in God. My friend, all the striving, anxiety and worry has to go. Repent of the unbelief in your soul which doubts that God is really there for you. Of course, you didn't intentionally doubt Him. It's not like you programmed yourself to not trust God. But we still must repent for it not because it's to our shame, but because it is contrary to truth. Repenting is rejecting the lie. It's establishing that you no longer agree with it.

Are you ready to see the works of your hands become fruitful? Are you ready to become the lender and not the borrower? Are you ready to be more and more blessed so that you can be more and more of a blessing? Then here's what you need to do:

1) Repent for the unbelief in your soul and all the years of "believing God, but not believing God"; not trusting, comprehending or perceiving Him

2) Repent for all the striving after everything you've done

3) Ask God to expose whatever is in your soul that still believes all the devil taught you, and what it is that compels you to strive, taking matters into your own hands, trying to figure things out on your own

4) Declare to your soul that God cared about you all the years that you were dominated by darkness, that He wanted to be there for you in every way, and that it hurt Him to see you suffering under its dominion

5) Declare to your soul the truth, that God really is there for you 100% and meditate upon this constantly until it sinks in

6) Make a list of all the things you tend to strive after so to recognize if you fall into it

7) Ask God to convict you when you operate out of doubt, striving after things on your own, even relying on Him like a Genie out of a bottle in the process

8) Repent the moment He corrects you

9) Stop striving immediately

10) Rest in God

Scriptures establishing that we who walk with God are super blessed are:

- Deuteronomy 2:7
- Deuteronomy 7:13
- Deuteronomy 7:14
- Deuteronomy 14:29
- Deuteronomy 15:10
- Deuteronomy 23:20
- Deuteronomy 24:19

Just be sure to find out whatever it is in your soul that is preventing you from being fully secure, confident and at rest in God. And realize - **the more confidence you truly have in God, the more the goodness, plans, blessings, resources and provisions He has for you can manifest.** Striving is a blockade which keeps you from laying hold of or hearing all that God has for you. ~So rest, my friend. Rest in God. Amen.

Notes/Prayers

Notes/Prayers

"If I Had Dreams and Visions Like God Gave You
I Would Have Overcome By Now, Too"
Final Thoughts and Prayer for You

Writing the following closing thoughts was a bit painful...

The only reason I bring this up is because, strangely, in a matter of one week around the time of this writing, three different ODJ members expressed that surely they wouldn't be so stuck had they experienced the supernatural things from God that I did. Though it seems logical to conclude that, it's sincerely not the case.

Understand...

Before I was saved at 19 years of age and like most ODJ members, I lived in torment. Even in moments where good things transpired, inside I was dead, full of shame, self-hatred, taunted by evil spirits, clothed with despair, and utterly aimless. When the sun shined down on me, I was glad at the surface for its goodness, but inwardly remained in darkness, totally insecure, feeling dirty, ugly, inferior, and destitute. Constantly plagued with negative, condescending voices in my mind that left me feeling alone, inadequate, and despising my existence. This woman knelt down in front of me when I was around 5 years old and said, "Jesus loves you!" and I was blank. I remember hearing the words, but they were devoid of form or meaning. I didn't even calculate that Jesus was a who or a what. She may as well have said, "Calculus and Trigonometry are high school math courses". Math? High school? I got nothing. Just empty, formless sounds in one ear and out the other. In addition to my severe lack of comprehension of God and His goodness, I was terrorized in my sleep with paralyzation and things like black dots growing in the sky, taking over the sky, and swallowing me up. People who've visited hell say they are alarmed by the awareness of their complete separation from God and it being horrific. I obviously was never completely separated from God. But I sure relate.

After I was born again, ALL OF THE ABOVE CONTINUED FOR OVER 20 YEARS **despite** Christ in me. Despite the dreams and visions, I lived in torment and injustice for decades. **Those encounters didn't whisk me out of torment or defeat!**

The torment continued. The self-loathing remained. Defeat (no matter my skill, application, qualifications) was my lot in this life. The emotional, spiritual and mental rollercoaster ensued.

But, throughout it all...

I cried out relentlessly in blind faith. And I mean I CRIED OUT. I'm sure you relate! But, here's the thing: I KNEW something was not right. I knew Christians weren't supposed to be pressed down and hindered at every turn, locked in an aimless cycle of abuse and defeat, and I wanted it rectified. More than that, I KNEW Christians were supposed to be putting the devil out - and we weren't! I had this knowing, this certainty, this FAITH that the problem wasn't with God, but me and the Church, and that I would hunt Him down to get the answer. I didn't just pursue deliverance, I chased it with a vengeance because I KNEW the answer existed. My point is my faith and perseverance were the keys to attaining manifest freedom in Christ. Not the sporadic encounters.

Way back then, I thought repenting, seeking God, going to church, worshiping, praying, serving, learning His Word, obeying God and being humble and forgiving was alignment with God wherein the devil has no authority. What I didn't yet understand was *believing* God was equally, if not more, important. Jesus said our work is TO BELIEVE (John 6:29). Believe what? Believe that not only did He die for our sins and was raised from the dead, **but that He loves us, is on our side, truly DOES have**

374

amazing plans for us, and has imparted His kingdom POWER into us. I didn't realize that I doubted *He was on my side*, that He cared about me on a personal level. It took years for me to understand that **my soul did not trust God much at all -even though my mind did**.

Further, I didn't understand self-hatred was alignment with darkness, not God. I didn't understand that rejecting my life in God to get me a husband was idolatry. I didn't understand that worrying about lack was disobedience to scripture and bowing to darkness. I didn't understand that, in God's kingdom, you process the pain at the altar but simultaneously choose divine joy and peace in the face of and despite adversity and injustice. I didn't understand how much I looked and acted like the world! I didn't realize how much pride I was in despite my conscious effort to be humble. I wasn't aware that I subconsciously doubted God would ever show up on my behalf (because I'd never experienced it). And that, as a result, I always had to take control and figure things out for myself, or make things happen the way I needed despite it hardly ever working. I didn't realize I was "still seeking my life" as I was in such soulish desperation to be counted as valuable as everyone else in the world, sometimes demanding to be heard, loved, and understood. And on and on I could go.

God's grace is sufficient. Had I died and left earth while messed up like that, I'd have gone to heaven because I was submitted and lived in repentance (aside from seasons of backsliding). But the problem was that even while I was emphatically on the straight and narrow, my soul was severely double-minded. I believed God - yet - I didn't! I knew the Word of God - yet - I didn't! I had one foot in the kingdom of God - living according to HIS precepts, by faith, obedience, repentance - and one foot in the kingdom of darkness - living according to Satan's precepts, doubting God, obedient to lies, and ignorant to so much of God's truth. I was unwittingly aligned with the dark kingdom and had no idea. But, that's why the dark kingdom had legal rights. I gave the authority of darkness platform.

Yet, despite my ignorance and wrongfully thinking I was abiding in Christ, I KNEW there was something I was missing - that it wasn't God's fault that the enemy still had the upper hand in my life; and I was determined to get to the bottom of it no matter what it took. I never gave up. In *that* way, I never doubted God. Perhaps that faith was what got me here.

In a nutshell, I fought my way out. **The supernatural encounters were sparse.** And though they helped me in various ways, they had nothing to do with my pursuit for and laying hold of the answers. They, in and of themselves, were not the answer. They were a few pieces of a huge puzzle. My faith and perseverance was the vehicle that carried me through to the place of putting the puzzle together.

Though I was thick-headed and stubborn, which is why it took me as long as it did to walk out from the dominion of darkness and into manifest, experiential victory, I did it by fighting my way through, acquiring great insight and wisdom along the way and being transformed through my submission to the whole of God's Word - *not the dreams and visions.*

It hurts to hear people say, "If God would have given me dreams and visions or talked to me like He did to you, then I would..." when, from my end, it wasn't the dreams, visions, or what He said that delivered me. You know, the pain I was in when God finally revealed that the one vision I'd had was my idolatry was excruciating, after which I had to walk through six months of severe discipline! The vision didn't spare me any pain! Nor did it thrust me forward into victory at that time. No, there were many profound lies and programs still dominating my soul after that season of discipline that had yet to be undone.

Imagine my confusion over the fact that I WAS having visions and dreams, but felt I was STILL LEFT IN THE DARK. I tell you - thinking "if God would just speak to me that would make all the difference in my life" is an insult to both God and me - because He *is* speaking to you, first of all, and secondly, because I went through hell to learn and APPLY all I have in order to be where I am today. It wasn't because I had some extra special supernatural handouts.

Finally, I want to say that despite no longer being oppressed by darkness and finally experiencing manifest victory, my life isn't perfect and neither am I. I'm STILL learning so much. But I'm no longer giving the enemy a platform via a double-minded soul that doubts God and bows to demonic spirits such as self-loathing, rejection, inferiority, insecurity, shame, religion, traditions of man, pagan worship, idolatry, false teachings, and all else. And I pray regularly that God would reveal any other ways I unwittingly align with the liar. I have prayed this same prayer since BEFORE I was born again to this day: God, show me the truth and nothing but the truth.

The Lord spoke to me in 2012, "Paula, you will be blessed because you believed when you had no reason to". In other words, while all was against me, WHILE I was still totally defeated and despised living, WHILE injustice after injustice prevailed against me, I never gave up on God. Though I never understood why the devil looked bigger than God, I KNEW **he really wasn't** and I was determined to lay hold of that reality. Despite the pain, while God was seemingly quiet, when I was lost in the wilderness, I believed it had to be something on my end, not God's. And I chose to persevere in the moments when He was silent. I had to trust blindly that He was still on my side - even while I had a spirit of abandonment and didn't experience Him standing or showing up for me - ever. In the face of every false accusation, I LOST. Where was He? Yet, I praised Him. And how could the devil prevail? I didn't know. Yet, I praised God. That's KEY.

For those who say God doesn't speak to them, give them visions or dreams - YES HE DOES. Sometimes we're just too cluttered and surrounded by darkness due to the false programming of our souls and unbelief to perceive Him! If you haven't been hearing God, don't give up and don't doubt Him.

Don't conclude or believe that God isn't speaking to you. He is. Realize and take responsibility for it, knowing that the muffling or lack of seeing is on your end - not His. This may be all it takes for you to finally connect with your visions and dreams.

That said, I'd like to close by saying no matter where you are in your walk with Christ, please determine to come into His full stature. Know that alignment with the truth is imperative. God desires that we prosper even as our souls prosper. You and I are victorious through Christ. But the manifestation of this victory is via BELIEVING IT. And it's via alignment with the kingdom of God. And to align, we must truly lay ourselves down, truly get to know and become one with truth and OUT of false teachings, religious traditions, out of guilt and into confidence, and so on. We need to stop listening to the lies and stupidity that the devil whispers into our ears. We need to stop being negative, defeated, and insecure - no matter what happened in our pasts. We need to stop doubting God's love and to, instead, chase it, and comprehend it.

We know Jesus is coming back soon. Things are going to get pretty bad, far worse than they are right now, before He returns. Indeed, He will gather those who are without spot or blemish (which is only possible through genuine repentance) before He pours out His wrath upon the earth. But the years preceding this will be severe - as Christians all over the globe will be under great persecution as has never been seen. Therefore, alignment with the kingdom of God is a MUST! There's no time to play with fire any longer. God intends to flow through His ALIGNED body in great power. Those who are aligned with the kingdom of God will flow in the power of the Spirit as a testimony of the kingdom of God. They will do works greater than Jesus Christ. The hour is upon us. Alignment with the kingdom of God is crucial.

I pray you are conscious of the kingdom of God in you. I pray all false programming and indoctrination of the dark kingdom has been dismantled in your soul. I pray you recognize where you tend to step over into agreement with the dark kingdom and that you'll stop. I pray that you now understand how real and relevant the two invisible kingdoms are - and that you make every effort to live exclusively for King Jesus from here on out. I pray from this moment forward you walk in the fear of the Lord like never before. I pray God will give you great, supernatural wisdom, knowledge, and revelation. And finally, I pray you know how high, how wide, how deep and how long is God's love for you.

In Jesus' Name, Amen.

Notes/Prayers

_____

_____

_____

_____

_____

_____

_____

_____

_____

_____

_____

_____

_____

_____

_____

_____

Notes/Prayers

Made in the USA
Monee, IL
12 March 2021